Work Out

Numeracy

The titles
in this
series

MACMILLAN
WORK OUT
SERIES

Work Out

Numeracy

F. E. Penketh

MACMILLAN

First published 1987

Published by
MACMILLAN EDUCATION LTD
Houndmills, Basingstoke, Hampshire RG21 2XS
and London
Companies and representatives
throughout the world

Typeset by TecSet Ltd, Wallington, Surrey
Printed in Great Britain by The Bath Press, Avon

British Library Cataloguing in Publication Data
Penketh, F. E.
Work out numeracy.—(Macmillan work out
series)
1. Arithmetic—Examinations, questions,
etc.
I. Title
513'.076   QA139
ISBN 0-333-41245-1

To Margaret and Anne

Contents

Acknowledgements

The author and publishers wish to thank the following, who have been of assistance in the compilation of this book or who have kindly given permission for the use of copyright material: Central Office of Information, National Westminster Bank plc, HMSO, British Railways Board, British Airways, Loganair Ltd, Brymon Airways, Townsend Thoresen Car Ferries Ltd, Ribble Bus Company, Market Research Review and the Post Office.

Extracts from PP7307:1982 are reproduced by permission of the British Standards Institution. Complete copies can be obtained from the BSI at Linford Wood, Milton Keynes, MK14 6LE. The cover photograph is by Alan Thomas.

Every effort has been made to trace all the copyright holders but if any have been overlooked the publishers will be pleased to make the necessary arrangements at the first opportunity.

I should like to thank Mary Waltham of Macmillan Education Ltd for help and advice regarding the format of the book and the following for their own individual contributions: Jack Topping, Michael Gray, Robert Thompson and Graham Penketh, but especially Madge Nelson for typing and interpreting my script.

F. E. P.

Groups Responsible for Numeracy Examinations at this Level

In the United Kingdom the following examining groups are responsible for Numeracy examinations at this level and syllabuses and examination papers can be ordered from the addresses given here.

City and Guilds of London Institute
76 Portland Place
London W1N 4AA

The Royal Society of Arts Examinations Board
Publications Office
Murray Road
Orpington
Kent BR5 3RB

University of Cambridge Local Examinations Syndicate
Hills Road
Cambridge
Cambs CB1 2EU

The Associated Examining Board
Stag Hill House
Guildford
Surrey GU2 5XJ

General Introduction

How to Use the Book

The book is aimed at students who intend taking one of the Numeracy Examinations that are offered by CPVE, RSA, City & Guilds, and BTech general courses.

Each chapter begins with a short revision section, followed by a number of worked examples which illustrate the different types of question that may be asked. Exercises at the end of each chapter give plenty of practice in basic calculations, in multiple choice type questions, and in questions which may need some thought before beginning the calculations. All are at an appropriate level for examinations in numeracy.

The final chapter consists of a number of assignments and, because these are likely to be more difficult than other previous exercises, hints are given at various stages to help with the working out. All the answers are at the back of the book but you should not look at them until you have written your own. If your answer is wrong go back to one of the worked examples in the beginning of the chapter to see if you can spot where you may have made a mistake.

Revision

The old saying 'practice makes perfect' probably applies more in mathematics than in any other subject. Aim at doing some questions every day since this is bound to give revision in addition, subtraction etc. It is better working for thirty minutes every day rather than three hours at the end of the week.

The Examination

The time given for any examination is most important and so if you cannot answer a question, or you become confused when answering it, move on to the next question without wasting time. You probably have a good idea which questions you are good at; look out for such questions, answer them first and this should put you in the right frame of mind to answer the other questions.

1 Number

1.1   How Big is a Number?

The size of a number depends on the position (place value) of the figures and the size of the figures.

Example 1.1

Write 68 in words.

68 is 6 tens and 8 units and is written sixty-eight.

Example 1.2

Write 437 in words.

437 is 4 hundreds, 3 tens and 7 units and is written four hundred and thirty-seven.

Example 1.3

Write 2006 in words.

2006 is 2 thousands, 0 hundreds, 0 tens and 6 units and is written two thousand and six.

Remember that the place value headings can be written in order of size:

Millions	Hundred thousands	Ten thousands	Thousands	Hundreds	Tens	Units
2	4	6	3	8	5	1

The number 2 463 851 is two million, four hundred and sixty-three thousand, eight hundred and fifty-one.

Example 1.4

Write eight hundred and twenty-five in figures.

Eight hundred and twenty-five is 825.

Example 1.5

Write two million six hundred thousand three hundred and ninety-six in figures.

Two million six hundred thousand three hundred and ninety-six is 2 600 396.

1

Exercise 1.1

Write the following in words. The first two are completed for you.

1 46 is forty-six.

2 508 is five hundred and eight.

3 72	4 48	5 84	6 267	7 503
8 670	9 309	10 821	11 1463	12 2506
13 3084	14 1009	15 27 283	16 40 713	17 20 058
18 372 542	19 620 491	20 5 926 473		

Exercise 1.2

Write the following numbers in figures. The first two are completed for you.

1 Seventy-three is 73.

2 One hundred and nine is 109.

3 Three hundred and forty-four.
4 One thousand three hundred and eight.
5 Four thousand nine hundred and twenty-three.
6 Two thousand and four.
7 Twelve thousand and sixty-five.
8 Sixty two thousand five hundred and ninety-one.
9 Twenty thousand and two.
10 One hundred and fifty thousand.
11 Two hundred and sixty-nine.
12 Two hundred and eighty thousand five hundred and thirty-four.
13 Five hundred and six thousand and twenty-seven.
14 Eight hundred and thirty-two thousand nine hundred and three.
15 One million three hundred and forty-two thousand.
16 Three million.
17 Six hundred and seven thousand six hundred and seven.
18 What does the figure 4 represent in 3420?
19 What does the figure 1 represent in 71 396?
20 What does the figure 0 represent in 406 582?

1.2   Addition

Begin by adding figures in the right-hand column.

Example 1.6

```
  54      2 and 4 make 6. Write 6 in the units column of the answer.
+ 32      3 and 5 make 8. Write 8 in the tens column of the answer.
  86      Answer   86
```

Example 1.7

```
  51     7 and 1 make 8
+ 47     4 and 5 make 9
  98     Answer   98
```

Where figures have to be carried from one column to the next then use the method with which you are familiar.

Example 1.8

```
   47          47
 + 26        + 26
  ₁
   73          73
                ₁
```

6 and 7 make 13. Write figure 3 in the answer and carry 1 into the next column, putting it either alongside and slightly below the next figure or beneath the answer line as shown.
Thus 1 and 2 make 3 and 4 makes 7.
Answer   73

Example 1.9

Find the sum of 127, 32, 79 and 256.

Where numbers are not given in columns then put them into columns before beginning the addition.

```
   127
    32
    79
 + 256
   ₁₂
   494     Answer   494
```

As a matter of habit I always begin at the bottom of the column and add upwards.
   Where there are a lot of numbers I always *check* the addition by starting at the top and adding downwards. If the two answers do not coincide then repeat the additions until they do.

Example 1.10

Find the sum of 4275, 384, 1009, 369 and 57.

Write the numbers in columns.

```
  4275     7 and 9 make 16, and 9 makes 25, and 4 makes 29, and 5 makes 34.
   384     Write 4 in the answer and carry 3.
  1009     Check: 5 and 4 make 9, and 9 makes 18, and 9 makes 27, and 7 makes
   369     34.
 +  57
  ₁₂₃
  6094     Answer   6094
```

Exercise 1.3

Complete the following additions. The first two are completed for you.

1	36	2	15	3	24	4	52	5	47
	+ 12		+ 9		+ 33		+ 37		+ 35
	48		24						

6	95	7	53	8	26	9	55	10	24
	+ 69		+ 27		+ 74		132		95
							+ 17		+ 336

11	37	12	59	13	507	14	142	15	23
	205		273		238		307		247
	+ 528		+ 103		16		1295		8
					+ 83		+ 68		+ 7

16	721	17	83	18	424	19	6	20	727
	35		201		38		409		2813
	216		95		3916		380		609
	+ 7		+ 3260		+ 77		+ 54		+ 35

Exercise 1.4

Find the sum of the following numbers. The first two are completed for you.

1 15 + 48 + 27

$$\begin{array}{r} 15 \\ 48 \\ + 27 \\ \hline 90 \end{array}$$

Answer   90

2 9 + 84 + 16 + 305

$$\begin{array}{r} 9 \\ 84 \\ 16 \\ + 305 \\ \hline 414 \end{array}$$

Answer   414

3 44 + 165 + 8   4 11 + 35 + 27   5 23 + 129 + 8 + 2719
6 327 + 625 + 22 + 8   7 4303 + 9 + 271 + 64   8 90 + 361 + 5274 + 6
9 52 + 75 + 804 + 9   10 2107 + 4638 + 590 + 63   11 78 + 506 + 32 + 114
12 425 + 2 + 3007 + 86

1.3 Addition from Information Given

Many questions are written in sentences and it becomes a matter of sorting out which things have to be added together.

Example 1.11

A darts player in a pub throws six darts. He scores 20, 5 and 1, and then 19, 17 and 3. How many does he score?

He scores on each of the six darts.
The scores are 20, 5, 1, 19, 17 and 3.

Add them together:
$$
\begin{array}{r}
20 \\
5 \\
1 \\
19 \\
17 \\
+ \quad {}_2 3 \\
\hline
65 \\
\hline
\end{array}
$$

Answer   65

Example 1.12

A salesman in the course of a week had to travel from Oxford to London (57 miles), then to Cambridge (54 miles), then to Leeds (145 miles), then to Manchester (40 miles), then to Birmingham (80 miles), and then home to Oxford (another 64 miles). How far did he travel in the week and, using his route, how far is it from Manchester to Oxford?

There are two questions being asked:
(a) How far did he travel in the week?

Total distance he travelled = 57 miles + 54 miles + 145 miles
+ 40 miles + 80 miles + 64 miles
= 440 miles.

(b) How far is it from Manchester to Oxford using his route?
The route is Manchester–Birmingham–Oxford.

Manchester to Birmingham =   80 miles
Birmingham to Oxford   =   64 miles
Manchester to Oxford   = 144 miles

Exercise 1.5

1 John with his first three darts of a darts match threw 20, 19 and 17. What did he score?
2 The attendances at Manchester United's ground for the first four home games of the season were 47 216, 51 783, 44 825 and 42 974. What was the total attendance for the four home games?
3 Simon reckoned that in a six-day period which covered Christmas he smoked 18, 22, 35, 33, 17 and 24 cigarettes on successive days. His girlfriend smoked 14, 16, 27, 24, 12 and 14 cigarettes over the same period.
   How many did each smoke?
4 A family has 3 pints of milk on Monday, 2 pints on Tuesday, 3 pints on Wednesday, 2 pints on Thursday, 3 pints on Friday and 6 pints on Saturday. How many pints of milk do they use in a week?

5 After potting a red ball at snooker you can then try and pot any coloured ball, followed by another red, and so on. A red counts one point, yellow 2 points, green 3 points, brown 4 points, blue 5 points, pink 6 points and black 7 points.

Steve Davis made the following break: red, black, red, black, red, pink, red, blue, red, yellow, red, black, red, black, red, brown, red, black, red. How many points did he score?

6 A rugby union team consists of 15 players and a soccer team of 11 players. The leisure centre hired a coach to take a rugby team and two reserves, and a soccer team and two reserves, together with eight officials. How many passengers did the coach carry?

7 A journey from London and back went as follows. London to Bournemouth (100 miles), then to Bristol (82 miles), then to Birmingham (81 miles), then to Carlisle (196 miles), then to Newcastle (57 miles), then to York (84 miles), then to Gt Yarmouth (201 miles), then to London (128 miles).

Using the same route, and going the same way, how far is it from

(a) London to Bristol;   (b) Birmingham to York;
(c) Carlisle to Gt Yarmouth;   (d) Gt Yarmouth to Birmingham;
(e) Bristol to Newcastle;   (f) London and back to London?

8 A class's attendances for the ten sessions in a week were 28, 28, 27, 26, 26, 26, 27, 27, 28, 28.

What was the total attendance for the week?

What was the likely number of students in the class?

9 A newsagent has the following delivery of daily newspapers: fifty-five *Mirrors*, forty-six *Suns*, thirty-two *Expresses*, twenty-eight *Mails*, twenty-five *Stars*, twelve *Guardians*, six *Times* and two *Financial Times*. What is the total of daily papers?

10 Two dice when thrown show a total of 7. What could each dice face have been showing?

1.4 Subtraction

Subtract using the method you have been taught.

Example 1.13

What is the difference between 88 and 43?

88	8 take away 3 leaves 5. Write 5 in the units column of the answer.
− 43	8 take away 4 leaves 4. Write 4 in the answer.
45	Answer 45

Example 1.14

From 659 take 237.

659	9 take away 7 leaves 2. Write 2 in the answer.
− 237	5 take away 3 leaves 2. Write 2 in the answer.
422	6 take away 2 leaves 4. Write 4 in the answer.
	Answer 422

Example 1.15

From 73 take away 28.

Two methods can be used in this example and I would advise continuing the method you have been taught.

Method 1

$$
\begin{array}{r}
{}^{6}\cancel{7}3 \\
-\ 28 \\
\hline
45 \\
\hline
\end{array}
$$

3 take away 8 cannot be done, so a 10 is used from the 7 in the next column and added to the 3 to make 13.
13 take away 8 is 5. Place 5 in the answer.
The 7 in the tens column has become 6.
6 take away 2 is 4. Place 4 in the answer.
Answer   45

Method 2

$$
\begin{array}{r}
73 \\
-28 \\
\hline
45 \\
\hline
\end{array}
$$

3 take away 8 cannot be done so 10 is added to the 3 to make 13.
13 take away 8 is 5. Place 5 in the answer.
Because we added 10 to the top line we must add one 10 to the bottom line and the 2 becomes 3.
7 take away 3 is 4. Write 4 in the answer.
Answer   45

Example 1.16

$$
\begin{array}{r}
2\cancel{4}7 \\
-\ 169 \\
\hline
78 \\
\hline
\end{array}
$$
Answer   78

Example 1.17

$$
\begin{array}{r}
1001 \\
-\ 257 \\
\hline
744 \\
\hline
\end{array}
$$
Answer   744

Exercise 1.6

Find the difference between the numbers given. The first two have been completed for you.

1	45 − 28 17	2	216 − 38 178	3	67 − 35	4	89 − 53	5	63 − 36
6	174 − 92	7	327 − 119	8	452 − 365	9	300 − 143	10	954 − 618

11	1242	12	1000	13	5000	14	38	15	628
	− 735		− 164		− 3576		− 19		− 435

16	3006	17	243	18	501	19	3258	20	625
	− 428		− 65		− 244		− 2319		− 339

Exercise 1.7

The first two are completed for you.

1 A newsagent starts the day with 260 newspapers and when the shop closes he has 43 left. How many has he sold?

   The number sold is the difference between the number of papers at the start of the day and the number left at the end of the day:

$$2\overset{5}{\cancel{6}}0$$
$$-\ 43$$
$$\overline{217}$$ Number of newspapers sold is 217.

2 A shop buys 200 sweaters at a special price for the sales week. On Monday 27 were sold, Tuesday 32 sold, Wednesday 18 sold, Thursday 35 sold, Friday 26 sold and Saturday 55 sold. How many were left at the end of the sale?

   First, find the total number sold:

Monday	27
Tuesday	32
Wednesday	18
Thursday	35
Friday	26
Saturday	55
Total sold	193

   There were 200 sweaters

$$-\ 193 \text{ sold}$$
$$\overline{\ \ 7}$$ Answer   7 left

3 From a bag of 20 sweets John ate 7 the first day and 5 the second day. How many were left?

4 In a darts match of first to score 501, Carol had already scored 248 and Sheila 315. How many did each still have to score?

5 Out of a possible 360 attendances one girl had 283 attendances. How many times was she absent?

6 A signpost points in the direction of Brackley 12 miles, Buckingham 21 miles and Milton Keynes 34 miles. How far is it from Brackley to Milton Keynes? From Buckingham to Milton Keynes?

7 In a recent test match the West Indies scored 424 runs in their first innings and England scored 287. By how many runs did West Indies lead?

8 There are 312 steps to the top of a church tower. When I have climbed 137 how many more are there?

9 A two-man bricklaying team reckon to lay 1200 bricks between them in a day. By mid-afternoon one has laid 417 bricks and the other 385. How many bricks are still to be laid for the target to be reached?

10 A CND group marched from Birmingham to Greenham – a total of 95 miles – in four days. On the first day they walked 28 miles, on the second 32 miles and on the third 21 miles. How far did they walk on the fourth day?

11 A lady won first prize of £100 000 on a premium bond and the next day bought a bungalow for £53 280. How much did she have left?

12 The table shows the bottom four clubs in Division Four, how many goals they have scored and how many goals have been scored against them. Which club has the biggest goal difference?

	Goals for	Goals against
Chester	24	61
Torquay United	30	57
Northampton	35	68
Wrexham	35	42

1.5 Multiplication

To multiply two numbers together, if it needs to be worked out on a piece of paper, make sure the units in each number are underneath one another; that is, the last figures of each number must be underneath one another.

Example 1.18

Multiply 257 by 3.

```
  257
×   3
  12
  771
```

3 times 7 is 21; write 1 in the answer and carry 2.
3 times 5 is 15, add the 2 carried, making 17.
Write 7 in the answer and carry 1.
3 times 2 is 6, add the 1 carried, making 7.
Write 7 in the answer.

Answer   771

Example 1.19

Multiply 38 by 24.

Method 1

Begin by multiplying 38 by 4.

```
   38
×  24
  13
  152
  760
  912
```

4 times 8 is 32; write 2 in the answer and carry 3.
4 times 3 is 12, add the 3 carried, making 15.
Write 15 in the answer
Now multiply 38 by 2, which is really 2 tens, so write a 0 in the units column and then you cannot put any tens in the unit column by mistake.
2 times 8 is 16; write 6 in the answer in the tens column and carry 1.
2 times 3 is 6, add the 1 carried, making 7.
Add the two results together.

Answer   912

9

Method 2

Multiply by the 2 first.

```
    38
×  ₃ ₁24
   760
   ₁152
   912
```

Use the method with which you are familiar.
The carrying figures can be placed wherever you feel they will not be forgotten.

Example 1.20

You will rarely have to do multiplication of numbers with more than two figures in each, except by using a calculator.

But however many figures there are in each number make sure the units of each number are underneath one another.

```
      567
×  ₂₁₅₅84
   45 360
    2 268
   47 628
```
Answer   47 628

Exercise 1.8

Find the value of the following. The first two are completed for you.

```
1     36
   ×   9
      ₅
     324
```
Answer   324

```
2     18
   ×  ₃₂34
     540
      ₁72
     612
```
Answer   612

3	43	4	43	5	43	6	32	7	56
	× 5		× 6		× 7		× 8		× 9

8	34	9	67	10	41	11	95	12	78
	× 46		× 39		× 76		× 48		× 34

13	82	14	97	15	26	16	135	17	267
	× 64		× 30		× 78		× 24		× 43

18 80	**19** 59	**20** 137
× 49	× 78	× 152

Exercise 1.9

The first two are completed for you.

1 A youth earns £46 a week. How much is this per month (4 weeks)?

If he earns £46 a week he will earn 4 times as much in 4 weeks.

```
  £46
×   4
   2
  184
```
Answer   £184 per month

2 A milk float carries 26 crates of milk and in each crate there are 24 bottles. How many bottles of milk are being carried?

1 crate contains 24 bottles
26 crates will be 26 times 24 bottles.

```
   26
×  24
  2 1
  520
  104
  624
```
Answer   Float carries 624 bottles

3 A girl starting work for the first time is determined to save £3 a week. How much is saved in a year (52 weeks)?

4 A ship carries a cargo of 32 lorries with each one weighing 18 tons. What is the total weight of the cargo?

5 A darts player throws 19, treble 19 (i.e. 3 times 19) and double 17 (i.e. twice 17). What is his score?

6 A family of 2 adults and 2 children go on holiday to Tenerife. The cost for each adult is £347 and for each child is £210. Other charges in the holiday come to £59. What is the total cost of the holiday?

7 Rates paid on a house each month total £65. How much is this for a year (12 months)?

8 Brian boasts that he smokes 27 cigarettes a day. How many is this in a week (7 days)?

9 There are 24 bottles in a crate. How many bottles are there in 36 crates?

10 A skilled mechanic is paid £7 an hour. How much does he earn in a 35-hour week?

11 There are 4 car parks in town and each one will hold 320 cars. At 10.00 a.m. on Saturday morning there are only 27 spare places on the car parks. How many cars are parked?

12 A hotel quoted a price of £9 for each guest at a wedding. If there were 87 guests, how much did this part of the wedding cost?

13 A jumbo jet holds 446 passengers. In summer there are 14 jumbo jets crossing from England to America in a day. What is the maximum number of passengers that can fly in one day from England to America?

14 A mother arranged to do a buffet party for her teenage daughter for 22 guests, which included all the family. Mother allowed £3 per head for food, £25 for drinks, £7 to cover decorations, flowers, etc., and £10 for last-minute items. How much was needed to cover the cost of the party?

1.6 Division

Example 1.21

Divide 245 by 5. (Can also be written 245 ÷ 5.)

Method 1   Short Division

```
   49
5)2⁴⁴5
```

Divide by 5. The small figures show the remainder each time 5 is divided into the figure beginning at the left.

Answer   49

Method 2   Long Division

```
   49
5)245
   20      (5 × 4)
   ──
   45
   45      (5 × 9)
   ──
   ··
```

5 will not divide into the first figure 2.
5 will divide into the first two figures (24) 4 times (5 × 4 = 20), leaving a remainder of 4. The next figure 5, is brought down and 5 is divided into 45.
This goes exactly 9 times.

Answer   49

Example 1.22

23076 ÷ 9.

```
    2564
9)2⁵³⁵³076
```

Answer   2564

Example 1.23

8992 ÷ 16.

```
    562
16)8992
   80        (16 × 5)
   ──
    99
    96       (16 × 6)
    ──
     32
     32      (16 × 2)
     ──
     ··
```

Answer   562

Sometimes you have to bring down more than one number.

Example 1.24

$7696 \div 37$.

```
        208
   37)7696
      74      (2 × 37)
      ___
      296
      296      (8 × 37)
      ___
      ...
```

37 into 76 goes 2 (2 × 37 = 74).
Bring down 9.
37 will not go into 29.
Put 0 in the answer.
Bring down the next figure 6.
37 into 296 goes 8 times.

<u>Answer   208</u>

Occasionally there is a remainder and in this case the answer is shown together with the remainder.

Example 1.25

$6430 \div 18$.

```
        357
   18)6430
      54          (3 × 18)
      ___
      103
       90         (5 × 18)
      ___
      130
      126         (7 × 18)
      ___
        4 remainder.
```

<u>Answer   357, remainder 4</u>

Exercise 1.10

Find the value of the following. The first two are completed for you.

1 $192 \div 8$
```
        24
     8)19²2
```

2 $322 \div 14$
```
          23
      14)322
         28
         ___
         42
         42
         ___
         ..
```

3 $175 \div 7$ 4 $304 \div 8$ 5 $402 \div 6$ 6 $747 \div 9$ 7 $2975 \div 7$
8 $4536 \div 9$ 9 $4856 \div 8$ 10 $3152 \div 8$ 11 $702 \div 13$ 12 $1292 \div 19$
13 $8512 \div 16$ 14 $14\,124 \div 22$ 5 $8289 \div 27$ 16 $7488 \div 36$ 17 $13\,244 \div 28$
18 $26\,226 \div 31$ 19 $32\,128 \div 64$ 20 $4171 \div 43$

Exercise 1.11

The first two are completed for you.

1 An electricity bill is £208 per quarter (13 weeks). How much is this per week?

The electricity is £208 for 13 weeks.
To find how much it is for one week divide £208 by 13.

```
        16
   13)208
       13      (13 × 1)
      ───
       78
       78      (13 × 6)
      ───
       ··
```
Answer   £16 per week

2 Daffodil bulbs are delivered to a garden centre in sacks and then they are sold in packets, each one containing 12 daffodils. If a sack contains 3900 bulbs, how many packets can you make up from one sack?

There are 3900 bulbs in one sack,
and there are 12 bulbs in each packet.
To find how many packets divide 3900 by 12.

```
         325
   12)3900
        36      (12 × 3)
       ───
        30
        24      (12 × 2)
       ───
        60
        60      (12 × 5)
       ───
        ··
```
Answer   325 packets in one sack

3 A garden is 216 feet long. How many 6 ft wooden fencing panels are needed to fence one side?

4 A lorry can carry 18 tons of sand. How many lorry loads are needed to shift 1026 tons?

5 A woman earns £4888 a year (52 weeks). How much is this a week?

6 A householder pays £348 a year for gas and he arranges to pay it in equal amounts each calendar month. How much does he pay each month?

7 A teacher buys a roll of material 187 ft long for her 17 pupils. How much material has been allowed for each pupil?

8 A shopkeeper prepacks his sweets and allows 24 per packet. How many packets did he get from a tin containing 1728 sweets?

9 A rugby team (15 players), 6 reserves and 2 officials paid £5612 for a rugby tour abroad. If each paid the same how much did each person pay?

10 Rock salt for gritting roads is dumped in 15-ton loads in a hilly area. How many dumps are created from 1125 tons?

11 Spain said that last year nine million tourists had flown to Spain. If each plane can hold 180 passengers, how many flights, at least, were there to Spain?
    Is this more than 130 a day or less than 130?

12 British Telecom need eighteen million telephone directories. The printer packages them in bundles of eight. How many bundles are there?

1.7 Priorities

In an expression such as

$$(4 + 2) \times (9 \div 3)$$

we must decide which parts to deal with first.

A *first priority* is a bracket (   ). Everything in a bracket must be worked out before further calculation.

14

A *second priority* is multiplication and division and they are done before addition and subtraction.

Example 1.26

Find the value of $5 + 4 \times 3$.

$5 + 4 \times 3$ Multiplication is done first.
$= 5 + 12$
$= 17.$

Example 1.27

Find the value of $(5 + 4) \times 3$.

$(5 + 4) \times 3$ Bracket is done before multiplication.
$= 9 \times 3$
$= 27.$

Example 1.28

Find the value of $(5 + 6) \times (2 + 7)$.

$(5 + 6) \times (2 + 7)$ Everything in a bracket must be worked out before further
$= (11) \times (9)$ calculation.
$= 99.$

Contrast this with example 1.28a.

Example 1.28a

Find the value of $5 + 6 \times 2 + 7$.

$5 + 6 \times 2 + 7$ Multiplication is done before addition.
$= 5 + 12 + 7$
$= 24.$

Example 1.29

Find the value of $10 + 9 \div 3 - 2$.

$10 + 9 \div 3 - 2$ Division is done before addition and subtraction.
$= 10 + 3 - 2$
$= 13 - 2$
$= 11.$

Example 1.30

Find the value of $(8 + 7) \div (9 - 4) + 3$.

$(8 + 7) \div (9 - 4) + 3$	Brackets first.
$= 15 \div 5 + 3$	Division before addition.
$= 3 + 3$	
$= 6.$	

Exercise 1.12

Find the value of the following. The first two are completed for you.

1 $9 + 6 \div 3 = 9 + 2 = 11.$
2 $7 - (3 + 2) + 5 = 7 - 5 + 5 = 7.$
3 $3 + (7 \times 3)$ 4 $7 + (2 \times 5)$ 5 $(9 + 6) - 3$ 6 $(4 \times 4) - 6$
7 $15 - (3 \times 4)$ 8 $18 \div (4 + 2)$ 9 $18 \div (4 - 2)$ 10 $8 + 4 \times 3 - 2$
11 $15 \div 3 + 2$ 12 $24 \div (4 \times 2)$ 13 $24 \div 6 + 2$ 14 $12 \div 4 - 3$
15 $(7 + 6) \div (9 - 8)$ 16 $6 \times 5 - 2 \times 9$ 17 $(16 - 6) \div 5$ 18 $3 \times (8 - 4) + 6$
19 $16 \div 4 + 3 \times 2$ 20 $(18 \div 6) - 3$

1.8   Multiplication of Whole Numbers by 10, 100, 1000, etc

This section shows how to multiply whole numbers by 10, 100, etc.
To multiply any whole number by 10 simply write 0 after the number.

Example 1.31

$7 \times 10 = 70.$ $9 \times 10 = 90.$ $15 \times 10 = 150.$

$290 \times 10 = 2900.$ $107 \times 10 = 1070.$ $1237 \times 10 = 12\,370.$

To multiply any whole number by 100 simply write 00 after the number.

Example 1.32

$7 \times 100 = 700.$ $9 \times 100 = 900.$ $15 \times 100 = 1500.$

$290 \times 100 = 29\,000.$ $107 \times 100 = 10\,700.$ $1237 \times 100 = 123\,700.$

To multiply any whole number by 1000 simply write 000 after the number.

Example 1.33

$7 \times 1000 = 7000.$ $9 \times 1000 = 9000.$ $15 \times 1000 = 15\,000.$

To multiply by 1 000 000 simply write 000 000 after the number.

1.9 Multiplication of Numbers Ending in 0

Example 1.34

$$30 \times 20 = 3 \times 10 \times 2 \times 20$$

There is one 0 in 30 and one 0 in 20.

$$= 6 \times 10 \times 10$$

Multiply 2×3 and then add two 0s.

$$= 6 \times 100$$
$$= 600.$$

Example 1.35

$60 \times 70 = 4200$	$6 \times 7 = 42$	Add on two 0s.
$300 \times 50 = 15\,000$	$3 \times 5 = 15$	Add on three 0s.
$150 \times 30 = 4500$	$15 \times 3 = 45$	Add on two 0s.
$300 \times 750 = 225\,000$	$3 \times 75 = 225$	Add on three 0s.
$400 \times 600 = 240\,000$	$4 \times 6 = 24$	Add on four 0s.

1.10 Division of Whole Numbers Ending in 0 by 10, 100, 1000, etc.

Where a whole number ends in 0 then to divide by 10 simply take off one 0.

Example 1.36

$40 \div 10 = 4.$	4Ø take off one 0.
$370 \div 10 = 37.$	37Ø take off one 0.
$37\,000 \div 10 = 3700.$	37 00Ø take off one 0.

To divide by 100 take off 00 *provided* there are sufficient 0s at the end of the number.

Example 1.37

$600 \div 100 = 6.$	6ØØ take off two 0s.
$3500 \div 100 = 35.$	35ØØ take off two 0s.
$328\,000 \div 100 = 3280.$	328 0ØØ take off two 0s.

For division by 1000 take off 000 *provided* there are sufficient 0s at the end of the number.

1.11 Division of Two Whole Numbers Ending in 0

Take off *the same number of 0s from each number* and then divide as usual.

Example 1.38

$$2800 \div 70 = 280 \div 7$$

Taking one 0 off each number.

$$= 40.$$

$$270 \div 90 = 27 \div 9$$
$$= 3.$$

Taking one 0 off each number.

$$4000 \div 500 = 40 \div 5$$
$$= 8.$$

Taking two 0s off each number.

Exercise 1.13

Find the value of the following. The first two are completed for you.

1 $40 \times 90 = 4 \times 10 \times 9 \times 10$
$\qquad\qquad = 36 \times 100$
$\qquad\qquad = 3600.$

2 $3600 \div 60 = 360 \div 6$
$\qquad\qquad\quad = 60.$

3 15×10	4 290×10	5 162×100	6 92×1000
7 20×70	8 40×60	9 30×200	10 80×90
11 320×100	12 30×500	13 70×9000	14 110×20
15 170×300	16 $290 \div 10$	17 $7800 \div 10$	18 $150 \div 10$
19 $27\,000 \div 100$	20 $3100 \div 100$	21 $197\,000 \div 100$	22 $320\,000 \div 1000$
23 $5\,200\,000 \div 1000$	24 $1600 \div 4$	25 $1800 \div 90$	26 $32\,000 \div 400$
27 $5600 \div 8$	28 $24\,400 \div 40$	29 $350\,000 \div 700$	30 $17\,500 \div 50$

1.12 Approximations

When we have completed a calculation we often wonder whether the answer is right or wrong. To give some idea whether it could be right we can find a rough estimate of the answer. For example, there is a big difference between 2 and 200.

There is no hard and fast rule about finding a rough estimate but one method is to 'round off' each number to the nearest 10, or 100, or 1000, etc.

As a general rule, if a figure is 5 or more we round up and if 4 or less we round down.

28 is 30 to the nearest 10   (28 is nearer to 30 than 20.)

22 is 20 to the nearest 10.

51 is 50 to the nearest 10.

168 is 200 to the nearest 100.

352 is 0 to the nearest 1000.

Using such work may help in multiplication and division in providing a check as to whether an answer may be correct or not.

Example 1.39

79×53 is roughly 80×50 (rounding off each number to the nearest 10),
and $80 \times 50 = 4000$
so 79×53 is roughly 4000.
$\approx$ is a symbol which means approximately.
$79 \times 53 \approx 4000$.
The actual answer is 4187.

Example 1.40

73 × 47 is roughly 70 × 50 = 3500
so   73 × 47 ≈ 3500   (actual answer is 3431).

Example 1.41

      99 × 99 ≈ 100 × 100 = 10 000
so   99 × 99 ≈ 10 000   (actual answer is 9801).

Example 1.42

      3156 ÷ 79 ≈ 3200 ÷ 80 = 40
so   3156 ÷ 79 ≈ 40   (actual answer is 39.9).

Example 1.43

      87 862 ÷ 99 ≈ 88 000 ÷ 100 = 880
so 87 862 ÷ 99 ≈ 880   (actual answer is 887.5).

Exercise 1.14

Round off the following. The first two are completed for you.

  1 64 to the nearest 10   is 60.

  2 127 to the nearest 100   is 100.

  3 86 to the nearest 10   **4** 15 to the nearest 10
  5 265 to the nearest 100   **6** 580 to the nearest 100
  7 391 to the nearest 10   **8** 391 to the nearest 100
  9 391 to the nearest 1000   **10** 756 to the nearest 1000
 11 5275 to the nearest 1000   **12** 4501 to the nearest 1000
 13 1831 to the nearest 10   **14** 1831 to the nearest 100
 15 1831 to the nearest 1000   **16** 77 to the nearest 10
 17 77 to the nearest 100   **18** 2489 to the nearest 100
 19 2489 to the nearest 1000   **20** 167 to the nearest 10

Exercise 1.15

Give approximate answers for the following. The first two are completed for you.

  1 27 × 32 ≈ 30 × 30 = 900.   27 × 32 ≈ 900.

  2 3357 ÷ 82 ≈ 3400 ÷ 80 ≈ 42.   3357 ÷ 82 ≈ 42.

  3 19 × 51   **4** 28 × 52   **5** 37 × 73   **6** 44 × 66
  7 162 × 99   **8** 155 × 49   **9** 175 × 199   **10** 59 × 81
 11 6384 ÷ 99   **12** 36 892 ÷ 101   **13** 4853 ÷ 49   **14** 6824 ÷ 29
 15 15 621 ÷ 91   **16** 4739 ÷ 28   **17** 76 849 ÷ 203   **18** 2805 ÷ 70
 19 3715 ÷ 62   **20** 105 × 105

Exercise 1.16   Multiple-choice Questions

Work out which is the correct answer in the following questions.
1 What is 32 137 expressed in words?

    A   Thirty-two thousand and thirty-seven.
    B   Three hundred and twenty-one thousand and thirty-seven.
    C   Thirty-two thousand one hundred and thirty-seven.
    D   Thirty-two thousand one hundred and seventy.

2 Last Wednesday Arsenal had forty-three thousand and eighty-seven spectators but on Saturday the crowd was 4348 less. Was Saturday's gate

    A 38 739   **B** 47 435   **C** 38 639   **D** 47 535?

3 A cricketer had scores of 26, 13, 43 not out, 0 and 15. Was his total

    A 328   **B** impossible to say   **C** 54   **D** 97?

4 A hockey team won 5 matches, drew 4 and lost 3. Did they play

    A 5 matches   **B** 12 matches   **C** 4 matches   **D** 3 matches?

5 If 258 is multiplied by 77 is the answer

    A 19 877   **B** 19 888   **C** 19 866   **D** 19 855?

6 If 24 552 is divided by 88 is the answer

    A 279   **B** 280   **C** 278   **D** 277?

7 A signpost in York points to Barlby 14 miles, Howden 25 miles and North Cove 36 miles. The number of miles from Barlby to North Cove is

    A 14 miles   **B** 25 miles − 14 miles   **C** 36 miles − 14 miles
    D 36 miles − 25 miles.

8 A school canteen menu said:
coffee 14p, tea 12p, sandwich 23p, soup 18p.
   The bill came to 53p. Did the pupil buy

    A 2 teas and a sandwich   **B** sandwich, soup and coffee
    C coffee and 2 sandwiches   **D** tea, soup and sandwich?

9 At the beginning of a week a shopkeeper had 300 packets of tea and he had delivery of another 200 packets in the middle of the week. During the week he has sold 280 packets. How many does he need to get his stock up to 300 packets?

    A 300 packets   **B** 220 packets   **C** 80 packets   **D** 20 packets.

10 A darts player at the beginning of a game of 501 up throws double twenty, treble nineteen, and seventeen with his first three darts. Does he still need

    A 387   **B** 445   **C** 287   **D** 390?

11 The meter at the side of a petrol pump showed 21 706. After a tanker delivery it showed 27 432. Did the tanker deliver

    A 4274   **B** 5138   **C** 5726   **D** 4976?

12 A gambling machine gives back 7 coins after it has accepted 10 coins. In the course of a day it accepted 1400 coins. Is the number of coins left in the machine

    A 980   **B** 420   **C** 1400   **D** 70?

13 Is the answer to $5 + 3 \times 2 + 6$

   A 17   **B** 64   **C** 16   **D** 27?

14 How much is 70×900?

   A 16 000   **B** 6400   **C** 63 000   **D** 630

15 Is 249 to the nearest 100

   A 300   **B** 200   **C** 250   **D** 240?

16 Is $6395 \div 91$ roughly

   A 80   **B** 60   **C** 70   **D** 50?

17 55×85 is roughly

   A 4500   **B** 4000   **C** 5400   **D** 5500.

18 A page of a book has 54 lines with 70 letters on each line. The number of letters on the page is

   A 124   **B** 3780   **C** 378   **D** 5470.

19 In a quiz game a competitor was asked to add 127 to 54, and then add 32, and then to subtract 94, and then add 104 and, finally, to subtract 127. Was the correct answer

   A 106   **B** 94   **C** 96   **D** 102?

20 On a normal day there are half a million copies of a newspaper printed. On one day 127 000 copies were lost because of industrial action. The number of copies printed on that day was

   A 627 000   **B** 127 000   **C** 500 000   **D** 373 000.

2 Fractions

2.1 Changing Fractions to Equivalent Fractions

A fraction can be changed to another fraction and yet have exactly the same value; this is said to be changing one fraction to an equivalent fraction.

Example 2.1

Change $\frac{3}{4}$ to an equivalent fraction of sixteenths.

We want to make $\frac{3}{4}$ = so many sixteenths = $\frac{}{16}$.
The denominator of the second fraction is 4 times the size of the first. To make them equal the numerator of the second fraction, therefore, has to be 4 times the size of the second.
So $\frac{3}{4} = \frac{12}{16}$.

Example 2.2

Complete as equivalent fractions $\frac{3}{5} = \frac{}{25}$.

The denominator of the second fraction is 5 times the size of the first; therefore, the numerator of the second fraction has to be 5 times the size of the first:

$\frac{3}{5} = \frac{15}{25}$.

Exercise 2.1

Change to equivalent fractions; the first two are completed for you.

1   $\frac{1}{2} = \frac{}{16}$.   The denominator has been multiplied by 8 so multiply the numerator by 8.

    $\frac{1}{2} = \frac{8}{16}$. $1 \times 8 = 8$.
            $2 \times 8 = 16$.

2   $\frac{4}{3} = \frac{12}{}$.   The numerator has been multiplied by 3 so multiply the denominator by 3.

    $\frac{4}{3} = \frac{12}{9}$. $4 \times 3 = 12$.
            $3 \times 3 = 9$.

3 $\frac{1}{2} = \frac{}{4}$.	4 $\frac{1}{3} = \frac{}{9}$.	5 $\frac{1}{4} = \frac{}{16}$.	6 $\frac{3}{2} = \frac{}{6}$.
7 $\frac{3}{2} = \frac{12}{}$.	8 $\frac{3}{4} = \frac{}{12}$.	9 $\frac{2}{3} = \frac{12}{}$.	10 $\frac{2}{5} = \frac{}{10}$.
11 $\frac{4}{5} = \frac{16}{}$.	12 $\frac{7}{8} = \frac{}{16}$.	13 $\frac{3}{5} = \frac{6}{}$.	14 $\frac{11}{8} = \frac{33}{}$.
15 $\frac{6}{5} = \frac{24}{}$.	16 $\frac{5}{3} = \frac{15}{}$.	17 $\frac{3}{8} = \frac{6}{}$.	18 $\frac{5}{8} = \frac{}{32}$.
19 $\frac{5}{2} = \frac{10}{}$.	20 $\frac{3}{4} = \frac{}{8}$.		

21 Change $\frac{3}{4}$ into sixteenths.

22 Change $\frac{4}{5}$ into tenths.

23 Change $\frac{5}{8}$ into thirty-seconds.

24 Change two-thirds into sixths.

25 Change three-quarters into twelfths.

26 Change five-halves into tenths.

27 Change four-thirds into twelfths.

28 Change seven-eighths into sixteenths.

29 Change sixteen thirty-seconds into eighths.

30 Change five-quarters into sixteenths.

2.2   Cancelling Fractions

A fraction should be given in its lowest terms, that is, the denominator and numerator should be looked at to see whether the same number will divide into both of them.

Example 2.3

Reduce $\frac{6}{10}$ to its lowest terms.

$\frac{6}{10} = \frac{3}{5}$.   Divide numerator and denominator by 2.
This is cancelling by 2.

Note: The cancelling is usually done on the fraction itself: $\dfrac{\overset{3}{\cancel{6}}}{\underset{5}{\cancel{10}}} = \dfrac{3}{5}$.

Sometimes it is necessary to cancel more than once.

Example 2.4

Give $\frac{24}{60}$ as a fraction in its lowest terms.

$\dfrac{\cancel{24}}{\cancel{60}} = \dfrac{2}{5}$. Cancelling by 2, then 2, and then 3.

Where both numbers are even you can always cancel by 2.

Exercise 2.2

Reduce the following fractions to their lowest terms. The first two have been completed for you.

1   $\dfrac{6}{8}$ $\dfrac{\overset{3}{\cancel{6}}}{\underset{4}{\cancel{8}}} = \dfrac{3}{4}$.   Cancelling by 2.

2   $\dfrac{24}{18}$ $\dfrac{\cancel{24}}{\cancel{18}} = \dfrac{4}{3}$.   Cancelling by 2 and then 3.

3   $\dfrac{4}{6}$ 4 $\dfrac{9}{12}$ 5 $\dfrac{6}{4}$ 6 $\dfrac{10}{15}$ 7 $\dfrac{12}{16}$

8 $\frac{14}{16}$	9 $\frac{8}{10}$	10 $\frac{14}{32}$	11 $\frac{25}{10}$	12 $\frac{12}{4}$
13 $\frac{16}{10}$	14 $\frac{8}{12}$	15 $\frac{8}{20}$	16 $\frac{6}{16}$	17 $\frac{20}{8}$
18 $\frac{6}{15}$	19 $\frac{18}{24}$	20 $\frac{5}{8}$		

2.3 Comparison of Fractions

A comparison of fractions can be made by making use of equivalent fractions to change all of the fractions to the same denominator.

Example 2.5

Arrange in order of size $\frac{1}{3}, \frac{3}{4}, \frac{5}{8}$.

First, find a denominator into which all three denominators will divide. How do we do this?

A practical way is to look at the largest denominator and see if all the other denominators will divide into it.

If they will not then double the largest denominator and try again.

If they will not then multiply the largest denominator by 3.

If all the other denominators will still not divide into it then multiply by 4, and so on.

For $\frac{1}{3}, \frac{3}{4}$ and $\frac{5}{8}$ a suitable denominator is 24.

Now express each fraction with a denominator of 24:

$$\frac{1}{3} = \frac{8}{24}, \qquad \frac{3}{4} = \frac{18}{24}, \qquad \frac{5}{8} = \frac{15}{24};$$

$\frac{18}{24}$ is bigger than $\frac{15}{24}$ which is bigger than $\frac{8}{24}$.

Fractions in order of size are $\frac{3}{4}, \frac{5}{8}, \frac{1}{3}$.

Example 2.6

Arrange in order of size $\frac{2}{3}, \frac{4}{5}, \frac{3}{4}$.

First, look for a denominator into which all three denominators will divide.

A suitable denominator is 60.

Change all three fractions to sixtieths:

$\frac{2}{3} = \frac{40}{60}, \qquad \frac{4}{5} = \frac{48}{60}, \qquad \frac{3}{4} = \frac{45}{60}.$

Fractions in order of size are $\frac{4}{5}, \frac{3}{4}, \frac{2}{3}$.

Exercise 2.3

Put the following fractions in order of size, smallest first. The first two have been completed for you.

1 $\frac{1}{4}, \frac{1}{3}$.

Change each fraction to the same denominator, then place in order.

Change each fraction to twelfths:

$\frac{1}{4} = \frac{3}{12}, \quad \frac{1}{3} = \frac{4}{12}$.

Fractions in order of size are $\frac{1}{4}, \quad \frac{1}{3}$.

2 $\frac{3}{8}, \frac{3}{4}, \frac{1}{2}, \frac{7}{10}$.

Change each fraction to fortieths:

$\frac{3}{8} = \frac{15}{40}, \qquad \frac{3}{4} = \frac{30}{40}, \qquad \frac{1}{2} = \frac{20}{40}, \qquad \frac{7}{10} = \frac{28}{40}$.

Fractions in order of size are $\quad \frac{3}{8}, \frac{1}{2}, \frac{7}{10}, \frac{3}{4}$.

3 $\frac{2}{3}, \frac{4}{5}$	4 $\frac{3}{8}, \frac{5}{12}, \frac{1}{3}$	5 $\frac{3}{4}, \frac{5}{6}, \frac{5}{8}$	6 $\frac{2}{3}, \frac{5}{8}$
7 $\frac{1}{3}, \frac{3}{5}, \frac{1}{2}$	8 $\frac{5}{8}, \frac{2}{3}, \frac{4}{5}$	9 $\frac{1}{3}, \frac{1}{4}, \frac{5}{12}$	10 $\frac{5}{8}, \frac{7}{16}, \frac{1}{2}$
11 $\frac{3}{4}, \frac{9}{16}, \frac{7}{8}, \frac{1}{2}$	12 $\frac{7}{24}, \frac{5}{8}, \frac{1}{4}$	13 $\frac{7}{12}, \frac{2}{5}, \frac{1}{4}, \frac{9}{20}$	14 $\frac{2}{3}, \frac{3}{4}$
15 $\frac{3}{2}, \frac{15}{8}, \frac{7}{4}$	16 $\frac{2}{3}, \frac{4}{5}, \frac{3}{4}$	17 $\frac{5}{6}, 1, \frac{3}{4}, \frac{11}{12}$	18 $\frac{1}{2}, \frac{7}{16}, \frac{5}{8}, \frac{3}{8}$
19 $\frac{3}{4}, \frac{23}{32}, \frac{9}{16}, \frac{5}{8}$	20 $\frac{6}{5}, \frac{11}{10}, 1, \frac{17}{20}$		

2.4 Improper Fractions and Mixed Numbers

An improper fraction is a fraction where the numerator is bigger than the denominator.

These improper fractions can be changed into a whole number plus a proper fraction; it is then called a mixed number.

Example 2.7

Change $\frac{15}{8}$ into a mixed number.

We divide the denominator into the numerator, but instead of finding a remainder we put this remainder over the denominator so making a proper fraction:

$\frac{15}{8} = 1\frac{7}{8}$.   8 into 15 goes 1 with a remainder of 7.

Put this 7 over the denominator.

Examples 2.8

$\frac{4}{3} = 1\frac{1}{3}$.   Divide 4 by 3.

$\frac{10}{3} = 3\frac{1}{3}$.   Divide 10 by 3.

$\frac{15}{4} = 3\frac{3}{4}$.   Divide 15 by 4.

Example 2.9

Change $3\frac{3}{4}$ to an improper fraction.

In changing a mixed number to an improper fraction the denominator of the fraction is all-important:

25

$3\frac{3}{4} = 3 + \frac{3}{4}$.

Now change the 3 whole ones into quarters, making 12:

$3\frac{3}{4} = \frac{12}{4} + \frac{3}{4}$.

$\quad = \frac{15}{4}$.

In other words, multiply the whole number by the denominator and then add the numerator part of the fraction.

Examples 2.10

$1\frac{2}{3} = \frac{5}{3}$.   (3 × 1 and then add 2.)

$2\frac{7}{8} = \frac{23}{8}$.   (8 × 2 and then add 7.)

$4\frac{3}{4} = \frac{19}{4}$.   (4 × 4 and then add 3.)

Exercise 2.4

Change the improper fractions to mixed numbers; the first two have been completed for you.

1 $\frac{5}{4}$.

Divide the denominator into the numerator and put any remainder over the denominator:

$\frac{5}{4} = 1\frac{1}{4}$.   (4 into 5 goes 1 with a remainder of 1)

2 $\frac{28}{10}$.

$\frac{28}{10} = 2\frac{8}{10} = 2\frac{4}{5}$.   (10 into 28 goes 2 with a remainder of 8. See if the remaining fraction will cancel.)

3 $\frac{5}{2}$	4 $\frac{7}{4}$	5 $\frac{11}{3}$	6 $\frac{13}{10}$	7 $\frac{12}{8}$	8 $\frac{14}{10}$
9 $\frac{21}{8}$	10 $\frac{7}{3}$	11 $\frac{26}{8}$	12 $\frac{9}{2}$	13 $\frac{14}{6}$	14 $\frac{18}{4}$
15 $\frac{21}{6}$	16 $\frac{15}{8}$	17 $\frac{10}{4}$	18 $\frac{54}{10}$	19 $\frac{26}{4}$	20 $\frac{7}{2}$

Exercise 2.5

Change the mixed numbers to improper fractions; the first two have been completed for you.

1 $2\frac{3}{4}$

Multiply the whole number by the denominator of the fraction and then add the numerator part of the fraction.

$2\frac{3}{4} = \frac{11}{4}$.   (2 × 4 and then add 3.)

2 $3\frac{5}{6} = \frac{23}{6}$.   (3 × 6 and then add 5.)

3 $2\frac{1}{2}$	4 $3\frac{1}{4}$	5 $1\frac{5}{6}$	6 $1\frac{2}{3}$	7 $3\frac{2}{5}$	8 $2\frac{3}{8}$
9 $5\frac{2}{3}$	10 $6\frac{3}{4}$	11 $3\frac{5}{8}$	12 $1\frac{4}{5}$	13 $3\frac{3}{10}$	14 $2\frac{7}{8}$
15 $3\frac{3}{4}$	16 $1\frac{7}{16}$	17 $2\frac{1}{5}$	18 $3\frac{1}{3}$	19 $5\frac{1}{4}$	20 $3\frac{7}{8}$

2.5 Addition and Subtraction

Before adding or subtracting it is important to make sure that the denominators of the fractions involved are all the same.

Example 2.11

$\frac{1}{4} + \frac{3}{8}$.

Change each fraction to eighths (look at example 2.5):

$$\frac{1}{4} + \frac{3}{8} = \frac{2}{8} + \frac{3}{8} \qquad (\frac{1}{4} = \frac{2}{8}.)$$
$$= \frac{5}{8}.$$

Example 2.12

$\frac{1}{4} + \frac{1}{3}$.

Change each fraction to twelfths:

$$\frac{1}{4} + \frac{1}{3} = \frac{3}{12} + \frac{4}{12} \qquad (\frac{1}{4} = \frac{3}{12}, \qquad \frac{1}{3} = \frac{4}{12})$$
$$= \frac{7}{12}.$$

It is usual to use only one line when the common denominator has been chosen, so

$$\frac{1}{4} + \frac{1}{3} = \frac{3+4}{12}$$
$$= \frac{7}{12}.$$

Example 2.13

$$\frac{1}{4} + \frac{1}{3} + \frac{1}{5} = \frac{15+20+12}{60} \qquad (\frac{1}{4} = \frac{15}{60}, \qquad \frac{1}{3} = \frac{20}{60} \qquad \frac{1}{5} = \frac{12}{60})$$
$$= \frac{47}{60}.$$

When adding mixed numbers, add together the whole numbers first followed by the fractions.

Example 2.14

$$2\frac{1}{4} + 3\frac{5}{8} = 5 + \frac{1}{4} + \frac{5}{8} \qquad \text{Add whole numbers first.}$$
$$= 5\frac{2+5}{8}$$
$$= 5\frac{7}{8}.$$

Example 2.15

$$\frac{2}{3} - \frac{1}{4} = \frac{8-3}{12}$$
$$= \frac{5}{12}.$$

More care may have to be taken when subtracting mixed numbers.

Example 2.16

$3\frac{1}{2} - 2\frac{1}{3} = 1\frac{3-2}{6}$ This example is straightforward.
$\phantom{3\frac{1}{2} - 2\frac{1}{3}} = 1\frac{1}{6}.$

Example 2.17

$4\frac{1}{2} - 2\frac{2}{3} = 2\frac{3-4}{6}.$ Care is needed because 4 cannot be taken from 3.
Use one of the whole numbers and change it into sixths:
$\phantom{4\frac{1}{2} - 2\frac{2}{3}} = 1\frac{6+3-4}{6}$
$\phantom{4\frac{1}{2} - 2\frac{2}{3}} = 1\frac{9-4}{6}$
$\phantom{4\frac{1}{2} - 2\frac{2}{3}} = 1\frac{5}{6}.$

Exercise 2.6

Add together the following fractions; the first two have been completed for you.

1 $\frac{1}{3} + \frac{1}{5}.$

   Change each fraction to the same denominator, in this case fifteenths:
   $\frac{1}{3} + \frac{1}{5} = \frac{5}{15} + \frac{3}{15} = \frac{8}{15}.$

2 $1\frac{1}{2} + \frac{3}{4} + 1\frac{1}{8}.$

   Add whole numbers together. Change fractions to the same denominator, in this case eighths:
   $1\frac{1}{2} + \frac{3}{4} + 1\frac{1}{8} = 2\frac{4+6+1}{8}$
   $\phantom{1\frac{1}{2} + \frac{3}{4} + 1\frac{1}{8}} = 2\frac{11}{8}$
   $\phantom{1\frac{1}{2} + \frac{3}{4} + 1\frac{1}{8}} = 3\frac{3}{8}.$ $(\frac{11}{8} = 1\frac{3}{8})$

3 $\frac{1}{2} + \frac{1}{4}$	4 $\frac{1}{4} + \frac{5}{8}$	5 $\frac{2}{3} + \frac{1}{4}$	6 $\frac{7}{16} + \frac{3}{4}$
7 $\frac{1}{2} + \frac{1}{4} + \frac{3}{8}$	8 $\frac{5}{6} + \frac{2}{3}$	9 $\frac{2}{3} + \frac{3}{4} + \frac{1}{2}$	10 $1\frac{1}{4} + 2\frac{3}{8}$
11 $4\frac{1}{2} + 1\frac{1}{3}$	12 $2\frac{1}{5} + 3\frac{3}{10}$	13 $\frac{3}{4} + 2\frac{7}{16} + 1\frac{1}{2}$	14 $1\frac{1}{2} + 2\frac{1}{4} + \frac{3}{4}$
15 $\frac{9}{16} + 1\frac{7}{8} + 2\frac{1}{2}$	16 $\frac{7}{8} + \frac{2}{3} + 2\frac{1}{6}$	17 $1\frac{3}{4} + 2\frac{5}{8}$	18 $\frac{3}{10} + 1\frac{4}{5}$
19 $\frac{1}{2} + \frac{7}{10} + 1\frac{2}{5}$	20 $3\frac{3}{4} + 1\frac{7}{8}$		

Exercise 2.7

Subtract the following fractions; the first three have been completed for you.

1 $\frac{3}{4} - \frac{2}{3}$

   Change each fraction to the same denominator, in this case 12:
   $\frac{3}{4} - \frac{2}{3} = \frac{9-8}{12} = \frac{1}{12}.$

2 $2\frac{1}{2} - 1\frac{1}{8}$

   Subtract the whole numbers first, and then subtract one fraction from the other:
   $2\frac{1}{2} - 1\frac{1}{8} = 1\frac{4-1}{8}$
   $\phantom{2\frac{1}{2} - 1\frac{1}{8}} = 1\frac{3}{8}.$

3 $3\frac{1}{4} - 1\frac{5}{8}$

Subtract the whole numbers first, and put the fractions over the same denominator:

$3\frac{1}{4} - 1\frac{5}{8} = 2\frac{2-5}{8}$.

But 5 cannot be taken from 2, so use one of the whole numbers and change to eighths (8 is the denominator):

$= 1\frac{8+2-5}{8}$

$= 1\frac{5}{8}$.

4 $\frac{7}{8} - \frac{5}{16}$	**5** $\frac{3}{4} - \frac{3}{8}$	**6** $\frac{9}{16} - \frac{1}{4}$	**7** $\frac{2}{3} - \frac{1}{4}$
8 $2\frac{1}{2} - \frac{3}{16}$	**9** $3\frac{5}{8} - 1\frac{1}{3}$	**10** $2\frac{11}{16} - 1\frac{1}{4}$	**11** $3\frac{2}{3} - 2\frac{1}{4}$
12 $1\frac{3}{4} - \frac{1}{3}$	**13** $3\frac{1}{2} - 1\frac{9}{16}$	**14** $2\frac{2}{3} - \frac{7}{8}$	**15** $3\frac{1}{4} - 1\frac{7}{8}$
16 $2\frac{1}{3} - 1\frac{5}{8}$	**17** $1\frac{1}{2} + \frac{3}{4} - 1\frac{9}{16}$	**18** $2\frac{1}{4} - 3\frac{1}{2} + 2\frac{3}{4}$	**19** $\frac{11}{16} - 2\frac{1}{4} + 3\frac{5}{16}$
20 $3 - 4\frac{1}{8} + 2\frac{1}{3}$			

2.6 Multiplication

For proper fractions multiply all the numerators together and all the denominators together; if mixed numbers are involved convert them to improper fractions before multiplying.

The working can be made easier by cancelling and you can cancel any number in a numerator with any number in a denominator.

Example 2.18

$\frac{1}{3} \times \frac{4}{5} = \frac{4}{15}$. $(1 \times 4 = 4)$
$\phantom{\frac{1}{3} \times \frac{4}{5} = \frac{4}{15}.}$ $(3 \times 5 = 15)$

Example 2.19

$\frac{3}{4} \times \frac{4}{9} = \frac{12}{36} = \frac{1}{3}$.

or $\dfrac{\cancel{3}^{1}}{\cancel{4}_{1}} \times \dfrac{\cancel{4}^{1}}{\cancel{9}_{3}} = \dfrac{1 \times 1}{1 \times 3} = \dfrac{1}{3}$.

Example 2.20

$\dfrac{\cancel{2}^{1}}{\cancel{3}_{1}} \times \dfrac{\cancel{9}^{3}}{\cancel{10}_{5}} = \dfrac{3}{5}$.   Cancelling by 3 for 3 and 9.
 Cancelling by 2 for 2 and 10.

Example 2.21

$2\frac{1}{2} \times 1\frac{1}{3}$ These are mixed numbers; change to improper fractions.

$= \dfrac{5}{\cancel{2}_{1}} \times \dfrac{\cancel{4}^{2}}{3} = \dfrac{10}{3} = 3\dfrac{1}{3}$.

Exercise 2.8

Multiply the following fractions; the first three have been completed for you.

1 $\frac{3}{4} \times \frac{2}{3} = \frac{6}{12}$ Multiply the numerators together.
                          Multiply the denominators together.

   $= \frac{1}{2}$.   Cancelling by 6.

or $\frac{\cancel{3}^1}{\cancel{4}_2} \times \frac{\cancel{2}^1}{\cancel{3}_1} = \frac{1}{2}$.   Cancelling before multiplying.

2 $2\frac{1}{8} \times 1\frac{1}{3} = \frac{17}{\cancel{8}_2} \times \frac{\cancel{4}^1}{3}$ Change mixed numbers to improper fractions and then cancel.

   $= \frac{17}{6}$

   $= 2\frac{5}{6}$.

3 Find $\frac{3}{4}$ of 120.   In this context 'of' means multiply.

   $\frac{3}{4}$ of $120 = \frac{3}{\cancel{4}_1} \times \cancel{120}^{30}$

   $= 90$.

4 $\frac{5}{8} \times \frac{3}{5}$	5 $\frac{3}{4} \times \frac{5}{6}$	6 $\frac{3}{4} \times \frac{10}{13}$	7 $2\frac{1}{4} \times 1\frac{1}{3}$
8 $2\frac{1}{2} \times 1\frac{1}{3}$	9 $1\frac{1}{8} \times 4$	10 $2\frac{1}{4} \times \frac{1}{2}$	11 $3\frac{1}{8} \times 1\frac{3}{5}$
12 $\frac{7}{8} \times 1\frac{3}{4}$	13 $\frac{3}{4}$ of $2\frac{1}{3}$	14 $\frac{1}{2}$ of $2\frac{3}{8}$	15 $\frac{1}{3}$ of $2\frac{1}{2}$
16 Find $\frac{2}{3}$ of 180	17 What is $\frac{3}{5}$ of 120?		18 Find $\frac{1}{3}$ of 135
19 How much is $\frac{3}{8}$ of £120?		20 What is $\frac{3}{5}$ of £90?	

2.7 Division

To divide by a fraction, whether a proper or an improper fraction, all we have to do is invert the fraction and then multiply. (A mixed number should be changed first to an improper fraction.)

Example 2.22

$\frac{3}{4} \div \frac{1}{2} = \frac{3}{\cancel{4}_2} \times \frac{\cancel{2}^1}{1}$ (Inverting $\frac{1}{2}$ and then multiplying.)

   $= \frac{3}{2} = 1\frac{1}{2}$.

Example 2.23

$1\frac{1}{5} \div 1\frac{1}{10} = \frac{6}{5} \div \frac{11}{10}$ Changing to improper fractions.

   $= \frac{6}{\cancel{5}_1} \times \frac{\cancel{10}^2}{11}$ Inverting $\frac{11}{10}$ and then multiplying.

   $= \frac{12}{11} = 1\frac{1}{11}$.

30

Exercise 2.9

Divide the following fractions; the first two have been completed for you.

1 $2\frac{3}{4} \div 1\frac{1}{4} = \frac{11}{4} \div \frac{5}{4}$ Change to improper fractions.

$\quad\quad = \frac{11}{4} \times \frac{4}{5}$ Insert divisor and multiply.

$\quad\quad = \frac{11}{5} = 2\frac{1}{5}$.

2 $2\frac{1}{4} \div \frac{2}{3} = \frac{9}{4} \div \frac{2}{3}$

$\quad\quad = \frac{9}{4} \times \frac{3}{2}$

$\quad\quad = \frac{27}{8} = 3\frac{3}{8}$.

3 $2\frac{1}{3} \div 6$ $\quad$ 4 $3\frac{1}{2} \div 1\frac{1}{4}$ $\quad$ 5 $2\frac{5}{6} \div 1\frac{1}{3}$ $\quad$ 6 $2\frac{1}{4} \div \frac{1}{2}$

7 $1\frac{1}{3} \div \frac{2}{3}$ $\quad$ 8 $\frac{5}{6} \div \frac{2}{3}$ $\quad$ 9 $1\frac{1}{5} \div 2\frac{1}{10}$ $\quad$ 10 $2\frac{3}{4} \div 3\frac{2}{3}$

11 $\frac{3}{4} \div \frac{1}{2}$ $\quad$ 12 $4 \div \frac{2}{3}$ $\quad$ 13 $10 \div 3\frac{1}{3}$ $\quad$ 14 $\frac{3}{4} \div \frac{2}{3}$

15 $2\frac{1}{4} \div 1\frac{1}{3}$ $\quad$ 16 $3\frac{1}{2} \div 2\frac{1}{4}$ $\quad$ 17 $\frac{7}{16} \div \frac{1}{4}$ $\quad$ 18 $\frac{1}{4} \div \frac{7}{16}$

19 $2\frac{1}{8} \div \frac{3}{4}$ $\quad$ 20 $\frac{3}{4} \div 2\frac{1}{2}$

2.8 Priorities

If we are asked to work out an expression such as
$(1\frac{2}{3} + \frac{3}{4}) \times (\frac{1}{2} + 1\frac{1}{4})$

then we must know the order in which to work out the different parts of the expression.

The order of priorities for fractions is exactly the same as that used for numbers.

First, complete work in the brackets.

Second, complete multiplication and division.

Finally, complete addition and subtraction.

Example 2.24

$1\frac{3}{4} \times (1\frac{1}{2} - \frac{1}{6})$

$= 1\frac{3}{4} \times (1\frac{3-1}{6})$ Complete work in brackets first.

$= 1\frac{3}{4} \times 1\frac{2}{6}$ $(1\frac{2}{6} = 1\frac{1}{3})$

$= \frac{7}{4} \times \frac{4}{3} = \frac{7}{3} = 2\frac{1}{3}$.

Exercise 2.10

Priorities:

First, complete work in the brackets.

Second, do multiplication and division.

Third, do addition and subtraction.

Complete the following questions; the first three have been completed for you.

$$1 \quad \frac{1}{2} + \frac{3}{4} \text{ of } \frac{2}{3} = \frac{1}{2} + \frac{\cancel{3}^1}{\cancel{4}_2} \times \frac{\cancel{2}^1}{\cancel{3}_1} \qquad \text{Do multiplication first.}$$

$$= \frac{1}{2} + \frac{1}{2}$$

$$= 1.$$

$$2 \quad \left(\frac{1}{2} + \frac{3}{4}\right) \text{ of } \frac{2}{3} = \left(\frac{1}{2} + \frac{3}{4}\right) \times \frac{2}{3} \qquad \text{Complete work in brackets first.}$$

$$= \left(\frac{2+3}{4}\right) \times \frac{2}{3}$$

$$= \frac{5}{\cancel{4}_2} \times \frac{\cancel{2}^1}{3}$$

$$= \frac{5}{6}.$$

$$3 \quad 4 \div \frac{2}{3} + 3 \quad = \cancel{4}^2 \times \frac{3}{\cancel{2}_1} + 3 \qquad \text{Do division first.}$$

$$= 6 + 3$$

$$= 9.$$

4 $\frac{1}{2}$ of $1\frac{1}{2} + \frac{1}{2}$ 5 $\frac{3}{4}$ of $6 - 2$ 6 $1\frac{1}{2} + 2 \div 1\frac{3}{4}$ 7 $1\frac{1}{4} + (2\frac{1}{4} - 1\frac{1}{2})$

8 $\frac{5}{16} \times (2\frac{1}{4} + 1\frac{3}{4})$ 9 $1\frac{1}{4} \div \frac{1}{2} + \frac{1}{2}$ 10 $1\frac{1}{4} \div (\frac{1}{2} + \frac{1}{4})$ 11 $1\frac{1}{2} + \frac{1}{2} \times \frac{1}{4} + 1\frac{3}{4}$

12 $1\frac{1}{2} \div \frac{3}{8}$ of $1\frac{1}{3}$ 13 $3\frac{1}{4} \div \frac{3}{4} + 1\frac{1}{4}$ 14 $2\frac{1}{2} - (1\frac{1}{2} \times 1\frac{1}{4})$ 15 $2\frac{1}{2} \div \frac{3}{4} \times 1\frac{1}{3}$

16 $\frac{5}{8}$ of $80 - 16$ 17 $\frac{3}{4}$ of $1\frac{1}{3} \div \frac{1}{4}$ 18 $1\frac{1}{2} + \frac{1}{2} \times \frac{3}{4}$ 19 $(\frac{2}{3} + \frac{3}{4}) \times 1\frac{1}{2} + \frac{1}{2}$

20 $1\frac{1}{2} \times 2\frac{1}{4} + \frac{3}{4}$

Exercise 2.11

Complete the following questions; the first four are completed for you.

1 How much is $\frac{2}{3}$ of £60?

In this context 'of' means multiply.

The question now becomes $\frac{2}{\cancel{3}_1} \times £\cancel{60}^{20}$

$$= £40. \qquad \text{Don't forget the £ symbol.}$$

2 Find the cost of $1\frac{1}{2}$ lb of ham at 180p per lb.

You are given the cost of 1 lb.

To find the cost of $1\frac{1}{2}$ lb multiply the cost of 1 lb by $1\frac{1}{2}$:

Cost of $1\frac{1}{2}$ lb $= 1\frac{1}{2} \times 180$p

$$= \frac{3}{\cancel{2}_1} \times \cancel{180}^{90}\text{p}$$

$$= 270\text{p}. \qquad \text{Don't forget the p symbol.}$$

3 $\frac{2}{3}$ of a sum of money is £100. How much is $\frac{3}{5}$ of it?

In question 1 of this exercise it was said that 'of' means multiply; the question now asked can therefore be rewritten as

$\frac{2}{3} \times$ sum of money $=$ £100.

First, find the sum of money.

This can be done as follows:

$\frac{2}{3}$ = £100.

$\frac{1}{3}$ = £50.

$\frac{3}{3}$ = £150.

Having found the sum of money £150 now find $\frac{3}{5}$ of £150:

$$= \frac{3}{\cancel{5}_1} \times \cancel{£150}^{30}$$

= £90. Don't forget the £ symbol.

4 $\frac{1}{3}$ of a pole is red, $\frac{5}{12}$ is blue and the remaining 6 ft is white. How long is the pole and what length is painted red? First, find what fraction of the pole is painted red and blue:

$= \frac{1}{3} + \frac{5}{12} = \frac{4+5}{12} = \frac{9}{12} = \frac{3}{4}$.

This means that $\frac{1}{4}$ ($1 - \frac{3}{4}$) is painted white.

We are told the white-painted piece is 6 ft long, which means $\frac{1}{4}$ of the pole is 6 ft.

The length of the whole pole is 24 ft.

The red portion is $\frac{1}{3}$ of pole = $\frac{1}{3} \times 24$ ft

= 8 ft.

5 How much is $\frac{3}{4}$ of £120?

6 $\frac{3}{4}$ of a sum of money is £90. How much is $\frac{1}{2}$ of it?

7 Three students share a prize of £50. One student received $\frac{1}{2}$ of the prize, another $\frac{2}{5}$ of the prize; how much money did the third one receive?

8 One half of my money is spent on cigarettes, one third on sweets and I have £1 left. How much did I have to begin with?

9 In a bag of mixed sweets, one half are caramels, one third of the rest are chocolate éclairs, and the remainder are boiled sweets. There are twelve boiled sweets. How many chocolate éclairs and caramels are there?

10 A 15 ft pole is red and white. $\frac{2}{5}$ is painted red. What length of pole is painted white?

11 A family holiday cost £850. Accommodation took $\frac{3}{5}$ of this. $\frac{3}{10}$ was for travelling, and the rest on entertainment. How much was spent on (a) accommodation, (b) travelling, (c) entertainment?

12 A newsagent says that $\frac{2}{3}$ of his weekly sales comes from newspapers and the rest from tobacco and sweets. The newspaper sales amount to £1200 a week. What are the sales from tobacco and sweets? What are the annual sales (52 weeks) of everything?

13 In an hour of Thames Television there were advertising breaks of $1\frac{1}{2}$ minutes, $3\frac{1}{4}$ minutes and $2\frac{3}{4}$ minutes. How much advertising was there in one hour?

14 In a survey of 750 teenagers it was found that $\frac{2}{5}$ were heavy smokers, $\frac{1}{3}$ smoked occasionally, and the rest were non-smokers. How many were non-smokers?

15 A packet contains chocolate in $\frac{3}{4}$ lb boxes. If the packet weighs 12 lb, how many boxes of chocolate are there?

16 A $4\frac{1}{2}$ lb jar of caramels is prepacked into $\frac{1}{4}$ lb bags. How many bags are there?

17 A coal lorry carries 45 cwt of coal in $\frac{1}{2}$ cwt sacks. How many sacks on the lorry?

18 A survey among young children found the most popular colours are red, blue and yellow. A half liked red, a third liked blue and ten liked yellow. How many children were asked and how many liked red?

19 In 1984 it was found that 180 million pounds (£180m) was spent on baked

beans. Heinz account for $\frac{4}{10}$ of this total. How much was spent on Heinz baked beans?

20 In 1984 it was found that £140m was spent on canned soups. Heinz got $\frac{1}{2}$ of this market, Campbells and Crosse & Blackwells together got $\frac{1}{4}$ of the total, and own label got $\frac{3}{20}$ of the total. How much money did all the rest get and how much did Heinz get?

Exercise 2.12   Multiple-choice Questions

Work out which is the correct answer in the following questions.

1 Which of the following is $\frac{3}{5}$ equal to?

    A $\frac{15}{20}$ B $\frac{10}{15}$ C $\frac{9}{15}$ D $\frac{9}{12}$

2 Is $\frac{12}{32}$ equal to

    A $\frac{5}{16}$ B $\frac{3}{8}$ C $\frac{1}{3}$ D $\frac{7}{16}$

3 Is $\frac{2}{3}$

    A   bigger than $\frac{3}{4}$ B   same as $\frac{3}{4}$ C   smaller than $\frac{3}{4}$

    D   impossible to work out?

4 Is $\frac{12}{8}$ equivalent to

    A $1\frac{1}{2}$ B $1\frac{3}{8}$ C $1\frac{5}{8}$ D $1\frac{3}{4}$?

5 Is $4\frac{1}{2}$ equivalent to

    A $\frac{41}{2}$ B $\frac{8}{2}$ C $\frac{5}{2}$ D $\frac{9}{2}$?

6 Is $\frac{1}{2} + \frac{1}{3} + \frac{1}{4}$ equal to

    A $\frac{11}{12}$ B $1\frac{1}{12}$ C $1\frac{1}{6}$ D $\frac{9}{12}$?

7 Is $1\frac{1}{2} + 2\frac{5}{12} + \frac{5}{6}$ equal to

    A $4\frac{1}{12}$ B 5   C $4\frac{3}{4}$ D $4\frac{5}{12}$?

8 What needs to be added to $1\frac{1}{4}$ to make $2\frac{5}{6}$?

    A $4\frac{1}{12}$ B $1\frac{7}{12}$ C $1\frac{1}{2}$ D $3\frac{3}{4}$

9 What needs to be taken from $2\frac{1}{2}$ to make $\frac{11}{12}$?

    A $1\frac{13}{14}$ B $1\frac{1}{2}$ C $1\frac{7}{12}$ D $3\frac{5}{12}$

10 $\frac{1}{3}$ of a class wear navy cardigans, $\frac{1}{2}$ of the rest wear maroon, and the six that are left do not wear cardigans. How many wear maroon?

    A 12   B 8   C 6   D 10

11 How much is $2\frac{1}{4}$ lb of meat at £4 per lb?

    A £1.78   B £$6\frac{1}{4}$ C £9   D £$2\frac{3}{4}$

12 One half of my money is spent on cigarettes, one third on food and there is £3 left. Did I begin with

    A £20   B £15   C £18   D £21?

13 Is $2\frac{1}{2} \times 1\frac{1}{2} + \frac{1}{2}$ equal to

    A $4\frac{1}{4}$ B 5   C $4\frac{1}{2}$ D $3\frac{3}{4}$?

34

14 Pocket money was given among three children as follows:
$\frac{1}{2}$ to Mary, $\frac{1}{3}$ to John, $\frac{1}{6}$ to Harry.
What fraction of the money was left over?

A None **B** $\frac{1}{6}$ **C** $\frac{1}{3}$ **D** $\frac{1}{12}$

15 Is $\frac{1}{2}$ of $\frac{1}{2}$ equal to

A 1 **B** 2 **C** $\frac{1}{4}$ **D** $\frac{1}{2}$?

16 At one time in the miners' strike it was reported that $\frac{2}{5}$ of the 180 000 miners were working. How many were on strike at this time?

A 72 000 **B** 90 000 **C** 108 000 **D** 120 000

17 In a hospital $\frac{1}{8}$ of the personnel are doctors, $\frac{7}{16}$ are nurses, $\frac{1}{8}$ are administrators, and all remaining staff total 375. Is the number of personnel in the hospital

A 1000 **B** 1500 **C** 1200 **D** 1800?

18 A woman in her will left one half of her estate to her husband, two thirds of the remainder to her children, and the remainder to the RSPCA. If the RSPCA received £1200, did she leave

A £2400 **B** £120 000 **C** £7200 **D** £12 000?

19 A 20 lb pack is split into $\frac{1}{4}$ lb packets. Are there

A 5 packets **B** 80 packets **C** 24 packets **D** 20 packets?

20 A grand prix driver was placed first in $\frac{1}{4}$ of his races in one year, second in $\frac{1}{3}$ of his races, and third in all the remaining races. If he was third in 10 races was he first in

A 5 races **B** 10 races **C** 12 races **D** 6 races?

3 Decimals

3.1 Place Value

Decimal fractions are usually called decimals and are separated from the whole numbers by a dot called the decimal point.

The numbers to the right of the decimal point are a special way of writing fractions whose denominators are 10, 100, 1000, etc.

The place value table showing the relationship between whole numbers and decimals is:

Decimal point

Thousands Hundreds Tens Units ! Tenths Hundredths Thousandths

Example 3.1

Four point three (4.3) means 4 units and 3 tenths.
Six point three five (6.35) means 6 units, 3 tenths and 5 hundredths.
Thirty-six point nought eight seven (36.087) means 3 tens, 6 units, 0 tenths, 9 hundredths and 7 thousandths.

You may find a whole number written with the decimal point followed by 0, such as 4.0.

It is usual to put 0 in front of the decimal point if there are no whole numbers, for example 0.53, 0.824.

Exercise 3.1

Write down the following words in decimals, and decimals in words. The first two are completed for you.

1 Two point six four = 2.64

2 3.065 = three point nought six five

3 Twenty-five point six three
4 Eight point two five
5 Nought point five nine
6 One hundred and seven point nine six
7 Three point nought eight
8 Fourteen point two nought two
9 Sixty-three point nought seven eight
10 7.52   11 26.79   12 8.4   13 15.06   14 18.003   15 10.56
16 42.703   17 105.02   18 36.104
19 What does the 1 in 36.104 mean?
20 What does the 5 in 1.251 mean?

3.2 Converting Simple Fractions to Decimals and Decimals to Fractions

If a fraction is expressed in tenths, hundredths, thousandths, it can be written as a decimal immediately.

Example 3.2

Look at the place value table as these are written out:

$\frac{1}{10} = 0.1$ $\qquad\qquad$ $\frac{4}{10} = 0.4$

$\frac{36}{100} = 0.36$ $\qquad$ This is 36 hundredths and the 6 must go in the hundredths column.

$\frac{95}{100} = 0.95$ $\qquad\qquad$ $\frac{195}{100} = 1.95$

$\frac{387}{1000} = 0.387$ $\qquad\quad$ $\frac{37}{1000} = 0.037$

Look at the place value table and remember that

0.4 is 4 tenths or $\frac{4}{10}$;

0.09 is 9 hundredths or $\frac{9}{100}$;

0.36 is 36 hundredths or $\frac{36}{100}$;

0.012 is 12 thousandths or $\frac{12}{1000}$;

0.268 is 268 thousandths or $\frac{268}{1000}$.

Remember to cancel these fractions to their lowest terms.

Exercise 3.2

Change these fractions to decimals. The first two are completed for you.

1 $\frac{3}{10} = 0.3$

2 $\frac{182}{1000} = 0.182$

3 $\frac{4}{10}$	4 $\frac{8}{10}$	5 $\frac{1}{10}$	6 $\frac{15}{100}$	7 $\frac{27}{100}$	8 $\frac{35}{100}$
9 $\frac{58}{100}$	10 $\frac{11}{100}$	11 $\frac{72}{100}$	12 $\frac{125}{100}$	13 $\frac{303}{1000}$	14 $\frac{84}{1000}$
15 $\frac{6}{1000}$	16 $\frac{5}{100}$	17 $\frac{902}{1000}$	18 $\frac{22}{1000}$	19 $\frac{15}{10}$	20 $\frac{346}{100}$

Exercise 3.3

Change these decimals to fractions and reduce to lowest terms. The first three are completed for you.

1 $0.6 = \frac{6}{10} = \frac{3}{5}$ $\qquad$ Cancelling by 2.

2 $0.35 = \frac{35}{100} = \frac{7}{20}$ $\qquad$ Cancelling by 5.

3 $0.375 = \frac{375}{1000} = \frac{3}{8}$ $\qquad$ Cancelling by 5, and then 5, and then 5.

37

4 0.3	5 0.8	6 0.25	7 0.38	8 0.64	9 0.75
10 0.88	11 0.132	12 0.625	13 0.94	14 0.7	15 0.875
16 0.65	17 0.682	18 0.46	19 0.52	20 0.188	

3.3 Addition and Subtraction

The method is exactly the same as that for whole numbers (Sections 1.3 and 1.6) but remember to keep all the decimal points underneath one another; this ensures that all the units, all the tenths, all the hundredths, and so on will be underneath one another.

Example 3.3

Add together 8.24, 26.84, 7.3 and 2.625

Place the numbers in columns with the decimal points underneath one another.

```
   8.24
  26.84
   7.3
+  2.625
  2 2 1
  45.005     Answer    45.005
```

Example 3.4

Add together 3.72, 46, 0.294, 100.04 and 92.5.

Place the numbers in columns with the decimal points underneath one another. Note how a decimal point is placed behind the units of a whole number:

```
   3.72
  46.0
   0.294
 100.04
+ 92.5
  1 1 1 1
 242.554     Answer    242.554
```

In subtraction, again keep the decimal points underneath one another.

Examples 3.5

48.96 − 26.42

```
  48.96
− 26.42
  22.54
```

$$8.3 - 3.7$$

$$
\begin{array}{r}
\overset{7}{8}.\overset{1}{3} \\
-\ 3.7 \\
\hline
4.6
\end{array}
$$

Answer   4.6

Example 3.6

$$45.4 - 18.26$$

$$
\begin{array}{r}
\overset{3}{4}\overset{1}{5}.\overset{3}{4}\overset{1}{0} \\
-\ 18.26 \\
\hline
27.14
\end{array}
$$

Answer   27.14

Exercise 3.4

Find the value of the following. The first two are completed for you.

1 4.3 + 7.52 + 3.7

Add like ordinary numbers but make sure the decimal points of each number are underneath one another.

$$
\begin{array}{r}
4.3 \\
7.52 \\
+\ 3.7 \\
\overset{1\ 1}{} \\
\hline
15.52
\end{array}
$$

Answer   15.52

2 27.9 + 0.056 + 8.94 + 108.5

$$
\begin{array}{r}
27.9 \\
0.056 \\
8.94 \\
+\ 108.5 \\
\overset{2\ 2}{} \\
\hline
145.396
\end{array}
$$

Answer   145.396

3 8.7 + 1.2

4 7.5 + 6.9

5 12.28 + 14.31

6 37.85 + 9.67

7 27.92 + 6.38 + 4.6

8 0.28 + 27.61 + 4.0

9 134.6 + 0.02 + 5.78 + 15

10 9.004 + 24.16 + 0.507

11 52.81 + 15.14 + 0.32

12 8.06 + 102.8 + 0.52

13 92.5 + 16.7 + 0.26

14 0.02 + 0.75 + 6.29

15 14.16 + 83.24 + 0.74

16 9.06 + 11.052 + 3.65

17 27.18 + 46.85 + 0.092

18 0.062 + 5.07 + 25.48

19 15.86 + 2.04 + 108 + 0.006

20 64.28 + 0.751 + 7.08 + 0.052

Exercise 3.5

Find the value of the following. The first two are completed for you.

1 8.7 − 5.9

Subtract like ordinary numbers but make sure the decimal points of each number are underneath one another.

$$\begin{array}{r} {}^7\!\!\!\not8.^1\!7 \\ -\ 5.9 \\ \hline 2.8 \end{array}$$ Answer   2.8

2 20 − 12.74

$$\begin{array}{r} {}^1\!\not2\,{}^9\!\not0.{}^9\!\not0\,{}^1\!0 \\ -\ 12.74 \\ \hline 7.26 \end{array}$$ Answer   7.26

3 9.7 − 4.3	**4** 28.64 − 12.41	**5** 17.52 − 12.32	**6** 63.13 − 40.58
7 32.56 − 18.75	**8** 25.84 − 9.92	**9** 175.2 − 97.84	**10** 200 − 138.22
11 36.1 − 19.53	**12** 40 − 24.38	**13** 528 − 75.29	**14** 64.97 − 35
15 225.08 − 157.20	**16** 146.7 − 88.95	**17** 22.5 − 17.84	**18** 100 − 54.62
19 40.1 − 25.93	**20** 72.1 − 54.18		

3.4   Multiplication

Ignore the decimal point and multiply the numbers as if they were whole numbers. Place the decimal point in the answer after multiplying.

How to place the decimal point?

Count how many figures, including 0s, there are to the right of the decimal point in each number and add together. This total gives the number of figures which must be to the right of the decimal point in the answer.

Example 3.7

2.4 × 4

$$\begin{array}{r} 24 \\ \times\ {}_1\,4 \\ \hline 96 \end{array}$$ Multiply as if whole numbers.

There is 1 figure behind the decimal point in 2.4.
There are no figures behind the decimal point in 4 (4.0).
There has to be 1 + 0 = 1 figure behind the decimal point in the answer.
Count 1 figure from the right: Answer   9.6

Example 3.8

3.8 × 5.2

$$\begin{array}{r} 38 \\ \times\ 52 \\ {}^{4\ 1} \\ \hline 1900 \\ 76 \\ \hline 1976 \end{array}$$ Multiply as if whole numbers.

Answer   1976

40

There is 1 figure behind the decimal point in 3.8.
There is 1 figure behind the decimal point in 5.2.
There must be 1 + 1 = 2 decimal places in the answer.
Answer   19.76

Exercise 3.6

Multiply the numbers given. The first three are completed for you.

1 8.6 x 2.4

Multiply as if whole numbers:

```
      86     Add together the number of decimal places in each number:
x     24     1 + 1 = 2.
    1720     There have to be 2 decimal places in the answer.
     344
    2064     Answer   20.64
```

2 39.5 x 7.64

Multiply as if whole numbers:

```
       395      Add the number of decimal places in each number:
x      764      1 + 2 = 3.
   276 500      There have to be 3 decimal places in the answer.
    23 700
     1 580
   301 780      Answer   301.780
```

3 0.37 x 4.8

Multiply as if whole numbers:

```
       37     There have to be 2 + 1 = 3 decimal places in the answer.
x      48
     1480
      296
     1776     Answer   1.776
```

4 2.3 x 3	5 8.6 x 7	6 25.3 x 8	7 7.4 x 16
8 4.3 x 2.8	9 9.6 x 1.5	10 3.96 x 6	11 8.24 x 3.6
12 7.3 x 6.8	13 5.6 x 0.4	14 0.8 x 9.2	15 0.35 x 8.6
16 0.57 x 0.26	17 7.6 x 0.83	18 25.1 x 12	19 1.7 x 0.4
20 0.8 x 0.52			

3.5 Multiplication and Division by Powers of 10

10×1	$= 10$	$= 10^1$.
10×10	$= 100$	$= 10^2$.
$10 \times 10 \times 10$	$= 1000$	$= 10^3$.
$10 \times 10 \times 10 \times 10 \times 10$	$= 100\,000$	$= 10^5$.

The small figures 1, 2, 3 and 5 are said to be the powers of 10; the power gives the number of times the base number (10) is multiplied to itself. The power of 10 corresponds to the number of 0s after the figure 1.

Any decimal number can be multiplied by a power of 10 by moving the decimal point to the right — the number of places corresponding to the power of 10.

Examples 3.9

$1.3 \times 10 \quad = 13$ Move decimal point in 1.3 one place to right.

$1.3 \times 100 \quad = 130$ Move decimal point 2 places to right.

$1.3 \times 1000 = 1300$

$1.3 \times 10^5 \quad = 130\,000$

Any decimal number can be divided by a power of 10 by moving the decimal point to the left — the number of places to correspond to the power of 10.

Examples 3.10

$12.62 \div 10 \quad = 1.262$ Move decimal point 1 place to left.

$12.62 \div 100 \quad = 0.1262$ Move decimal point 2 places to left.

$12.62 \div 1000 = 0.012\,62$

$12.62 \div 10^5 \quad = 0.000\,126\,2$

Exercise 3.7

Find the value of the following. The first two are completed for you.

   1   $3.7 \times 100 = 370$

   2   $3.7 \div 100 = 0.037$

3 5.6×100	4 2.34×1000	5 0.173×10	6 0.58×1000
7 $21.6 \times 10\,000$	8 395.51×10	9 $0.07 \times 10\,000$	10 3.6×100
11 0.5×100	12 $375 \div 10$	13 $375 \div 100$	14 $375 \div 1000$
15 $0.28 \div 100$	16 $5.6 \div 1000$	17 $92.4 \div 10$	18 $38.06 \div 10\,000$
19 $0.06 \div 1000$	20 $3.20 \div 100$	21 2.58×10^5	22 8.309×10^4
23 $428 \div 10^3$	24 $2.31 \div 10^3$		

3.6   Division

Division of a decimal number by a whole number is similar to the method shown in 1.6 but care has to be taken in placing the decimal point.

Example 3.11

   $76.8 \div 8$.

If we are dividing by a number less than 10 then we do it similarly to worked example 1.21:

$$\begin{array}{r} 9.6 \\ \hline 8\overline{)76.8} \end{array}$$

Put a decimal point in the answer immediately above the one in the number being divided.

Answer   9.6

Example 3.12

$737.1 \div 7$

$$\begin{array}{r} 105.3 \\ 7\overline{)737.1} \end{array}$$

Put decimal point in answer.
7 into 7 goes 1.
7 into 3 won't go.
Put 0 in the answer and carry 3.

Answer   105.3

If dividing by a large number then use long division as in worked examples 1.23, 1.24 and 1.25.

Example 3.13

$849.42 \div 27$

$$\begin{array}{r} 31.46 \\ 27\overline{)849.42} \\ 81 \\ \hline 39 \\ 27 \\ \hline 124 \\ 108 \\ \hline 162 \\ 162 \\ \hline \cdots \end{array}$$

Put decimal point in answer.

3×27

1×27

4×27

6×27

Answer   31.46

When dividing by a decimal number, move the decimal point to make it into a whole number and adjust the position of the decimal point of the other number in the same way.

Example 3.14

$75.66 \div 0.6$

Make 0.6 into a whole number by moving the decimal point 1 place to the right.

If this is done then 75.66 also has to have the decimal point moved one place to the right.

$75.66 \div 0.6$ is exactly the same as $756.6 \div 6.0$

Now that we are dividing by a whole number continue as in the previous examples:

$$\begin{array}{r} 126.1 \\ 6\overline{)756.6} \end{array}$$

Answer   126.1

43

Example 3.15

   4.158 ÷ 0.18

Make 0.18 a whole number by moving the decimal point 2 places to the right.
4.158 becomes 415.8 when the decimal point moved 2 places to the right.

4.158 ÷ 0.18 is the same as 415.8 ÷ 18

```
      23.1              Put the decimal point in the answer.
 18)415.8
     36        2 × 18
     ——
     55
     54        3 × 18
     ——
     18
     18        1 × 18     Answer    23.1
     ··
```

Exercise 3.8

Find the value of the following. The first three have been completed for you.

   1 95.2 ÷ 7

```
    13.6
       2 4
 7)95.2        Answer    13.6
```

   2 8.64 ÷ 2.4

Change the divisor (2.4) into a whole number 24 — this has meant moving the decimal point 1 place.
   Now move the decimal point 1 place in the dividend (8.64) to 86.4:
8.64 ÷ 2.4 is the same as 86.4 ÷ 24.

```
      3.6
 24)86.4
    72        3 × 24
    ——
    14.4
    14.4      6 × 24
    ····               Answer    3.6
```

   3 5.6 ÷ 0.4 is the same as 56 ÷ 4.

```
    14.0
 4)56.0        Answer    14.0
```

4 82.8 ÷ 6	**5** 93.6 ÷ 4	**6** 114.8 ÷ 7	**7** 198.4 ÷ 8
8 5.6 ÷ 1.6	**9** 18.36 ÷ 3.6	**10** 17.68 ÷ 2.6	**11** 19.32 ÷ 2.8
12 35.5 ÷ 0.5	**13** 72.8 ÷ 0.4	**14** 44.8 ÷ 0.7	**15** 747 ÷ 0.9
16 498.4 ÷ 1.4	**17** 181.7 ÷ 2.3	**18** 0.1118 ÷ 4.3	**19** 0.2368 ÷ 37
20 3.312 ÷ 4.8			

3.7   Corrected Decimals

In section 1.20 we saw how numbers can be rounded off. For most decimals it is usual to work to only 2 or 3 decimal places and give an answer to a certain degree of accuracy.

A 'corrected' answer means giving an answer to a given number of decimal places.

Examples 3.16

4.31 is 4.3 correct to one decimal place.

4.37 is 4.4 correct to one decimal place.

As in rounding off, if the last figure is a 5 or more put the previous figure up by one; if the last figure is 4 or less leave the previous figure as it was.

When correcting to one decimal place look at the figure in the second decimal place.

When correcting to two decimal places look at the figure in the third decimal place.

When correcting to three decimal places look at the figure in the fourth decimal place.

Examples 3.17

3.26 is 3.3 correct to one decimal place.

3.264 is 3.26 correct to two decimal places.

3.2645 is 3.265 correct to three decimal places.

Exercise 3.9

Write the following correct to one decimal place. The first three are completed for you.

1 7.68 = 7.7 correct to one decimal place.

2 2.97 = 3.0 correct to one decimal place.

3 3.549 = 3.5 correct to one decimal place.

4 3.66	**5** 5.94	**6** 0.25	**7** 0.96	**8** 8.048
9 0.76	**10** 15.08	**11** 28.97	**12** 3.047	**13** 0.16
14 0.06	**15** 2.58	**16** 10.84	**17** 9.96	**18** 3.27
19 1.018	**20** 28.73			

Exercise 3.10

Write the following correct to two decimal places. The first three are completed for you.

1 2.928 = 2.93 correct to two decimal places.

2 0.7249 = 0.72 correct to two decimal places.

3 7.996 = 8.00 correct to two decimal places.

4 18.757	**5** 9.085	**6** 76.184	**7** 0.8548	**8** 2.996
9 0.097	**10** 15.328	**11** 1.075	**12** 0.2098	**13** 29.178
14 5.397	**15** 12.085	**16** 10.097	**17** 0.006	**18** 9.2049
19 75.477	**20** 35.063			

3.8 Significant Figures

A number may have a lot of figures but some of the figures may not be important in relation to the others and we may be asked to express it to so many significant figures, i.e. important figures.

For example, a person winning one million and three pounds on the football pools can afford to ignore the three pounds.

The number of significant figures must be stated for an answer to be given.

Significant figures include all figures in a number except noughts at the beginning and end.

Examples 3.18

800 and 0.08 each have 1 significant figure; ignore noughts at beginning and end.
370 and 0.0037 each have 2 significant figures; ignore noughts at beginning and end.
A nought between figures is significant.
4060 and 0.0406 each have 3 significant figures.
3008 and 0.030 08 each have 4 significant figures.

Examples 3.19

2324 is 2300 when given to 2 significant figures.
171 is 170 to 2 significant figures.
103 is 100 to 2 significant figures.
0.0152 is 0.015 to 2 significant figures.
0.0104 is 0.010 to 2 significant figures.

3.9 Corrected Significant Figures

Most answers ask for 'correct to so many significant figures' and so we have to combine the knowledge of 1.50 and 1.52.

Examples 3.20

What is 42.53 correct to 3 significant figures?

We only want 3 figures in the answer, including any in-between noughts, and since the fourth figure is less than 5 the answer is 42.5

What is 42.765 correct to 3 significant figures?

The fourth figure is 6 and in 'rounding up' the 7 becomes 8 and so the answer is 42.8

What is 6038 correct to 3 significant figures?

The answer is 6030

Exercise 3.11

Write the following numbers correct to two significant figures; the first three are completed for you.

1 6520 = 6500 correct to two significant figures.

2 503 = 500 correct to two significant figures.

3 0.0767 = 0.077 correct to two significant figures.

4 964	**5** 2846	**6** 36972	**7** 308	**8** 18.38
9 18.83	**10** 3.06	**11** 7.032	**12** 0.0573	**13** 0.0688
14 4048	**15** 5.007	**16** 0.1008	**17** 2070	**18** 15.52
19 7.88	**20** 2.507			

Exercise 3.12

Write the following numbers correct to three significant figures; the first four are completed for you.

1 72.835 = 72.8 correct to three significant figures.

2 72.875 = 72.9 correct to three significant figures.

3 7004 = 7000 correct to three significant figures.

4 0.023 86 = 0.0239 correct to three significant figures.

5 32.51	**6** 7.635	**7** 0.2977	**8** 8084	**9** 8088
10 35.009	**11** 0.050 62	**12** 50 725	**13** 4097	**14** 2.0654
15 5.8282	**16** 791.49	**17** 75.06	**18** 30.04	**19** 5996
20 3.083				

3.10   Changing Any Fraction to a Decimal

The denominator is divided into the numerator to give the decimal equivalent of the fraction.

Example 3.21

Find $\frac{3}{4}$ as a decimal.

The fraction $\frac{3}{4}$ means $3 \div 4$.
Divide 3 by 4 as in Example 1.21:

$$\frac{0.75}{4)\overline{3.00}} \qquad \text{Answer} \quad 0.75$$

Example 3.22

Change $\frac{1}{8}$ to a decimal.

$\frac{1}{8}$ means $1 \div 8$.

$$\begin{array}{r} 0.125 \\ 8\overline{)1.000} \end{array}$$

Answer   0.125

Exercise 3.13

Change the following fractions to decimals; the first three are completed for you.

1 $\frac{3}{5} = 3.0 \div 5 = 0.6$ Divide 5 into 3.

2 $\frac{3}{8} = 3.0 \div 8 = 0.375$ Divide 8 into 3.

3 $\frac{2}{3} = 2.0 \div 3 = 0.6666 = 0.66$. This is a recurring decimal.

4 $\frac{1}{2}$	5 $\frac{2}{5}$	6 $\frac{1}{4}$	7 $\frac{3}{4}$
8 $\frac{5}{8}$	9 $\frac{1}{3}$	10 $\frac{7}{10}$	11 $\frac{7}{8}$
12 $\frac{4}{5}$	13 $\frac{5}{3}$	14 $\frac{7}{4}$	15 $\frac{7}{5}$
16 $\frac{11}{8}$	17 $\frac{3}{2}$	18 $\frac{5}{4}$	19 $\frac{4}{3}$
20 $\frac{9}{5}$			

3.11 Standard Form

Standard form is a neat way in which we write very large or very small numbers (such as those used in astronomy, physics or engineering, for example).

To put a number into standard form we rewrite the number to have a value between 1 and 10 and then make the necessary adjustments by multiplying by a power of 10; the adjustment makes sure that the number is not altered.

Look at section 3.5 as a reminder:

1000 is 10^3,

100 is 10^2,

10 is 10^1,

and, continuing the sequence,

1 is 10^0,

0.1   is 10^{-1},

0.01 is 10^{-2},

0.001 is 10^{-3}.

and so on.

Now we use this to write any number in standard form:

$38 = 3.8 \times 10   = 3.8 \times 10^1$.   This is standard form.

$380 = 3.8 \times 100   = 3.8 \times 10^2$.   Standard form.

$3800 = 3.8 \times 1000 = 3.8 \times 10^3$.   Standard form.

Remember that the power of 10 coincides with the number of places the decimal point has been moved in order for the number to be written between 1 and 10.

If the number is originally less than 1, the decimal point has to be moved the other way, hence a negative power of 10.

Example 3.23

Write 4685.0 in standard form.

To rewrite 4685.0 as a number between 1 and 10 the decimal point has to be after the 4 and so we get 4.685.
But this has meant moving the decimal point of the original number 3 places to the *left*.

4685.0 is the same as 4.685×1000.

$1000 = 10^3$.

$4685.0 = 4.685 \times 1000 = 4.685 \times 10^3$.

Answer 4.685×10^3

Example 3.24

Write 39 600.0 in standard form.

$39\,600.0 = 3.96 \times 10\,000 = 3.96 \times 10^4$.

Answer 3.96×10^4

Example 3.25

Write 0.0582 in standard form.

To rewrite 0.0582 as a number between 1 and 10 it has to be 5.82
The decimal point has been moved 2 places, but this time to the *right*. So this time use a negative power of 10.

$0.0582 = 5.82 \times 10^{-2}$.

(In effect this is the same as saying $5.82 \div 100$.)

Example 3.26

Write 0.007 25 in standard form.

$0.007\,25 = 7.25 \times 10^{-3}$.   Decimal point was moved 3 places to right.

Exercise 3.14

Write the following numbers in standard form; the first two are completed for you.

1 $3725 = 3.725 \times 10^3$

2 $0.003\,725 = 3.725 \times 10^{-3}$

3 7864.0   4 2975.0   5 372.5   6 37 250.0

7 98.7	8 569 000	9 852.6	10 5798.6
11 28.8	12 0.004 72	13 0.009 65	14 0.0246
15 0.000 65	16 0.000 07	17 0.0125	18 0.003
19 0.000 142	20 0.036		

Exercise 3.15

Write the following as actual numbers; the first two are completed for you.

1 $2.3 \times 10^3 = 2300$

2 $4.64 \times 10^{-4} = 0.000\,464$

3 6.4×10^2	4 8.25×10^4	5 3.96×10^3	6 2.0×10^1
7 4.125×10^2	8 5.8×10^4	9 7.9×10^7	10 5.25×10^5
11 3.4×10^3	12 1.7×10^{-2}	13 3.4×10^{-4}	14 9.4×10^{-3}
15 4.3×10^{-1}	16 5.9×10^{-3}	17 6.87×10^{-5}	18 7.23×10^{-4}
19 4.7×10^{-2}	20 9.4×10^{-3}		

Exercise 3.16 Multiple-choice Questions

Work out which is the correct answer in the following questions:

1 24.36 is

    A Twenty-four and thirty-six.
    B Two thousand four hundred and thirty-six.
    C Twenty-four point three six.
    D Two four three six.

2 Does the 1 in 36.102 mean

    A one-hundredth   **B** one   **C** one-tenth   **D** ten?

3 How much is 3.94 + 15.06 + 4.8?

    A 23.80   **B** 24.34   **C** 24.80   **D** 23.76

4 If you change 0.36 to a fraction is the answer

    A $\frac{36}{10}$ **B** $\frac{9}{20}$ **C** $\frac{9}{25}$ **D** $3\frac{6}{10}$?

5 Three pieces of timber are 5.96 metres, 2.08 metres and 3.74 metres. Is the total length

    A 12 metres   **B** 11.78 metres   **C** 10.78 metres   **D** 11.68 metres?

6 From twenty is taken 6.38; is the answer

    A 26.38   **B** 3.62   **C** 14.38   **D** 13.62?

7 What needs to be added to 18.75 to make 23.40?

    A 4.65   **B** 42.15   **C** 5.35   **D** 4.95

8 Which of the following is nearest to 49.7×14?

    A 50   **B** 1400   **C** 560   **D** 700

9 Which of the following is nearest to $39714 \div 99$?

    A 39   **B** 100   **C** 397   **D** 3971

10 $220.02 \div 5.7$ is exactly

    A 44.6   **B** 38.6   **C** 24.6   **D** 30.6

11 How much is $1.7 + 1.3 \times 2.4 + 0.6$?

    A 9.0   **B** 6.0   **C** 5.42   **D** 5.46

12 The number of people attending a rugby international was 32 594. The press gave the figure to the nearest hundred as

    A 32 590   **B** 33 000   **C** 32 500   **D** 32 600

13 29.564 correct to 2 significant figures is

    A 29.00   **B** 30.00   **C** 29.6   **D** 29.56

14 34 000 in standard form is

    A 3.4×10^4 **B** 3.4×10^3 **C** 0.34×10^4 **D** 34×10^3

15 $\frac{5}{8}$ as a decimal is

    A 0.5   **B** 1.6   **C** 0.625   **D** 0

16 0.7×10^{-3} is

    A 700   **B** 0.73   **C** 0.07   **D** 0.0007

17 0.8 of a line is 16 cm. How long is the line?

    A 12.8 cm   **B** 2 cm   **C** 20 cm   **D** 16.8 cm

18 A salesman earns £1200 in commission and next year he expects to increase this figure by 1.2 times. His commission will then be

    A £1320   **B** £1440   **C** £1220   **D** £1000

19 A woman drove 6000 miles in one year but the following year this fell by 0.4. Did she then drive

    A 5999.6 miles   **B** 2400 miles   **C** 3600 miles   **D** 6000.4 miles?

20 300×500 is

    A 150   **B** 1500   **C** 15×10^3 **D** 150 000

4 Money

4.1 Money and Decimals

All operations on decimals (addition, subtraction, multiplication and division) can be applied to our money system. Note that there will be only two places of decimals.

£4.12 means 4 pounds and 12 pence.

£15.03 means 15 pounds and 3 pence.

£0.42 means 42 pence.

Exercise 4.1

Complete the following; the first two are completed for you.

1 Find the total of £27, £16.49 and £25.46

```
    £
  27.00
  16.49
  25.46
 £68.95    Answer   £68.95
```

2 From £50 take £23.47

```
    £
  50.00
  23.47
 £26.53    Answer   £26.53
```

3 £6.24 + £3.32	**4** £8.43 + £7.23
5 £27.46 + £10.72	**6** £14.48 + £38.56 + £24.99
7 £3.47 + £108.84 + £45.50	**8** £9.99 + £5.65 + £2.87 + £7.30
9 £145.20 + £33.56 + £62.00 + £7.99	**10** £630 + £126.80 + £9.08
11 £12.99 + £3.99 + £7.99 + £4.38	**12** £36.85 − £14.52
13 £48.26 − £24.37	**14** £72 − £46.34
15 £50 − £18.37	**16** £183 − £92.75
17 £12.99 − £6.48	**18** £45 − £28.64
19 £100 − £72.83	**20** £33.25 − £9.87

Exercise 4.2

Complete the following; the first four are completed for you.

1   How much is £12.85 x 4?
    (This could be how much you pay in a four-week month if you pay £12.85 a week.)
    £12.85 x 4.
    Multiply without the decimal point (see section 3.4):
    1285 x 4 = 5140.
       Total number of decimal places in the original question was 2, therefore, there has to be 2 places in the answer.
    Answer   £51.40

2   How much is £33.40 x 12?
    (This could be a payment of £33.40 a month and you are trying to find the cost per year.)
    £33.40 x 12.
    Multiply without the decimal point:
    Either   3340 x 12 = 40 080   (if you know your 12 times table),
    or   3 340
             x   12
              33 400
               6 680
              40 080

    There were 2 decimal places in the original question so there must be 2 decimal places in the answer.
    Answer   £400.80

3   £1667.82 ÷ 7.
    (This could be trying to find the cost per day if £1667.82 is the cost for a week.)
    £1667.82 ÷ 7.
    Divide as for ordinary decimals:
        238.26   Place decimal point in answer; see section 3.6.
    7)1667.82
    Answer   £238.26

4   £82.42 ÷ 13
    (This could be finding how much electricity costs per week if £82.42 is the cost per quarter, 13 weeks.)
    £82.42 ÷ 13.
    Divide as for ordinary decimals:
          6.34
    13)82.42
       78   6 x 13   Place decimal point in answer.
       44
       39   3 x 13
       52
       52   4 x 13
       ··
    Answer   £6.34

| 5 £2.40 x 4 | 6 £1.99 x 6 | 7 £36.45 x 4 | 8 £52.60 x 7 |
| 9 £146.27 x 4 | 10 £0.75 x 12 | 11 £0.33 x 24 | 12 £9.52 x 8 |

13 £2.65 × 24	14 £27.90 × 12	15 £36.75 × 24	16 £8.65 × 36
17 £15.62 × 13	18 £7.20 ÷ 4	19 £151.40 ÷ 4	20 £17.43 ÷ 7
21 £188.32 ÷ 8	22 £41.76 ÷ 12	23 £280.2 ÷ 12	24 £61.75 ÷ 13
25 £199.55 ÷ 13	26 £440.4 ÷ 24	27 £654 ÷ 24	28 £3754.87 ÷ 7
29 £127.44 ÷ 36	30 £677.4 ÷ 12		

Exercise 4.3

The following items were offered on a college menu board:

Coffee	22p	Chocolate	24p
Tea	19p	Fruit juice	14p

Toast (2 slices)	24p	Sausage and chips	42p
Cheese and onion sandwich	35p	Fish and chips	48p
Egg sandwich	35p	Cottage pie	40p
Ham sandwich	38p	Steak and kidney pie and chips	46p
Cheese and onion barm cake	42p	Curry and rice	33p
Egg barm cake	42p	Cheese and tomato pizza	32p
Salmon barm cake	45p	Chips	26p
		Boiled potatoes	24p
Sausage roll	26p		
Cornish pasty	30p	Mars bar	19p
		Kit Kat	18p
Soup, roll and butter	28p		
Ice cream	20p	Cheese and biscuits	22p
Sponge pudding	24p	Cheesecake portion	26p
Apple pie	24p		

From the menu find the cost of the following:
 1 Coffee, egg barm cake, ice cream.
 2 Sausage and chips, tea.
 3 Soup, roll and butter, cheese and biscuits, fruit juice.
 4 2 egg sandwiches, coffee, Mars bar.
 5 Cornish pasty, chips, apple pie, chocolate.
 6 Sausage roll and chips, ice cream, 2 coffees, Kit Kat.
 7 Cheese and tomato pizza, boiled potatoes, fruit juice.
 8 Ham sandwich, salmon barm cake, ice cream.
 9 Tea, toast, sponge pudding, Mars bar.
10 Fish and chips, cheese and biscuits, tea.
11 2 teas, 3 coffees, 4 egg sandwiches, 2 Mars, 2 Kit Kats.
12 Chocolate, salmon barm cake, cheesecake portion.
13 Fruit juice, ham sandwich, curry and rice, apple pie.
14 2 coffees, sausage and chips, fish and chips, ice cream, sponge pudding.
15 2 cheese and onion sandwiches, chips, ice cream, Mars bar.
16 Steak and kidney pie and chips, soup, roll and butter, apple pie, chocolate.
17 Cornish pasty, boiled potatoes, tea, cheese cake portion.
18 Tea, ham sandwich, Cornish pasty, cheese and biscuits, coffee.
19 2 coffees, 3 teas, 2 egg sandwiches, 3 salmon barm cakes, ice cream.
20 What is the change from £5 after buying 4 teas, 3 coffees, and 6 ham sandwiches?

Exercise 4.4

1 Three teenagers held a sponsored swim for Famine Relief. They raised £18.57, £24.32 and £9.84. How much did they raise?

2 Mother spent £16.57 at Marks & Spencer, £4.38 at Boots, £12.07 at British Home Stores and £3.82 in a DIY shop. How much change was left out of £50?

3 The Youth Club spent £100 on their Saturday disco. Ticket sales were £64, raffle ticket sales £17.40 and refreshment sales £16.77. How much had to come out of club funds to cover the cost?

4 A check on household spending for a week in winter was electricity £10.32, gas £18.62, rates £7.26, water rates £2.15, telephone £2.96 and food £42.60. How much was spent in this one week on these items?

5 A teenager went to town on a Saturday morning with £15.48 in her purse. The bus fare was 56p each way, she spent £2.20 on cheap jewellery, £5.46 on a record tape, £1.18 on a snack, and £3.74 on make-up. How much was left?

6 A supermarket sells the following items:

pkt cornflakes	82p	250 g coffee	£2.89
250 g butter	56p	1 kg sugar	58p
80 tea-bags	£1.42	1 lb bacon	£1.42
1 doz. eggs	84p	8 oz cheese	72p
1 lb carrots	28p	1 pint milk	25p

How much did it cost for

(a) 1 pkt cornflakes, 80 tea-bags and 1 doz. eggs?

(b) 1 lb carrots, 1 lb bacon, 1 pint milk, 1 kg sugar?

(c) 250 g butter, 250 g coffee, 1 kg sugar, 8 oz cheese, 1 pkt cornflakes, 80 tea-bags?

(d) One amount of each item?

7 A man buys a daily newspaper costing 27p on six days and a Sunday paper costing 55p. What does he spend on papers in a week?

8 A woman earns £3.50 an hour for a 35-hour week. How much did she earn per week?

9 A person earns £345 per calendar month. What is his annual salary?

10 A woman pays £558.72 in tax per year. How much does she pay each calendar month?

11 The running costs of a car for a year are petrol £533, car tax £90, insurance £130, and repairs and servicing £315. What are the total running costs for (a) 1 year, (b) 1 month?

12 The rent of a small house is £18.40 per week, which includes the rates. How much is this a year of 52 weeks?

13 A woman reckons to spend £1.32 each week on a football pool. She has one win of £17.40 during the year. How much has she lost during the year (52 weeks)?

14 A householder pays £582.24 a year in rates. He pays it in 12 monthly instalments. How much does he pay each month?

15 An electricity bill was £43.81 for one quarter (13 weeks). How much was it per week?

16 Sale items were advertised at half the price of normal prices. What did it cost in a sale to buy a blouse, skirt and jeans if the normal prices were £17.60, £19.40 and £14.40 respectively?

17 Simon and Jane go for a pub lunch and the menu shows the following items:

Soup with roll and butter	95p
Paté with toast and butter	£1.35
Plaice, chips and peas	£2.45
Steak and kidney pie with potatoes and veg.	£2.15
Ham salad	£1.95
Any sweet	95p
Coffee	45p

Simon has paté, steak and kidney pie, sweet and coffee, while Jane has soup, ham salad and coffee. How much is the total bill?

18 A woman sales assistant earns £3.20 per hour for a 35-hour week. During Christmas week she works 6 hours overtime for which she is paid time-and-a-half, that is, for each hour of overtime she gets 1½ hours' pay. How much does she earn that week?

19 A two-week holiday in Majorca is priced at £276 for an adult, £225 for children aged 10 to 16, and half the adult price for children aged under 10. What is the cost for a family of two adults and three children aged 15, 13 and 9?

20 A salesman is able to claim 28p for every mile he travels on business. In one week he claimed for 950 miles. How much did he claim?
The petrol for these journeys cost £74.
How much does he 'make' out of his mileage allowance?

Exercise 4.5

1 Starting with £5 I spend 38p, £1.27 and 75p. Is the amount left

    A £2.40   B £3.60   C £2.60   D £4?

2 A fish and chip shop takes £125.38 for food served on the premises and £197.86 for take away food. Are the total takings

    A £323.24   B £323.14   C £322.24   D £324.24?

3 What is 9 × £4.30?

    A £38.20   B £38.40   C £38.70   D £38.90

4 A man earns £2.80 per hour for a 35-hour week. For overtime he gets time-and-a-half. In one week he earns £114.80. Is the amount of overtime

    A 2 h   B 3 h   C 4 h   D 5 h?

5 How much is $\frac{1}{2}$ of £38.50?

    A £77   B £39   C £40.50   D £19.25?

6 A new car tyre costs £32 and a further £2.50 to have it balanced. What does it cost to have four new tyres and have them all balanced?

    A £138   B £130.50   C £128   D £148

7 A day return to London is £14 for an adult and half price for children. Two adults and two children make the journey. Is the change from £50

    A £15   B £8   C £22   D £10?

8 A carpet costs £8.99 a metre. For 9 metres is the cost

    A £89.90   B £81.00   C £81.09   D £80.91?

9 A woman is paid by way of salary and commission. If the salary is £284 and commission is £68 is she paid

    A £352   **B** £216   **C** £176   **D** £312?

10 How much is £226.80 ÷ 7?

    A £32.10   **B** £32.20   **C** £32.30   **D** £32.40

11 A school trip to an ice rink is £2.60 per pupil. The teacher collects £124.80. How many pupils go on the trip?

    A 52   **B** 38   **C** 48   **D** 53

12 A rose bush costs £2.80 and a shrub £3.40. The bill came to £15.20. Did I buy

    A 2 roses and 3 shrubs   **B** 4 roses and 1 shrub
    C 3 roses and 2 shrubs   **D** 1 rose and 4 shrubs?

13 An electricity bill was £54.60 for one quarter (13 weeks). How much was this a week?

    A £4.10   **B** £3.90   **C** £4.00   **D** £4.20

14 A sale announces $\frac{1}{4}$ off all normal prices. The normal price of a coat is £36. Was the sale price

    A £9   **B** £35.75   **C** £27   **D** £32?

15 How much is 0.7 of £1500?

    A £1050   **B** £750   **C** £850   **D** £105

16 A person earns £86 per week. What is the annual salary (52 weeks) to the nearest £100?

    A £5000   **B** £4400   **C** £4500   **D** £4470

17 £34.60 is changed into 20 pence pieces. How many are there?

    A 176   **B** 173   **C** 346   **D** 692

18 A person earns £4176 per year. How much is this per calendar month?

    A £417.60   **B** £350   **C** £363   **D** £348

19 A woman pays £54.64 each month in tax. Does she pay in one year

    A £596.36   **B** £708.18   **C** £655.68   **D** £624.04

20 The running costs of a car for a year are petrol £746, car tax £100, insurance £138, repairs and servicing £473, and depreciation £628. What are the total running costs for the year?

    A £2085   **B** £746   **C** £1825   **D** £965

21 Stacking chairs are £43.80 a dozen. How much will a hundred chairs cost?

    A £438   **B** £520   **C** £365   **D** £288

5 Measurement

5.1 Imperial and Metric Measures

You should try and remember the various weights, lengths and capacity in imperial and SI units. The following are the most common units in use.

(a) SI Measure

Weight

1000 milligrams (mg) = 1 gram (g)
1000 grams = 1 kilogram (kg)
1000 kilograms = 1 tonne (t)

Length

10 millimetres (mm) = 1 centimetre (cm)
100 centimetres = 1 metre (m)
1000 metres = 1 kilometre (km)

Capacity

10 millilitres (ml) = 1 centilitre (cl)
1000 millilitres = 1 litre (ℓ)

(b) Imperial Measure

(remember 1 dozen = 12)

Weight

16 ounces (oz) = 1 pound (lb)
14 pounds = 1 stone (st)
112 pounds = 1 hundredweight (cwt)
20 hundredweights = 1 ton

Length

12 inches (in) = 1 foot (ft)
3 feet = 1 yard (yd)
1760 yards = 1 mile

Capacity

2 pints (pt)	= 1 quart (qt)
8 pints	= 1 gallon (gal)

Also, there are 20 fluid ounces (fl oz) in 1 pint.

5.2 Changing Units

To change units in imperial or SI measure multiply or divide by the appropriate figure.

Example 5.1

Change 3 kg to g.

What is the relation between kg and g?
1 kg = 1000 g.
Then 3 kg = 3 × 1000 g
$\qquad$ = 3000 g.
Answer   3000 g

Example 5.2

Change 2800 g to kg.

Again, 1000 g = 1 kg.
Then 2800 g = $\frac{2800}{1000}$ kg
$\qquad$ = 2.8 kg.
Answer   2.8 kg

Example 5.3

Change 100 in to ft.

12 in = 1 ft.
So 100 in = $\frac{100}{12}$ ft
$\qquad$ = 8 remainder 4.
The 4 units left over are inches.
Answer   8 ft 4 in or $8\frac{1}{3}$ ft

5.3 Changing Imperial Units to SI Units

Where you have to change from one set of units to another you will be given the relationship between the two; this is called the conversion factor.

Example 5.4

Change 3 km to miles given that 1 km = 0.62 miles.

1 km = 0.62 miles. This is the conversion factor.

Then 3 km = 3 × 0.62 miles
        = 1.86 miles
Answer   1.86 miles

Example 5.5

   Change 5 miles to km given that 1 km = 0.62 miles.

0.62 miles = 1 km.
Then 1 mile = $\frac{1}{0.62}$ km.
5 miles   = 5 × $\frac{1}{0.62}$ km
           = $\frac{5}{0.62}$
           = 8.06 km.
Answer   8.06 km

Example 5.6

   Change 200 litres to gallons given that 1 gallon = 4.54 litres.

4.54 litres = 1 gallon
Then 1 ℓ = $\frac{1}{4.54}$ gal.
So 200 ℓ = 200 × $\frac{1}{4.54}$ gal.
         = $\frac{200}{4.54}$
         = 44.05 gal
Answer   44.05 gal

Sometimes you have to multiply by the conversion factor and at other times divide by it. If you are not sure what to do then think whether you are looking for a bigger answer or a smaller answer.

Exercise 5.1

 1 Change to m   (a) 6 km   (b) 4 km   (c) 15 km   (d) 50 km.
 2 Change to m   (a) 3.6 km   (b) 9.5 km   (c) 0.83 km   (d) 0.586 km.
 3 Change to km   (a) 9000 m   (b) 12 000 m   (c) 25 000 m   (d) 100 000 m.
 4 Change to km   (a) 4800 m   (b) 600 m   (c) 2584 m   (d) 40 m.
 5 Change to m and cm   (a) 4.54 m   (b) 15.06 m   (c) 0.53 m   (d) 0.08 m.
 6 Change to kg   (a) 2000 g   (b) 6000 g   (c) 18 000 g   (d) 156 000 g.
 7 Change to kg   (a) 1750 g   (b) 3920 g   (c) 840 g   (d) 75 g.
 8 Change to g   (a) 2 kg   (b) 7 kg   (c) 12 kg   (d) 20 kg.
 9 Change to g   (a) 3.25 kg   (b) 0.94 kg   (c) 0.05 kg   (d) 6.952 kg.
10 Change to kg and g   (a) 3.58 kg   (b) 16.2 kg   (c) 8.405 kg   (d) 0.34 kg.
11 Change to ml   (a) 5 ℓ   (b) 18 ℓ   (c) 2 ℓ   (d) 7 ℓ.
12 Change to ml   (a) 6.25 ℓ   (b) 0.38 ℓ   (c) 7.051 ℓ   (d) 11.6 ℓ.
13 Change to ℓ   (a) 9000 ml   (b) 18 000 ml   (c) 32 000 ml   (d) 3000 ml.
14 Change to ℓ   (a) 4900 ml   (b) 2564 ml   (c) 380 ml   (d) 60 ml.
15 1$\frac{1}{2}$ litres is added to 40 cl. What is the total?
16 A cask of wine holds 168 litres. How many wine bottles, each holding 70 cl, can be filled from the cask?
17 2 kg of potatoes cost 25p. What is the cost of 12 kg?
18 From 5 kg is taken 150 g and then 0.52 kg. What weight is left?

19 In a 5000 m race a man reckons to run a 400 m lap in 61 seconds. If he keeps this up for the whole race in what time does he do the 5000 m race?

20 A brick is 220 mm long. How many, placed end to end without mortar, will cover a length 15.4 m?

Exercise 5.2

1 Change to in   (a) 5 ft   (b) 20 ft   (c) 8 ft   (d) 12 ft.

2 Change to in   (a) 2 ft 8 in   (b) 4 ft 9 in   (c) 6 ft 4 in   (d) 15 ft 6 in.

3 Change to ft and in   (a) 90 in   (b) 70 in   (c) 35 in   (d) 110 in.

4 Change to ft   (a) 6 yd   (b) 15 yd   (c) 2 yd 2 ft   (d) 12 yd 1 ft.

5 Change to yd and ft   (a) 18 ft   (b) 25 ft   (c) 32 ft   (d) 14 ft.

6 How many cwt are there in   (a) 2 tons   (b) 5 tons   (c) 1 ton 15 cwt   (d) 3 tons 12 cwt?

7 How many oz are there in   (a) 2 lb   (b) 5 lb   (c) 4 lb 8 oz   (d) 3 lb 12 oz?

8 How many pints are there in   (a) 2 gal   (b) 3 gal 3 pts   (c) 5 gal 1 pt   (d) 4 gal 5 pt?

9 How many fl oz are there in   (a) 2 pt   (b) 1 pt 8 fl oz   (c) 3 pt 4 fl oz   (d) 5 pt 15 fl oz?

10 An empty lorry weighs 10 ton 8 cwt. When loaded it is 19 ton 2 cwt. What is the weight of the load?

11 A packet weighs 6 oz. What is the weight of 50 packets in lb and oz?

12 A lorry carries 56 lb sacks of coal. Unloaded it is 9 ton 12 cwt and loaded it is 15 ton 8 cwt. How many sacks of coal does it carry?

13 An edging stone is 3 ft long and costs £1.80. What would it cost to edge one side of a path 12 yd long?

14 A room 4 yd 2 ft in length is extended by 8 ft. What is the new length of the room?

15 A piece of overlap fencing panel is 6 ft long. How many are required for one side of a garden which is 14 yd long?

16 A 5 gallon drum of oil has 3 pints, 6 pints and then 4 pints taken from it. How much oil is left?

17 Beer is sold at 85p a pint. The landlord sells a barrel of beer containing 36 gal in one night. How much does he take from the sale of beer?

18 Petrol is sold at 204p a gallon. A motorist fills up his tank with 13 gallons. How much does the petrol cost him?

19 A man weighs 14 st 2 lb. After he goes on a diet his weight goes to 12 st 8 lb. How much weight did he lose?

20 Small metal supports for shelves are made L-shaped from a piece of metal $7\frac{1}{2}$ in long. How many supports can be made from a strip 25 ft long?

Exercise 5.3

For the purpose of this exercise assume the following approximate conversion factors: 1 ft = 30 cm;   1 gal = 4.5 ℓ;   1 kg = 2.2 lb.

1 How many litres are there in a 5 gallon drum?

2 A piece of wood is measured as 270 cm. What is the length in ft?

3 Using the conversion factor at the top, how long is a mile in metres?

4 A bag of potatoes weighs 50 kg. What is the weight in lb?

5 A ceiling is 7 ft 6 in high. What height is this in metres? (Find the height in cm first.)

6 A woman weighs 10 st 3 lb. What is her weight in kilograms?

7 Butter is 45p a lb. How much is it a kilogram?

8 A wooden fencing post is £2.50 per metre. How much is this per yard? (First find the cost per cm.)

9 A cask of butter weighs 55 lb and costs £27.50. What is the cost per kilogram? (First find what is the weight in kilograms.)

10 A firm decided to label its 4 oz packets in grams as well. How many grams would this be to the nearest gram?

5.4 Time

All countries use the same measurements — seconds, minutes, hours, days and years.

Time of day can be given as morning (a.m.) or afternoon (p.m.) but a more usual way is to use the 24-hour clock, which runs from 0000 hours to 2400 hours midnight, and 1200 hours is mid-day (noon). The abbreviation for hour is h.

Thus for example:

0600 hours is 6 a.m.	1100 hours is 11 a.m.
1300 hours is 1 p.m.	1800 hours is 6 p.m.
2030 hours is 8.30 p.m.	2210 hours is 10.10 p.m.

Note: 8.30 p.m. means 8 hours 30 minutes after noon, or it might be called half-past eight at night. It does not mean 8 point 30 as in the decimal system.

Example 5.7

Change ten past five in the morning to a 24-hour clock time.

What is meant by ten past five?
It means ten minutes past five o'clock, that is, 5.10.
We are told it is a morning time so it becomes 5.10 a.m.
On the 24-hour clock this is 0510 hours.

Example 5.8

What is a quarter past one in the afternoon as a 24-hour clock time?

A quarter past one means a quarter of an hour past one o'clock.
That is, 15 minutes past one or 1.15.
It is an afternoon time which means 1.15 p.m. or 1.15 after noon (midday).
1200 hours is midday.
1.15 after midday is 1315 hours.

Example 5.9

How long is it, in hours and minutes, from 8.20 a.m. until 4.30 p.m.?

Work out in easy stages:

From 8.20 a.m. to 9.00 a.m. =	40 min
From 9.00 a.m. to 12 noon =	3 h
From 12 noon to 4.30 p.m. =	4 h 30 min
Total time =	8 h 10 min

Answer   8 h 10 min

Example 5.10

A flight is due to take off at 2130 hours but owing to fuelling problems it does not take off until 0120 hours the following day. How long was the delay?

From 2130 hours until 2200 hours =   30 min
From 2200 hours until 2400 hours = 2 h
From 2400 hours until 0120 hours = 1 h 20 min
Total delay   3 h 50 min

Answer   3 h 50 min

Note: After midnight 2400 hours you begin another day.

Exercise 5.4

Change the following times to those of a 24-hour clock:
1 8 o'clock in the morning.   2 10 o'clock in the morning.
3 4 o'clock in the afternoon.   4 9.00 p.m.
5 1.25 a.m.   6 7.36 a.m.
7 9.30 p.m.   8 2.45 p.m.
9 Half-past six in the morning.   10 A quarter to five in the afternoon.
11 Twenty past eight at night.
12 Eight minutes to nine in the morning.
13 8.30 in the morning.   14 9.20 at night.
15 Eighteen minutes past seven at night.   16 11.22 p.m.
17 Midday   18 A quarter past ten at night.
19 Fifteen minutes past midnight.   20 A quarter to eleven in the morning.

Exercise 5.5

Change these 24-hour clock times to morning or afternoon time.
1 0400 hours   2 1500 hours   3 1830 hours   4 2150 hours   5 0215 hours
6 0756 hours   7 2325 hours   8 0016 hours   9 0425 hours   10 2010 hours
11 1952 hours 12 0101 hours   13 1038 hours   14 2115 hours   15 1226 hours
16 1105 hours 17 0052 hours   18 0346 hours   19 1418 hours   20 2210 hours

Exercise 5.6

How long is it between these times? (Give answers in minutes or hours and minutes.)
1 9.00 a.m. to 11.30 a.m. on the same day.   15 1840 hours to 0220 hours on
2 10.00 a.m. to 3 p.m. on the same day.   the next day.
3 6.30 a.m. to 1.50 p.m. on the same day.   16 1226 hours to 1015 hours on
4 10.38 a.m. to 3.15 p.m. on the same day.   the next day.
5 11.15 a.m. to 7.06 p.m. on the same day.   17 0920 hours to 0750 hours on
6 8.25 p.m. to 2.15 a.m. on the next day.   the next day.
7 10.10 p.m. to 5.25 a.m. on the next day.   18 1150 hours to 1210 hours on
8 11.30 a.m. to 3.40 a.m. on the next day.   the next day.
9 0800 hours to 1500 hours on the same day.   19 1850 hours to 0015 hours on
10 0950 hours to 1614 hours on the same day.   the next day.
11 1140 hours to 1326 hours on the same day.   20 0925 hours to 1308 hours on
12 1013 hours to 1207 hours on the same day.   the same day.
13 1432 hours to 1924 hours on the same day.
14 0820 hours to 1610 hours on the same day.

6 Ratio and Proportion

6.1 Ratio as a Comparison

Ratio is a comparison of quantities; it can be written in a special way or as a fraction.

Proportion is what fraction of the whole is one part.

Example 6.1

In a garden there are 3 apple trees and 2 pear trees.

The ratio of apple trees to pear trees is said to be 3 : 2 (three to two) or $\frac{3}{2}$.

The number of trees in the whole garden is 5.

The proportion of apple trees in the garden is $\frac{3}{5}$ and that of pear trees is $\frac{2}{5}$.

Example 6.2

In a class there are 15 boys and 18 girls. What is the ratio of boys to girls? What is the proportion of girls in the class?

There are 15 boys, 18 girls.

Ratio of boys : girls = 15 : 18

                       = 5 : 6.

Ratios can be simplified in the same way as fractions.

In the class there are 15 boys and 18 girls, making a total of 33.

There are 18 girls out of a total of 33.

Proportion of girls = $\frac{18}{33} = \frac{6}{11}$.

Note: The proportion of boys is $\frac{15}{33}$ ($\frac{5}{11}$).

Ratios, like fractions, can be put in their simplest or lowest terms, or if they are in fractional form can be simplified.

Example 6.3

A ratio of 6 : 4 is the same as 3 : 2, dividing both parts by 2.

        4 : 12 is the same as 1 : 3.

        9 : 15 is the same as 3 : 5.

        $\frac{3}{4}$: 1 is the same as 3 : 4, multiplying both parts by 4.

        $\frac{2}{3}$: 1 is the same as 2 : 3, multiplying both parts by 3.

        $\frac{1}{2}$: $\frac{3}{4} = \frac{2}{4}$: $\frac{3}{4}$ = 2 : 3.

        $\frac{2}{3}$: $\frac{3}{4} = \frac{8}{12}$: $\frac{9}{12}$ = 8 : 9.

Example 6.4

Flaky pastry is made by mixing fat and flour in the ratio of 3 : 4. How much fat is required to 12 oz of flour?

Fat to flour is in ratio of 3 : 4.
This must always be kept.
If 12 oz of flour are used then we have multiplied the second part of the ratio by 3 oz (4 × 3 oz = 12 oz).
The first part of the ratio, which is fat, must also be multiplied by 3 oz in order to keep the same ratio.
Fat to flour is 3 : 4
Fat to flour is 9 oz : 12 oz.
Fat required is 9 oz.

Example 6.5

A garden compost is made up of loam, peat and coarse sand in the ratio of 7 : 3 : 2. If I use 4 buckets full of sand how much loam and peat is required?

Loam to peat to coarse sand is 7 : 3 : 2
Write down 4 buckets in place of the sand figure and the ratio then becomes
Loam to peat
to coarse sand   7   :   3   :   2
              14 buckets : 6 buckets : 4 buckets (each figure doubled)

Answer   14 bucketfuls of loam and 6 bucketfuls of peat.

Exercise 6.1

Simplify the following ratios:

1 2 : 4	2 8 : 6	3 12 : 4	4 15 : 20
5 18 : 12	6 15 g : 35 g	7 12 in : 8 in	8 15 kg : 1 kg
9 12 m : 8 m	10 1 litre : 250 ml	11 5 m : 80 cm	12 220 m : 1 km
13 3 ft : 2 ft 6 in	14 2 lb : 2 lb 8 oz	15 $\frac{1}{4}$: 1	16 1 : $\frac{3}{5}$
17 $1\frac{1}{3}$: 1	18 $1\frac{3}{4}$: 1	19 $\frac{1}{2}$: $\frac{5}{2}$	20 $\frac{1}{2}$: $\frac{5}{6}$
21 $\frac{3}{4}$: $\frac{2}{3}$	22 $2\frac{1}{2}$: $1\frac{1}{2}$	23 $\frac{2}{3}$: $1\frac{1}{2}$	24 $1\frac{1}{3}$: $2\frac{1}{4}$
25 30 : 40 : 50	26 15 : 25 : 45	27 8 : 16 : 24	28 2 : 8 : 10
29 $1\frac{1}{4}$: 5 : 10	30 $\frac{3}{4}$: $1\frac{1}{4}$: $1\frac{1}{2}$		

Exercise 6.2

1 In a class there are 8 girls and 6 boys. (a) What is the ratio of boys to girls? (b) What is the proportion of boys in the class?

2 In a motorway car park there are 28 cars and 16 lorries. (a) What is the ratio of cars to lorries? (b) What is the proportion of lorries in the car park?

3 A concrete can be made from 6 parts sand to one part cement. (a) What is the ratio of sand to cement? (b) What proportion of sand is in cement?

4 In a box of chocolates there are 12 soft centres to every 8 hard centres. (a) What is the ratio of soft centres to hard centres? (b) What is the proportion of hard centres in a box?

5 In an office there are 20 women and 4 men. (a) What is the ratio of women to men in the office? (b) What is the proportion of men in the office?

6 A pastry can be made by mixing fat and flour in the ratio of 1 : 2. (a) How much flour is required to 60 g of fat? (b) How much fat is required to 8 oz flour?

7 A concrete can be made from sand and cement in the ratio of 3 : 1. How much sand is required for 3 cwt of cement?

8 A fertiliser is made from nitrogen and phosphate in the ratio of 3 : 2. How much nitrogen is required for 6 oz of phosphate?

9 Shortbread is made from sugar, butter and flour in the ratio of 1 : 2 : 3. How much sugar is required if there is (a) 60 g of butter (b) 1½ lb of flour?

10 In the shortbread for question 9 how much butter is required if there is (a) 8 oz of sugar (b) 150 g of flour?

11 A concrete can be made from cement, sand and gravel in the ratio 1 : 3 : 16. How much cement and gravel is required if I use 9 buckets full of sand?

12 A farmer fattens young heifers on barley, sugar beet pulp and cattle cake in the ratio of 10 : 2 : 3. (a) How much cattle cake is required for 6 kg of sugar beet pulp? (b) How much barley and cattle cake are required for 2 cwt of sugar beet pulp?

6.2 Proportional Parts

This section looks at the calculation of how to find parts of a whole quantity when the proportions are given. The method is to add up all the individual proportions. This becomes the denominator of a fraction in which each individual proportion is the numerator. Examples will show this clearly.

Example 6.6

The ratio of fat to flour in shortcrust pastry is 1 : 2. How much of each is needed to make 450 g of pastry?

Ratio of fat to flour = 1 : 2.
Add the ratios together, $1 + 2 = 3$.
This means there are going to be 3 parts altogether, with 1 part fat and 2 parts flour.
Fat is $\frac{1}{3}$ of whole; flour is $\frac{2}{3}$; 450 g of pastry required.
1 part = $\frac{450}{3}$ g = 150 g.
Fat is 1 part = 150 g.
Flour is 2 parts = 2×150 g = 300 g.
Answer   150 g fat, 300 g flour

Example 6.7

Divide £30 in the ratio 7 : 3.

Ratio of 7 : 3 means there are 10 parts (7 + 3).
Divide £30 by 10 to find each part.
Each part = £$\frac{30}{10}$ = £3.
7 parts = $7 \times$ £3 = £21.
3 parts = $3 \times$ £3 = £9.
Answer   £21 and £9

Example 6.8

An alloy is made of copper and tin in the ratio of 3 : 2. How much copper and tin is there in 2 kg of alloy?

Ratio of 3 : 2 means there are 5 parts (3 + 2).
2 kg = 2000 g.
Now divide 2000 g by 5 to find each part:
Each part = $\frac{2000}{5}$ g = 400 g.
Copper is 3 parts = 3 × 400 g = 1200 g.
Tin is 2 parts   = 2 × 400 g = 800 g.
Answer   1200 g of copper, 800 g of tin

The method works for any number of figures in the ratio.

Example 6.9

Bandages are available in three sizes, large, medium and small, and they are ordered in the ratio 3 : 4 : 5. How many of each size are ordered in a total of 1800 bandages?

Ratio of 3 : 4 : 5 means there are 12 parts (3 + 4 + 5).
Divide 1800 by 12 to find each part:
Each part = $\frac{1800}{12}$ = 150 bandages.
Large bandages = 3 parts = 3 × 150 = 450 bandages.
Medium bandages = 4 parts = 4 × 150 = 600 bandages.
Small bandages = 5 parts = 5 × 150 = 750 bandages.
Answer   450 large bandages, 600 medium and 750 small

Example 6.10

Divide £300 in the ratio $1\frac{1}{2}$: 2 : $2\frac{3}{4}$.

With fractional ratios, first multiply to remove the fractions. In this case multiply every ratio by 4.
$1\frac{1}{2}$: 2 : $2\frac{3}{4}$ is the same as 6 : 8 : 11.
6 : 8 : 11 means there are 25 parts (6 + 8 + 11)
Divide £300 by 25 to find each part:
Each part = £$\frac{300}{25}$ = £12.
6 parts = £72.
8 parts = £96.
11 parts = £132.
Answer   £72, £96, £132

Exercise 6.3

1 Divide £10 in a ratio of 2 : 3.
2 Divide £40 in a ratio of 4 : 1.
3 Divide £36 in a ratio of 5 : 4.
4 Divide £60 in a ratio of $1\frac{1}{2}$: 1.
5 Divide £100 in a ratio of 5 : 3 : 2.
6 Divide £90 in a ratio of $\frac{3}{4}$: $1\frac{1}{2}$: $2\frac{1}{4}$.
7 Divide 500 ml in the ratio of 7 : 3.
8 Divide 135 m in the ratio of 4 : 5.
9 Divide 4 kg in the ratio of 3 : 2.
10 Divide 150 cm in the ratio of 8 : 7.
11 A liquid is made up of water and weedkiller in a ratio of 9 : 1 by volume. There are 20 litres of liquid. How much water and weedkiller was there?

12 500 g of alloy are made from copper and magnesium in the ratio 3 : 7. How much copper was needed?

13 135 sweets in a box of caramels contain rum and butter, vanilla, and strawberry flavour in the ratio 3 : 2 : 4. How many of each kind of sweet are there?

14 A questionnaire to 330 people found that red, blue and green colours were favourites in the ratio 5 : 4 : 2. How many people gave red as their favourite colour and how many gave green?

15 A survey of 500 householders found that owners, rented by the local authority, and rented by landlords were in the ratio 6 : 3 : 1. How many owners of houses were in that survey?

16 A drink is made up of water, gin and orange in the ratio 5 : 3 : 2. How much gin was there in a drink of 400 ml?

17 A housing estate of 450 dwellings consisted of houses, bungalows, and flats in the ratio 7 : 3 : 5. (a) How many houses and bungalows were there? (b) What proportion of the estate was flats?

18 A purse contained 50 p coins, 20 p coins and 10 p coins in the ratio of 2 : 4 : 6. The amount of money in the purse was £6. How many coins of each denomination were there?

19 The ratio of boys to girls in a cycling proficiency class is 2 : 6. There are 24 in the class. How many boys?

20 In a by-election result the proportion of people voting Conservative, Labour, Liberal/SDP, Others, was in the ratio $3 : 3 : 4 : \frac{1}{2}$. If 21 210 people voted, how many voted Others?

6.3 Scales and Maps

Maps, models and diagrams are often reduced in size in a fixed ratio. This reduction is then stated.

An Ordnance Survey map may show 1 : 50 000.

A drawing of a house may show 1 : 125.

A model may show 1 : 10.

Example 6.11

An Ordnance Survey map has a scale of 1 : 50 000. The distance between two towns on the map is measured as 2 cm. What is the actual distance between the two towns?

Scale is 1 : 50 000.

This means 1 unit on the map represents 50 000 units on the ground.

2 cm on the map represents 50 000 × 2 cm on the ground,

= 100 000 cm

= 1000 m

= 1 km.

Answer   1 km

Example 6.12

A walker is in Keswick and using an Ordnance Survey map of scale 1 : 25 000. He wants to walk to Buttermere which he finds, by using a piece of cotton, is 50 cm on the map. How far does he walk to get to Buttermere?

Scale is 1 : 25 000.

1 unit on the map is 25 000 units on the ground.

50 cm on the map = 25 000 × 50 cm on the ground,

= 1 250 000 cm

= 12 500 m

= 12.5 km.

Answer   12.5 km

Example 6.13

A map of the British Isles is on a scale of 1 : 5 000 000. A straight-line distance between London and Edinburgh is approximately 650 km. How far does this appear on the map?

Scale is 1 : 5 000 000.

1 unit on the map is 5 000 000 units on the ground,

or 5 000 000 units on the ground is 1 unit on the map.

1 unit on the ground = $\frac{1}{5\,000\,000}$ units on the map.

650 km on the ground = $\frac{650}{5\,000\,000}$ km on the map.

Change km into m and then cm:

$$= \frac{650 \times 1000 \times 100}{5\,000\,000} \text{ cm}$$

$$= \frac{65}{5} \text{ cm}$$

$$= 13 \text{ cm.}$$

Answer   13 cm

Example 6.14

A map of the British Isles is on a scale of 1 : 5 000 000. The straight-line distance between Land's End and John o'Groats is approximately 600 miles. How far apart are Land's End and John o'Groats on the map in inches? (To 1 decimal place.)

Scale is 1 : 5 000 000.

This means 1 unit on the map is 5 000 000 units on the ground.

5 000 000 units on the ground is 1 unit on the map.

1 unit on the ground = $\frac{1}{5\,000\,000}$ units on the map.

600 miles on the ground = $\frac{600}{5\,000\,000}$ miles on the map.

Now change 600 miles to yards and then to inches:

$$= \frac{600 \times 1760}{5\,000\,000} \qquad \text{Changing 600 miles to yd (1 mile = 1760 yd)}$$

$$= \frac{600 \times 1760 \times 36}{5\,000\,000} \qquad \text{Changing yd to in (1 yd = 36 in).}$$

$$= \frac{6 \times 176 \times 36}{5000} \text{ in}$$

$$= \frac{38\,016}{5000} \text{ in}$$

$$= \frac{38.016}{5} \text{ in}$$

$$= 7.6 \text{ in.}$$

Answer   7.6 in

Example 6.15

An aeroplane has a wingspan of 150 ft. A model of it is made on a scale 1 : 100. How big is the wingspan on the model?

Scale is 1 : 100.
1 unit on the model is 100 units on the aeroplane,
or 100 units on the aeroplane = 1 unit on the model.
1 unit on the aeroplane = $\frac{1}{100}$ unit on the model.
150 ft on the aeroplane = $\frac{150}{100}$ ft on the model.
                                = 1.5 ft on the model.

Answer   1.5 ft

Exercise 6.4

1 An Ordnance Survey map has a scale of 1 : 250 000. A straight road on the map is measured as 1 cm. What is the actual length of the road in km?

2 A continental map has a scale of 1 : 200 000. How much does 1 cm on the map represent in km?

3 Walkers using a map of scale 1 : 25 000 reckoned a distance on the map as 30 cm. What distance was this in km?

4 A map scale is given as 1 : 50 000. How far is it between two towns if it is measured as 12 cm on the map? (Answer in km.)

5 On an Ordnance Survey map of 1 : 50 000 two towns are 6 in apart. How far apart are they in actual fact? (Give answer to nearest mile.)

6 A house plan is drawn to a scale of 1 : 100. The lounge on the drawing is 3 in long and 2 in wide. What is (a) the length (b) the width, of the lounge in feet and inches?

7 An atlas contains a map of Europe on a scale of 1 : 5 000 000. How much, in km, does 1 cm on the map represent?

8 A house is to be drawn on a scale of 1 : 100. The main bedroom is 4 m long and 3.8 m wide. What lengths will these be drawn on a drawing? (Answer in mm.)

9 A model is to be made of an oil tanker which is 120 m long. The suggested scale is 1 : 250. How long will the model be? (Answer in cm.)

10 A book of AA road maps is on a scale of 1 : 250 000. The direct distance between Manchester and Liverpool is 56 km. How far will this be on one of the road maps?

6.4   Direct Proportion

Two quantities are said to be in direct proportion if an increase (or decrease) in one quantity makes the second quantity increase (or decrease) in the same ratio.

Example 6.16

I pay 40p for 4 oz sweets. How much will 8 oz cost?

In this case the weight is doubled and so the cost has to be doubled. But the best method for working out is as follows:
4 oz of sweets cost 40p.
1 oz of sweets cost $\frac{40}{4}$p = 10p. (Find what 1 unit costs.)
8 oz of sweets cost 8 × 10p = 80p.
Answer   80p

Example 6.17

The cost of a holiday is £63 for a week. How much would it cost for 10 days?

7 days cost £63.
1 day costs £$\frac{63}{7}$ = £9.
10 days will cost 10 × £9 = £90.
Answer   £90

Example 6.18

7 empty barrels weigh 336 lb. What will 5 empty barrels weigh?

7 barrels weigh 336 lb.
1 barrel weighs $\frac{336}{7}$ lb = 48 lb.
5 barrels weigh 5 × 48 = 240 lb.
Answer   240 lb

After some practice you may not want to divide at the second line but proceed directly to the third line.

Example 6.19

35 kg of tomatoes cost £55. How much will 21 kg cost?

35 kg of tomatoes cost £55.
1 kg cost £$\frac{55}{35}$.
21 kg cost 21 × £$\frac{55}{35}$ = £33.
Answer   £33

6.5 Inverse Proportion

Two quantities are said to be in inverse proportion if an increase in one quantity makes the second quantity decrease in the same ratio, or a decrease in one quantity makes the second quantity increase in the same ratio.

Quite often we have to make certain assumptions: that all men (or women) work at the same rate, that conditions do not change, that there are no breakdowns, and so on.

Example 6.20

If two men can load a lorry in 4 h, how long will it take 4 men?

We assume the men all work at the same rate.
2 men take 4 h.
1 man will take 2 × 4 h = 8 h.
4 men will take $\frac{8}{4}$ h = 2 h.
Answer 2 h

As the workforce is doubled, the time taken is halved. This is inverse proportion.

Example 6.21

Two mechanical diggers can move 200 tons of earth in 6 h. How long will it take three diggers to shift the same amount?

We assume the diggers work at the same rate and that they don't hinder one another.
2 diggers take 6 h.
1 digger will take 2 × 6 = 12 h.
3 diggers will take $\frac{12}{3}$ h = 4 h.
Answer   4 h

Hints

Ask yourself a series of questions: If I employ more people will it take less time or more time to complete the work? If I have more work to do will it take longer or less time to complete? Will it cost more or cost less to employ more people?

Example 6.22

4 women in a factory make 2400 components in a 6 hour shift. How long will it take 6 women to do the same work?

The time taken is 6 h to make 2400 components.
Will 6 women take longer or less time than 4 women to make the same amount?
It will take less time.

Then decrease 6 h in the ratio $\dfrac{4 \text{ women}}{6 \text{ women}}$.

Time taken = 6 × $\frac{4}{6}$
            = 4 h.
Answer   4 h

Example 6.23

If 6 bricklayers can build a wall in 8 days working 7 h a day, how long would you expect 8 bricklayers to take working 6 h a day?

Will it take 8 bricklayers less or longer than 6 bricklayers? Less. Then decrease 8 days in ratio $\frac{6}{8}$:
= 8 × $\frac{6}{8}$
= 6 days.

If they work 6 h a day instead of 7 h a day will it take longer or less time? Longer.
Then increase 6 days in the ratio $\frac{7}{6}$.

6 days $\times \frac{7}{6}$ = 7 days.

Answer   7 days

Exercise 6.5

1 5 oranges cost 35p. What do 7 cost?

2 4 m of material costs £24. What will 5 m cost?

3 A car costs £49 to hire for a week. What will it cost for 11 days?

4 3 beakers hold 24 fl oz. How much will 2 hold?

5 Nine fencing panels measure 54 ft. What will six measure?

6 Six containers weigh 15 kg. What will four weigh?

7 It costs £60 to hire a cement mixer for 5 days. How much would it cost, at the same rate, to hire it for 2 days?

8 A hotel bill is £56.70 for 3 days. How much is it at the same rate for 10 days?

9 A recipe for 6 people requires $\frac{3}{4}$ pt of water. How much water would be needed for 4 people?

10 $1\frac{1}{4}$ lb of tomatoes cost 50p. What will 3 lb cost?

11 $2\frac{1}{2}$ kg of grass seed costs £3. How much will 40 kg cost?

12 24 paving stones cover 14 ft. How long will 36 cover?

13 A recipe quotes 8 oz of flour to 1 lb of sugar. How much sugar would be required for 6 oz of flour?

14 3 wine glasses hold a maximum of 51 cl. What will 5 glasses hold?

15 Sweets are £1.44 a lb. How much will 90p buy?

16 Oil cost £4.95 for 5 litres. What is the cost of 2 litres?

17 4 pieces of timber of the same size weigh 56 kg. What will 7 pieces of the same size weigh?

18 5 ml of weedkiller has to be mixed with 2 pints of water. How much weedkiller is required for 2 gallons of water?

19 There are $2\frac{1}{5}$ lb in 1 kg. How many kg are there in 33 lb?

20 A 15-day holiday costs £213. How much will 10 days cost?

Exercise 6.6

1 A person can dig a small plot of land in 2 h. How long would it take 2 people to dig a similar plot?

2 A tractor can plough a field in 16 h. How long would it take 2 tractors?

3 4 men take 10 days to paint a number of houses. How long would you expect 5 men to take to paint the same number?

4 2 combine harvesters working together can cut a field of barley in 6 h. How long would you expect it to take 3 combine harvesters?

5 3 workers can build a wall in 2 days. How long would you expect 1 worker to take to build a similar wall?

6 A contractor said he could finish a road in 12 days using 9 men. How long would it take if he used 18 men?

7 3 diggers can shift a pile of earth in 8 h. How long would it take for 2 diggers to shift a similar pile?

8 Four men can load a lorry in 6 h. How long would it take three men to load a similar lorry?

9 Two mowing machines cut a school playing field in 6 h. How long would it have taken one machine?

10 A scout troop of 14 had enough food to last 6 days but then another 7 scouts arrived at the camp. How long would you expect the food to last now?

Exercise 6.7 *Multiple-choice Questions*

1 If 1 in = 2.5 cm, is 60 cm the same as

    A 24 in   **B** 150 in   **C** 62.5 in   **D** 30 in?

2 From 0925 h to 2315 h on the same day is

    A 32 h 40 min   **B** 10 h 10 min   **C** 13 h 50 min   **D** 12 h 10 min

3 A ratio of 3 : 4 is the same as

    A 8 : 6   **B** 6 : 10   **C** 6 : 7   **D** 9 : 12

4 A ratio of $1\frac{1}{2}$: $2\frac{1}{2}$ is the same as

    A 3 : 4   **B** 5 : 3   **C** 3 : 5   **D** 2 : 3

5 The ratio of sugar to fat in a recipe is 3 : 4. If there is 120 g of fat then the amount of sugar should be

    A 90 g   **B** 160 g   **C** 120 g   **D** 150 g

6 A wall can be built in 6 days by 4 workers. Will 3 workers take

    A 8 days   **B** $4\frac{1}{2}$ days   **C** 9 days   **D** 12 days?

7 I divide £100 in the ratio of 3 : 3 : 4. Is the biggest share

    A £60   **B** £50   **C** £40   **D** £30?

8 A map has a scale of 1 : 50 000. Is 3 cm on the map equivalent to

    A 15 km   **B** 5 km   **C** 3 km   **D** 1.5 km?

7 Averages

7.1 Arithmetic Mean

An average in mathematics can mean any kind of representative number but in everyday language when we find the word 'average' it is usually referring to arithmetic mean. To find the average (that is, the arithmetic mean) we add all the quantities together (money, weights, runs, people, etc.) and then divide by the number of quantities.

Example 7.1

Find the average of 9, 6, 5, 12, and 8.

First, add all the numbers together:
$9 + 6 + 5 + 12 + 8 = 40$.
There are 5 numbers.
To find the average divide the total by 5:
Average = $\frac{40}{5}$ = 8.

Answer   8

Example 7.2

Six sacks are found to contain 52 kg, 48 kg, 49 kg, 53 kg, 52 kg and 58 kg. What is the average weight in each sack?

Total weight = $52 + 48 + 49 + 53 + 52 + 58$ kg
             = 312 kgs.
Number of sacks = 6.
Average weight = $\frac{312}{6}$ kg = 52 kg.

Answer   52 kg

Example 7.3

Of six teenagers starting work, two earn £42 a week, two earn £46 a week, one earns £38 and the other earns £44. What is their average weekly pay?

In a question like this we find the total and divide by the number of quantities.
2 earn £42 a week = £84 in total.
2 earn £46 a week = £92 in total.
1 earns   = £38
1 earns   £44
Total earnings   = £258

Average pay = £$\frac{258}{6}$ = £43.

Answer £43

Example 7.4

A garage sold an average of 32 cars per month over a year. How many did it sell in a year?

The average of 32 cars a month means it is the equivalent of selling 32 cars every month.
1 month averaged 32 cars.
Total over 12 months = 12 × 32
$$= 384 \text{ cars.}$$
Answer   384 cars

Note: The garage may not have sold 32 cars in any one month.

Example 7.5

A mother gives an average of £1.20 pocket money a week to her 3 children. What is the total she gives per week?

Average is £1.20 for each child.
There are 3 children.
Total = 3 × £1.20 = £3.60
Answer   £3.60

Example 7.6

A garage has average sales of 42 cars a month for 11 months but in the 12th month it sells 78 cars. What is the average over 12 months?

Average for 11 months is 42 cars a month.
Total sold over this period = 11 × 42
$$= 462 \text{ cars.}$$
In the 12th month it sells 78 cars.
Total sold = 462 + 78
$$= 540 \text{ cars.}$$
Average over 12 months = $\frac{540}{12}$ = 45 cars.
Answer   45 cars

Example 7.7

An exam consists of three papers and to pass the exam needs an average of 50 marks over the three papers. After two papers the average is only 43 marks. What mark is required on the third paper?

To average 50 marks over 3 papers needs 3 × 50 marks = 150 marks.
Average of 2 papers is 43 marks = 2 × 43 = 86 marks.
Mark required on third paper = 150 − 86
$$= 64 \text{ marks.}$$
Answer   64 marks

Example 7.8

4 lb of coffee at £4.50 per lb is blended with 5 lb at £5.40 per lb. At what average price per lb should the mixture be sold to cover the cost?

4 lb at £4.50 per lb cost 4 × £4.50 = £18.00
5 lb at £5.40 per lb cost 5 × £5.40 = £27.00
                    Total cost   = £45.00

There are 9 lb altogether.
Average cost = £$\frac{45}{9}$ = £5.
Answer   £5

Example 7.9

A salesman has average sales over three weeks of £1300. What does he need to sell in the 4th week to increase this average by £200 over the four week period?

Sales over 3 weeks = 3 × £1300 = £3900.
He wants the average to be £1500 over 4 weeks.
Sales over 4 weeks = 4 × £1500 = £6000.
Sales needed in 4th week = £6000 − £3900
                         = £2100.

Answer   £2100

Example 7.10

The ratio of men to women in an office is 1 : 4. The men's average earnings were £160 while those of the women averaged £180. What was the average earnings of all the office staff?

The ratio of men to women is 1 : 4 and it doesn't matter how many there are altogether; the ratio remains the same.

Ratio of 1 : 4 means 5 parts,
1 part being men,
4 parts being women.
Earnings of the men: 1 part at £160 = £160
Earnings of the women: 4 parts at £180 = £720
                            Total = £880

Average of the 5 parts = £$\frac{880}{5}$ = £176.
Answer   £176

Exercise 7.1

1 Find the average of
    (a) 15, 19, 32   (b) 9, 14, 7, 26
    (c) 45, 53, 66, 52   (d) 12, 17, 9, 36, 21.
2 Find the average of
    (a) £25, £9, £20   (b) £154, £96, £208, £102
    (c) £3.24, £4.15, £2.08, £0.73   (d) £85, £162, £93, £17, £28.

3 Find the average of
   (a) 130 g, 112 g, 97 g, 151 g, 85 g
   (b) 2.7 kg, 8.9 kg, 6.4 kg, 0.88 kg
   (c) 2 lb 2 oz, 4 lb 7 oz, 5 lb 10 oz
   (d) 15 cwt, 18 cwt, 1 ton, 15 cwt.

4 Find the average of
   (a) 9 mm, 1 cm 2 mm, 1 cm 5 mm;
   (b) 12 km, 41 km, 27 km, 29 km, 36 km;
   (c) 4 ft 6 in, 5 ft 9 in, 4 ft 0 in, 6 ft 1 in;
   (d) 6 yd, 7 yd 2 ft, 9 yd 2 ft, 4 yd 2 ft.

5 Find the average of
   (a) 12 min, 20 min, 15 min, 13 min;
   (b) 6 pt, 1 gal, 3 pt, 9 pt, 4 pt;
   (c) 121 ml, 90 ml, 121 ml, 115 ml, 108 ml;
   (d) 11 yr 3 months, 12 yr, 12 yr 8 months, 11 yr 8 months, 11 yr 6 months, 11 yr 11 months.

6 A train covers a journey on different occasions in the following times: 2 h 5 min, 2 h 12 min, 2 h 6 min, 2 h 20 min and 2 h 12 min. What is the average time for the journey?

7 The highest summer temperatures recorded in a town on four consecutive days were 22.3 °C, 25.2 °C, 24.7 °C and 24.6 °C. Find the average of these temperatures.

8 The price of petrol at one garage is £2.05 per gallon. At two other garages it is £1.99 per gallon. What is the average price per gallon over the three garages?

9 A garage sold an average of 34 cars per month. How many did it sell in a year?

10 In an office 3 women are on one grade and earn £140 a week, 2 men are on a lower grade and earn £125 a week and the section head is on £266 a week. What is the average weekly pay in the office?

11 A book contains 72 000 words, averaging 450 words to the page. How many pages are in the book?

12 An exam consists of three papers and to pass the exam needs an average of 60 marks over the three papers. After two papers the average mark is 52. What mark is required on the third paper to make sure of a minimum pass?

13 A woman on a charity walk wants to average 28 miles a day over 10 days. In 4 days she averages 31 miles a day but then has to rest for 2 days because of blisters. What must she average over the last 4 days to keep to schedule?

14 The average pay of 5 workers is £130 a week. One earns £150. What is the average pay of the other four?

15 4 kg of tea at £1.60 per kg is blended with 3 kg of tea at £1.95 per kg. At what price per kg should the mixture be sold to cover the cost?

16 5 kg of coffee at £4.33 per lb is blended with 4 kg of coffee at £5.50. What price per lb should the mixture be?

17 The ratio of men to women in an office was 2 : 3. The men's average earnings were £190 a week while those of the women averaged £150 a week. What were the average earnings of all the office staff?

18 A student has 6 end-of-term exams and he would like to average 50 marks over the lot. After 4 exams his average is 53. What does he need to average over the remaining exams?

19 A grass seed is a mixture of ryegrass to fescue in the ratio of 4 : 3. If ryegrass is £2.29 per kg and fescue £3.34 per kg, what is the price per kg of the mixture?

20 A wine merchant blends red wine with a lighter wine in the ratio 3 : 2. The red wine is £1.20 a litre and the lighter wine is 90p a litre. The merchant wants 1000 litres of wine. What average price per litre is it for the blend?

Exercise 7.2   Multiple-choice Questions

1 The cost of a holiday is £98 for a week. Is the cost for 10 days

   A £196   B £63   C £140   D £162?

2 36 kg of tomatoes cost £66. Will 24 kg cost

   A £99   B £41.50   C £44   D £50?

3 A bus covers a journey on different occasions in the following times: 15 min, 16 min, $17\frac{1}{2}$ min, $16\frac{1}{2}$ min, 16 min. Is the average time for the journey

   A 16.4 min   B 16.2 min   C 16.3 min   D 16.5 min?

4 The average of four numbers is 16. The average of these four numbers and a fifth number is 18. What is the fifth number?

   A 18   B 23   C 26   D 22

5 3 lb of tea at £3.50 a lb is blended with 4 lb of tea at £4.20 a lb. The price of the mixture per lb is

   A £3.85   B £7.70   C £4.00   D £3.90

6 A grass seed mixture contains fine grass and ryegrass in the ratio 4 : 3. The fine grass is £3.85 a kg and the ryegrass £2.24 a kg. What is the price of mixture a kg?

   A £3.16   B £3.00   C £2.90   D £3.06

8 Speed, Distance and Time

8.1 Average Speed

Speed describes how far is travelled in a unit of time, the most common speeds being expressed in miles per hour or km per hour.

20 mile/h is 20 miles per hour or 20 miles in an hour.

20 km/h is 20 km per hour or 20 km in an hour.

$$\text{Average speed} = \frac{\text{distance}}{\text{time}}. \qquad (\text{Distance} \div \text{time.})$$

Example 8.1

A car travels 120 miles in 4 hours. What is its average speed?

Speed is how far it travels in a unit of time (1 h):

120 miles in 4 hours

is 30 miles in 1 hour

Average speed is 30 mile/h;

$$or \quad \text{Average speed} = \frac{\text{distance}}{\text{time}} = \frac{120 \text{ miles}}{4 \text{ hours}} = 30 \text{ miles per hour.}$$

Answer   30 mile/h

Example 8.2

An express coach leaves Leeds at 0930 hours and arrives in London at 1330 hours, which includes a short break.

The distance is 180 miles. What was the average speed of the coach?

Time taken is 1330 hours − 0930 hours = 4 h.

$$\text{Average speed} = \frac{\text{distance}}{\text{time}} = \frac{180 \text{ miles}}{4 \text{ h}} = 45 \text{ miles per hour.}$$

Answer   45 mile/h

Example 8.3

A racing car covers a 3 mile circuit in $1\frac{1}{2}$ minutes. What is the average speed for the circuit?

Average speed = $\dfrac{\text{distance}}{\text{time}}$ = $\dfrac{3 \text{ miles}}{1\frac{1}{2} \text{ min}}$ = 2 miles per minute.

2 miles per minute = 2 × 60 miles per hour
$$= 120 \text{ mile/h.}$$
Answer   120 mile/h

Example 8.4

A cyclist in a road race averages 24.7 mile/h over 5 h. How far does he travel?

Average speed is 24.7 mile/h.
This means 24.7 miles in an hour.
In 5 hours he will travel 5 × 24.7 miles
$$= 123.5 \text{ miles.}$$
Answer   123.5 miles

Example 8.5

A car travels 20 miles in 24 minutes. What is its average speed?

We want to find out how far it travels in one hour.
In 24 minutes it travels 20 miles,
in 1 minute it travels $\frac{20}{24}$ miles,

in 1 hour it travels $60 \times \dfrac{20}{24}$ = 50 miles.

Answer   50 mile/h

Example 8.6

A train travels for 220 miles at an average speed of 55 mile/h. How long does the journey take?

Average speed is 55 mile/h.
This means 55 miles in an hour.
To travel 220 miles will take $\frac{220}{55}$ = 4 h.
Answer   4 h

Example 8.7

How long does it take to travel 112 miles at an average speed of 30 mile/h?

Average speed 30 mile/h means 30 miles in an hour.
To travel 112 miles will take $\frac{112}{30}$ h = $3\frac{22}{30}$ h.
$\frac{22}{30}$ h = 44 min.
Answer $3\frac{22}{30}$ h = 3 h 44 min

Example 8.8

Where two average speeds are given and two times (or distances) then it is essential to work out the total distance and the total time.

A man runs for 2 h averaging 8 mile/h and then for 1 hour averaging 5 mile/h. What does he average over the whole run?
Averaging 8 miles per hour, in 2 h he covers 2 x 8 miles = 16 miles.
And then in 1 h he covers 5 miles.
Total distance he runs = 16 + 5 = 21 miles.
Total time taken = 2 h + 1 = 3 h.

$$\text{Average over the whole run} = \frac{21 \text{ miles}}{3 \text{ h}} = 7 \text{ mile/h.}$$

Answer   7 mile/h

Note that adding 8 mile/h and 5 mile/h and dividing by 2 does not give the right answer.

Example 8.9

A motorist travels 2 h at an average speed of 40 mile/h; he has a break for lunch of 1 h, and he completes his journey in another 3 h at an average speed of 45 mile/h. What is the average speed for the whole journey?

40 mile/h is 40 miles in an hour.
In 2 h he travels 2 x 40 miles = 80 miles.
In 3 h at 45 miles per hour he travels 3 x 45 = 135 miles.
Total distance = 80 miles + 135 miles = 215 miles.
Total time = 2 h + 1 h (lunch) + 3 h = 6 h.

$$\text{Average speed} = \frac{215 \text{ miles}}{6 \text{ h}} = 35\tfrac{5}{6} \text{ mile/h.}$$

Answer $35\tfrac{5}{6}$ mile/h

Example 8.10

A train travels for 90 miles at 45 mile/h and for 120 miles at 40 mile/h. What is the average speed for the journey?

45 mile/h is 45 miles in an hour.
To travel 90 miles would take $\frac{90}{45}$ = 2 h.
To travel 120 miles at 40 mile/h would take $\frac{120}{40}$ = 3 h.
Total distance travelled = 90 miles + 120 miles = 210 miles.
Total time taken = 2 h + 3 h = 5 h.

$$\text{Average speed} = \frac{210 \text{ miles}}{5 \text{ h}} = 42 \text{ mile/h.}$$

Answer   42 mile/h

Exercise 8.1

1 Find the average speed for travelling
   (a) 40 miles in 2 h   (b) 60 km in 3 h
   (c) 48 miles in 3 h   (d) 37 miles in 2 h
   (e) 50 miles in 4 h   (f) 62 miles in 3 h.

2 Find the average speed for travelling
   (a) 50 miles in $2\frac{1}{2}$ h   (b) 80 km in $2\frac{1}{2}$ h
   (c) 72 miles in $4\frac{1}{2}$ h   (d) 120 km in $1\frac{1}{2}$ h
   (e) 30 miles in 36 min   (f) 4 miles in 1 min 20 s.

3 What distance is travelled in
   (a) 3 h at 20 mile/h   (b) 4 h at 42 km/h
   (c) 2 h at 47 mile/h   (d) 3 h at 95 km/h
   (e) 5 h at 600 mile/h   (f) 3 h at 4.5 mile/h?

4 What distance is travelled in
   (a) $2\frac{1}{2}$ h at 20 mile/h   (b) $3\frac{1}{2}$ h at 48 km/h
   (c) $1\frac{1}{2}$ h at 32 mile/h   (d) 2 h 20 min at 45 mile/h
   (e) 3 h 45 min at 48 km/h   (f) 24 min at 40 mile/h?

5 How long does it take to travel
   (a) 60 miles at an average speed of 20 mile/h?
   (b) 90 miles at an average speed of 18 mile/h?
   (c) 135 miles at an average speed of 45 mile/h?
   (d) 200 km at an average speed of 25 km/h?
   (e) 148 km at an average speed of 37 km/h?
   (f) 90 miles at an average speed of 36 mile/h?

6 How long does it take to travel
   (a) 135 miles at an average speed of 30 mile/h?
   (b) 71 km at an average speed of 30 km/h?
   (c) 92 km at an average speed of 40 km/h?
   (d) 180 km at an average speed of 240 km/h?
   (e) 15 miles at an average speed of 36 mile/h?
   (f) 24 miles at an average speed of 32 mile/h?

7 A motorist travels 100 miles in 2 h 20 min. He has a break of 30 min and then he completes his journey by travelling 120 miles in 3 h 10 min. What is his average speed for the whole journey?

8 An aeroplane averages 420 mile/h for $2\frac{1}{2}$ h and 500 mile/h for the next $1\frac{1}{2}$ h. How far does it travel overall?

9 A cyclist manages to travel at 22 mile/h for 3 h and 12 mile/h for 2 h. What is the average speed for the journey? (Find total distance travelled and total time taken.)

10 A car left Glasgow at 0830 hours and after travelling for $3\frac{1}{2}$ h the driver had a break of one hour. He arrived in London at 1700 hours. The distance from Glasgow to London is 340 miles. What is (a) his average speed for the whole journey, (b) his average speed on the road?

11 A motorist travels for one hour at 50 mile/h and then for 2 h at 38 mile/h. Find the average speed.

12 A motorbike goes at 60 mile/h for 3 min and then covers the next two miles in 1 min 30 s. What was the average speed over the distance?

Exercise 8.2   *Multiple-choice Questions*

1 A car travels 100 miles between 0830 and 1100 hours. What is its average speed?

  A   50 mile/h   **B**   40 mile/h   **C**   60 mile/h   **D**   45 mile/h

2 A coach travels for $3\frac{1}{2}$ hours at an average speed of 40 mile/h. Does it travel

    A   40 miles   **B**   120 miles   **C**   140 miles   **D**   100 miles?

3 A motorcycle travels 2 miles at 60 mile/h and 3 miles at 30 mile/h. Is its average speed

    A   45 mile/h   **B**   42.5 mile/h   **C**   37.5 mile/h   **D**   40 mile/h?

4 A shop sold an average of 200 electric calculators per week over a period of four weeks. How many would need to be sold over a fifth week to increase this average by 20?

    A   300   **B**   240   **C**   220   **D**   225

9 Commercial Arithmetic

9.1 Introduction

'Money is the root of all evil' goes the chant of an old song; whether it is or not, we cannot manage without it.

This chapter shows how we use addition, subtraction, multiplication and division every day when we deal with money even though we may not realise it.

9.2 Payslips and Wages

Before any of us can use money we need to earn it; for those who are working or hope to work a typical payslip, whether paid weekly or monthly, will probably record the details shown in Fig. 9.1. Some payslips will record more information and others less; for example, the payslip of a person working part time in an evening in a bar will probably show only the hours worked each night, the rate of pay per hour, and the amount earned in the week.

Most of the terms explain themselves.

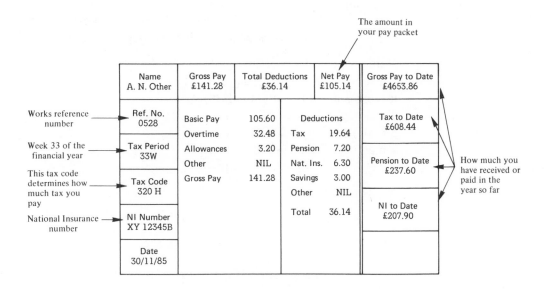

Figure 9.1 Typical payslip

Example 9.1

A woman is paid a basic wage of £2.20 an hour for a 35-hour week. Extra hours (overtime) are paid at time-and-a-quarter. What does she earn if she works 43 hours in one week?

Normal basic wage = 35 × £2.20   35 hours at £2.20 an hour.
                  = £77
Number of hours overtime = 43 − 35 = 8.
Overtime is paid at time-and-a-quarter and since the basic rate is
£2.20 an hour the overtime rate is £2.20 × $1\frac{1}{4}$.
£2.20 × $1\frac{1}{4}$ = £2.20 × $\frac{5}{4}$

$$= \frac{£11.00}{4} = £2.75.$$

There were 8 hours overtime, therefore she earned
8 × £2.75 = £22 in overtime.
Total pay = basic wage + overtime
          = £77 + £22
          = £99.

Answer   £99

Note: In the overtime calculation it does not matter if you increase the payment
per hour by a quarter or the hours by a quarter — the result is still the same.

There are 8 hours overtime.
This is paid at time and a quarter.
Overtime is equivalent to 8 × $1\frac{1}{4}$ hours = 8 × $\frac{5}{4}$ = 10 hours
10 hours at £2.20 an hour = £22.
Overtime is £22, same as before.

Example 9.2

A man works a 50-hour week and his pay is calculated as follows. The first 35
hours at £3 an hour, the next 8 hours at time-and-a-quarter, and the rest at
time-and-a-half. How much is his total pay for the week?

Number of hours overtime = 50 − 35 = 15 hours.
8 hours are at time-and-a-quarter ($1\frac{1}{4}$),
leaving 7 h at time-and-a-half ($1\frac{1}{2}$).
Total pay = 35 h at £3   = £105
8 h at $1\frac{1}{4}$ = 8 h at £3.75 =   £30
7 h at $1\frac{1}{2}$ = 7 h at £4.50 =   £31.50
                                    £166.51

Answer   £166.50

Example 9.3

A man earns a basic £180 a week, plus £45 in overtime. He pays £26.80 in tax,
£5.75 in national insurance, and his pension contribution is £5 for every £100
on basic pay. What is his net pay for the week?

Gross pay = basic + overtime
          = £180 + £45
          = £225.
Pension contribution on £100 basic pay is £5,
              on £180 basic pay is $\frac{180}{100}$ × 5 = £9.
Deductions = tax + national insurance + pension
           = £26.80 + £5.75 + £9
           = £41.55.

Net pay = Gross pay − deductions
       = £225 − £41.55
       = £183.45

Answer   £183.45

Exercise 9.1

1 A person has gross pay of £175.64 and deductions total £33.85. What is the nett pay?
2 My nett pay for a month is £415.56. The gross pay was £490.20. How much was deducted?
3 A woman works a 35-hour week at £2.80 an hour. How much does she earn in a week?
4 A man's basic pay is £2.80 an hour for a 37 hour week and time and a quarter for overtime. How much does he earn when he works 43 hours?
5 A man's basic rate of pay is £3.20 an hour but for weekend working he gets double time. In one week he works 50 hours, of which 12 were at the week-end. How much did he earn that week?
6 A woman has gross pay of £560 in a 4-week month. She pays National Insurance at £5.75 a week, she saves £6 a week, tax amounts to £87.80 a month, and her firm's pension costs her £33.60 a month. What is her nett pay?
7 A firm asks employees to contribute towards a pension at a rate of £6 for every £100 earned. A man earns £480 a month and in addition to pension contributions he pays £21.40 in national insurance and £64.24 in tax. What is his net pay for the month?
8 A man works a 52 hour week and his pay is calculated as follows: the first 36 hours at £3.20 an hour, the next 5 hours at time-and-a-quarter, the next 5 hours at time-and-a-half, and any further hours at double time. From this he pays £5.60 in National Insurance, and £12.42 in tax. What is his net pay?

9.3 Bank Paying-in Slips

When paying money into a bank for yourself or for your company the paying-in slip may want the information shown in Fig. 9.2. This has been fully completed for you.

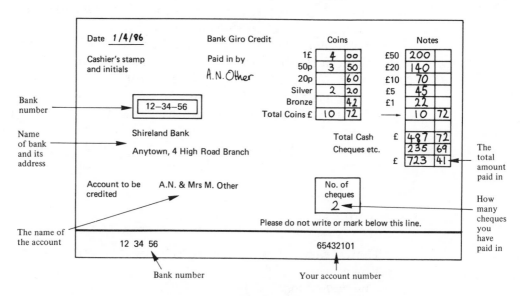

Figure 9.2   Typical bank paying-in slip

87

Example 9.4

Show how to fill in a bank paying-in slip for the following: 3 £1 coins, nine 50p coins, five 10p coins, six 5p coins, ten 2p coins, 6 £20 notes, 11 £10 notes, and 3 £1 notes.

The answer is shown in Fig. 9.3.

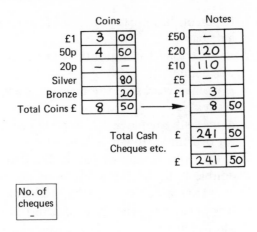

Figure 9.3 Paying-in slip (Example 9.4)

Exercise 9.2

Try and complete similar slips (ask for some at the bank or draw some as in the worked example) for the following amounts of cash and/or cheques.

1 5 £1 coins, four 50p coins, eight 20p coins, five 10p coins, six 5p coins, ten 2p coins, eight 1p coins, 3 £50 notes, 4 £20 notes, 3 £5 notes, and 6 £1 notes.

2 Three cheques, one for £125.35, one for £37.40 and one for £75.62.

3 25 £1 coins, 6 £50 notes, 4 £20 notes, 7 £5 notes, 32 £1 notes, and cheques for £65 and £45.

4 Twenty-five 50p coins, sixty-five 20p coins, fifty-five 10p coins, thirty 5p coins, 7 £20 notes, 15 £10 notes, 63 £1 notes, and a cheque for £32.40.

5 Cheques for £148.25, £96.48, £195.32, 12 £20 notes, 45 £10 notes, 32 £5 notes, 97 £1 notes, and 72 £1 coins, thirty-two 50p coins, twenty 20p coins, silver amounting to £15.65 and bronze to £3.28.

6 8 £50 notes, 9 £20 notes, 25 £5 notes, 97 £1 coins, forty-seven 50p coins, eighteen 20p coins, sixty-five 10p coins, and thirteen 5p coins.

7 Cheques for £35.87 and £107.56, with 47 £10 notes, 23 £5 notes, 104 £1 coins, and thirty-six 50p coins.

8 The total amount paid into a bank was £965.46p. There were cheques for £196.48, £205.29 and a third cheque, together with 15 £10 notes, 25 £5 notes, 80 £1 coins, fifteen 50p coins, thirty-two 20p coins and silver and bronze amounting to £18.46. For how much was the third cheque?

9.4 Postal Charges

All letters and parcels are charged as follows:
(a) by weight;
(b) by destination;
(c) whether first class or second class.

An inland destination is to anywhere in the UK, the Isle of Man, the Channel Islands and the Irish Republic.

An overseas destination is to anywhere that is not covered by inland mail.

First- and second-class letter post only applies to inland destinations.

First-class post is delivered as quickly as possible, whereas second-class has a delay of at least one day.

The Post Office provides two leaflets which include simple tables relating the cost of a letter or parcel to its destination. These tables are shown here as Tables 9.1 to 9.5.

Table 9.1   Inland letter post

Weight not over	1st class	2nd class
60 g	17p	13p
100 g	24p	18p
150 g	31p	22p
200 g	38p	28p
250 g	45p	34p
300 g	53p	40p
350 g	61p	46p
400 g	69p	52p
450 g	78p	59p
500 g	87p	66p
750 g	£1.28	98p
1000 g	£1.70	Not admissible
Each extra 250 g or part thereof	42p	over 750 g.

Table 9.2   Inland parcel post

Weight not over	National Rate
1 kg	£1.33
2 kg	£1.72
3 kg	£2.10
4 kg	£2.30
5 kg	£2.50
6 kg	£2.65
7 kg	£2.80
8 kg	£2.95
9 kg	£3.10
10 kg	£3.25
25 kg	£4.15

It may be slightly cheaper if you are sending a parcel to somewhere in the same county or an adjacent county — enquire at the Post Office.

Table 9.3 Overseas Postal Rates. Europe (by airmail) and surface mail to all other countries

Weight							
Not over		*Not over*		*Not over*		*Not over*	
20 g	22p	250 g	£1.06	500 g	£2.02	1750 g	£5.17
60 g	37p	300 g	£1.25	750 g	£2.77	2000 g	£5.72
100 g	53p	350 g	£1.44	1000 g	£3.52		
150 g	70p	400 g	£1.64	1250 g	£4.07		
200 g	88p	450 g	£1.83	1500 g	£4.62		

Table 9.4 Outside Europe (airmail)

	Airmail zone	Not over 10 g	Each additional 10 g or part thereof
Letters	A	29p	11p
	B	31p	14p
	C	34p	15p
Small packets	A	21p	5p
	B	23p	7p
	C	24p	8p

Table 9.5 Key to airmail zones (shown after the name of the country)

Australia (C)	Israel (A)	Saudi Arabia (A)
Brazil (B)	Japan (C)	South Africa (B)
Canada (B)	Korea (C)	Tonga (C)
Egypt (A)	Libya (A)	USA (B)
Falkland Islands (B)	Morocco (A)	Vietnam (B)
Gambia (B)	New Zealand (C)	Yemen (A)
Hong Kong (B)	Philippines (C)	Zimbabwe (B)

A full list of countries and airmail zones can be obtained from the Post Office.

How to find the postage cost of any letter or parcel to any country

The six steps to finding the postage cost of a letter or parcel are

(a) what is the weight of letter or parcel?
(b) where is it going?
(c) is it to be first-class or second-class post?
(d) is it to be airmail or surface mail?
(e) look at appropriate table;
(f) calculate cost.

Example 9.5

Find the cost of a first-class letter to Manchester posted in London, which weighs 200 g.

The weight is 200 g.
From London to Manchester is inland postage.
It is to be first class.

Airmail or surface mail does not apply.
Look at Table 9.1.
From Table 9.1 we see that the cost will be 38p.
Answer   38p

Example 9.6

Find the cost of a second-class letter from Edinburgh to London which weighs 380 g.

The weight is 380 g.
Edinburgh to London is inland postage.
It is to be second class.
Look at Table 9.1.
380 g is more than 350 g but it is not more than 400 g.
Table 9.1 says that not more than 400 g will cost 52p by second-class post.
Answer   52p

Example 9.7

Find the cost of sending a letter weighing 120 g from London to Paris.

Weight is 120 g.
London to Paris is European rates.
First or second class does not apply and all mail is airmail.
Look at Table 9.3.
120 g is more than 100 g but not more than 150 g.
Table 9.3 says that the cost will be 70p.
Answer   70p

Example 9.8

Find the cost of an airmail letter weighing 30 g from London to New Zealand.

Weight is 30 g. London to New Zealand is overseas mail.
This means either Table 9.3 or Table 9.4, but it is an airmail letter therefore Table 9.4 applies.
Which airmail zone does New Zealand come under?
The country key says New Zealand is zone C.
Cost for zone C is 34p not over 10 g and 15p for each additional 10 g.
Cost for 30 g is 34p (for 10 g) + 2 × 15p (2 × 10 g)
$$= 34p + 30p$$
$$= 64p.$$
Answer   64p

Example 9.9

Find the cost of sending a Christmas parcel by surface mail from England to Canada if the parcel weighs 1100 g.

Weight is 1100 g. England to Canada is overseas mail and it is to be sent by surface mail.

Look at Table 9.3.
Cost of parcel weighing 1100 g is £4.07.
Answer   £4.07

Exercise 9.3

Find the cost of sending the following:
 1 A first-class letter weighing 100 g from Newcastle to Bristol.
 2 A first-class letter weighing 400 g from London to Manchester.
 3 A first-class letter weighing 475 g from Stoke to an address in England.
 4 A second-class letter weighing 125 g from Scotland to Wales.
 5 A second-class letter weighing 285 g from England to Northern Ireland.
 6 A parcel weighing 4 kg from England to the Isle of Man.
 7 A parcel weighing 7.5 kg from Scotland to the Irish Republic.
 8 A parcel weighing 2.75 kg from England to the Channel Isles.
 9 A letter weighing 200 g from England to Germany.
10 A letter weighing 325 g from England to France.
11 An airmail letter weighing 40 g from England to Australia.
12 An airmail letter weighing 25 g from England to Egypt.
13 An airmail letter weighing 52 g from Wales to USA.
14 A parcel weighing 1 kg by surface mail from Scotland to Korea.
15 A small packet weighing 180 g by airmail from England to Hong Kong.
16 An airmail letter weighing 65 g from England to the Falkland Islands.
17 An airmail letter weighing 17 g from England to South Africa.
18 A small packet weighing 85 g by airmail from Wales to Brazil.
19 A small packet weighing 106 g by airmail from Scotland to Saudi Arabia.
20 A parcel weighing 390 g by surface mail from Scotland to Tonga.
21 A parcel weighing $4\frac{1}{2}$ kg from Land's End to John o'Groats.
22 A letter weighing 60 g from London to Oslo.
23 An air mail letter weighing 35 g from Manchester to New York.
24 A parcel weighing 425 g from Newcastle to Rome.

9.5   Foreign Currency and Exchange Rates

British currency can be exchanged for foreign currency and vice versa.
British currency is the pound (£) sterling and £1 = 100 pence.
The currencies of some other countries are as follows:

United States of America	dollars and cents	1 dollar = 100 cents
Germany	marks and pfennigs	1 mark = 100 pfennigs
Switzerland	francs and cents	1 franc = 100 cents.

For the purpose of this exercise use the following exchange rates and all calculations will work out exactly (check any daily paper to see what the exchange rate is now since it changes every day):

Austria	26.75	schillings
France	11.63	francs
Germany	3.81	marks
Italy	2445	lire
Spain	214	pesetas
United States	1.26	dollars

92

All these figures quote what you will receive for £1 sterling in the currencies of the countries named.

When you go abroad one of the major points of interest is money. You will want to know:

(a) how much foreign currency will you receive for your British money (£ sterling);

(b) when you return how much can you expect to receive in British money (£ sterling) for your foreign currency;

(c) how can you calculate an actual exchange rate.

Finding (a) entails a multiplication sum, while finding (b) entails a division sum.

When asked to convert one foreign currency to another foreign currency then still use £1 as the standard.

The worked examples show how these questions can be resolved.

The following examples use the exchange rates quoted above.

Example 9.10

How many French francs would you receive for £150?

£1 = 11.63 francs.
£150 = 150 × 11.63
     = 1744.50 francs

$$
\begin{array}{r}
1\,163 \\
\times\ \ \ \ 150 \\
\hline
116\,300 \\
58\,15 \\
\hline
174\,450
\end{array}
$$

Now move the decimal point 2 places.

Answer   1744.50 francs

Example 9.11

How many American dollars would you receive for £38?

£1 = 1.26 dollars.
£38 = 38 × 1.26
     = 47.88 dollars.

$$
\begin{array}{r}
126 \\
\times\ \ \ 38 \\
\hline
3780 \\
1008 \\
\hline
4788
\end{array}
$$

Now move the decimal point 2 places.

Answer   47.88 dollars

Example 9.12

How many £s will you get for 533.40 German marks?

3.81 marks = £1.
533.40 marks = £$\frac{533.40}{3.81}$
           = £140.

$$
\begin{array}{r}
140 \\
381\overline{)53340} \\
381\ \ \ \ \\
\hline
1524 \\
1524 \\
\hline
\cdots\cdots
\end{array}
$$

Answer   £140

Example 9.13

How many £s will you receive for 872.25 French francs?

11.63 francs = £1.
872.25 francs = £$\frac{872.25}{11.63}$
= £75.

$$\begin{array}{r} 75 \\ 1163\overline{)87225} \\ 8141 \\ \hline 5815 \\ 5815 \\ \hline \cdots \end{array}$$

Answer   £75

Example 9.14

Convert 228.6 German marks into American dollars.

Use £1 as the standard.
3.81 marks = £1
228.6 marks = £$\frac{228.6}{3.81}$
= £60.
£1 = 1.26 dollars.
£60 = 60 × 1.26 dollars
= 75.60 dollars.
Answer   75.60 dollars

Example 9.15

Convert 220 050 Italian lire into Spanish pesetas.

Use £1 as the standard.
2445 lire = £1
220 050 lire = £$\frac{220\,050}{2445}$
= £90.
£1 = 214 pesetas.
£90 = 90 × 214 pesetas
= 19 260 pesetas.
Answer   19 260 pesetas

As you can see, some currencies do involve large numbers.

Example 9.16

On returning from holiday I found that the bank gave me £65 in exchange for 208 Swiss francs. What was the exchange rate?

The exchange rate means how much is £1 worth?
£65 is worth 208 Swiss francs.
£1 is worth $\frac{208}{65}$ Swiss francs
= 3.20 Swiss francs.
Answer   The exchange rate is 3.20 Swiss francs for £1

94

Exercise 9.4

Using the exchange rates given, change the following currencies:
1 £100 into (a) Austrian schillings, (b) German marks, (c) French francs.
2 £300 into (a) US dollars, (b) Italian lire, (c) Spanish pesetas.
3 £170 into (a) French francs, (b) US dollars, (c) Spanish pesetas.
4 £2000 into (a) Austrian schillings, (b) French francs, (c) Italian lire.
5 £25 into (a) German marks, (b) Spanish pesetas, (c) Austrian schillings.
6 £60 into (a) Italian lire, (b) US dollars, (c) French francs.
7 £110 into (a) Austrian schillings, (b) Spanish pesetas, (c) German marks.
8 £240 into (a) US dollars, (b) French francs, (c) Austrian schillings.
9 £15 into (a) Italian lire, (b) German marks, (c) Spanish pesetas.
10 £180 into (a) French francs, (b) US dollars, (c) German marks.

Exercise 9.5

Using the exchange rates given, change the following currencies into £ sterling:
1 267.50 Austrian schillings
2 3810 German marks
3 214 000 Spanish pesetas
4 116.30 French francs
5 189 US dollars
6 61 125 Italian lire
7 266.70 German marks
8 13 375 Austrian schillings
9 2093.40 French francs
10 171 150 Italian lire
11 441 US dollars
12 5885 Spanish pesetas
13 495.30 German marks
14 26 750 Austrian schillings
15 523.35 French francs
16 856.80 US dollars
17 244.50 Italian lire
18 4708 Spanish pesetas
19 755.95 French francs
20 171.45 German marks.

Exercise 9.6

Using the exchange rates given, change the following currencies:
1 381 German marks into French francs.
2 252 US dollars into Italian lire.
3 1070 Spanish pesetas into German marks.
4 24 450 Italian lire into German marks.
5 5815 French francs into US dollars.
6 5350 Austrian schillings into Spanish pesetas.
7 126 US dollars into Italian lire.
8 762 German marks into US dollars.
9 11 630 French francs into German marks.
10 10 700 Spanish pesetas into US dollars.
11 733 500 Italian lire into US dollars.
12 1260 US dollars into French francs.
13 190.50 German marks into Austrian schillings.
14 26 750 Austrian schillings into French francs.
15 279.12 French francs into German marks.
16 6420 Spanish pesetas into US dollars.
17 195 600 Italian lire into Spanish pesetas.
18 504 US dollars into German marks.
19 1143 German marks into French francs.
20 116 300 French francs into Austrian schillings.

Exercise 9.7

Find the exchange rate to the pound in the following cases:
1 £100 is exchanged for 126 dollars.
2 £1000 is exchanged for 26 750 Austrian schillings.
3 £40 is exchanged for 128 Swiss francs.
4 261 Dutch florins are exchanged for £60.
5 £50 is exchanged for 10 550 Portuguese escudos.
6 £400 is exchanged for 4480 Swedish kronor.
7 1380 Danish krone are exchanged for £100.
8 31.50 US dollars are exchanged for £25.
9 4890 Yugoslavian dinars are exchanged for £15.
10 £70 is exchanged for 11 830 Greek drachmas.
11 485.20 French francs are exchanged for £40.
12 234 German marks are exchanged for £60.
13 66 000 Spanish pesetas are exchanged for £300.
14 £150 is exchanged for 495 Swiss francs.
15 £300 is exchanged for 3477 French francs.
16 £400 is exchanged for 740 Canadian dollars.
17 16 400 Belgian francs are exchanged for £200.
18 675 US dollars are exchanged for £500.
19 784 Hong Kong dollars are exchanged for £80.
20 £200 is exchanged for 63 000 Japanese yen.

9.6 Hire Purchase

Some items may be expensive to buy and usually it is possible to pay for such items by a number of equal payments spread over a number of months. An agreement is signed to do this and is called a hire purchase (h.p.) agreement or credit agreement.

You can take the goods home after the first payment.

Payments are made every month for 6 months or 12 months or 24 months.

The Consumer Credit Act 1985 gives a person the following rights:

(1) the right to cancel a credit agreement signed off the suppliers' premises; you have 5 days in which to change your mind;
(2) the right to pay off a debt early and usually receive a rebate;
(3) the right to a signed copy of the agreement, which will show how much you will repay;
(4) an end to small print.

When using hire purchase:

(1) you should expect to pay more than the normal cash price, although sometimes there are special offers with no extra charge;
(2) you may find it useful to look around to see which firm is charging least.

Buying through a mail order firm using a number of payments is a form of hire purchase.

Example 9.17

A stereo radio–cassette recorder is offered at £57.95 cash or with 6 monthly payments of £10.95 each. How much extra do you pay by buying it over 6 months?

Note that you can take the stereo radio home once you have made the first payment.
Cash price = £57.95
1 monthly payment   = £10.95
6 monthly payments = 6 × £10.95
                    = £65.70.
Total amount paid = £65.70.
Extra charge = £65.70 − £57.95
             = £7.75.
Answer   £7.75

Example 9.18

A 14-inch colour television is offered at £164.95 or for a deposit of £17 plus 11 monthly payments of £15.65. Find how much extra you pay under this hire purchase agreement.

Cash price = £164.95.
Deposit   = £17.
 1 monthly payment   = £15.65.
11 monthly payments = 11 × £15.65
                    = £172.15.
Total amount paid = deposit + monthly payments
                  = £17 + £172.15
                  = £189.15.
Extra charge   = £189.15 − £164.95
                  = £24.20.
Answer   £24.20

Example 9.19

A video tape recorder is £399.95 cash or it can be bought by 24 monthly payments of £20.99. How much would you save by paying in cash?

Cash price = £399.95.
 1 monthly payment   = £20.99.   2 099
24 monthly payments = 24 × £20.99   24
                    = £503.76.   41 980
Saving = £503.76 − £399.95   8 396
       = £103.81.   50 376
Answer   £103.81

In this case a considerable saving is made by paying cash.

Cars are probably the most expensive thing we buy, apart from a house, and they are often bought by hire purchase.

Example 9.20

A special offer for a car gave the cash price at £5985 or a deposit of $\frac{1}{5}$ the cash price, plus 36 monthly payments of £151.95. What was the total credit price and what was the saving by paying cash?

Cash price = £5985.
Deposit = $\frac{1}{5}$ of the cash price
         = $\frac{1}{5}$ × £5985
         = £1197.

97

1 monthly payment = £151.95,	15 195	
36 monthly payments = 36 × £151.95	36	
= £5470.20.	455 850	
	91 170	
	547 020	

Total credit price = deposit + monthly payments
$$= £1197 + £5470.20$$
$$= £6667.20.$$
Saving by paying cash = £6667.20 − £5985
$$= £682.20.$$

Answer   £682.20

Exercise 9.8

1 A radio is £24.95 cash, or it can be bought by 6 monthly payments of £5.00 each. Find the extra charge on buying by monthly payments.

2 A radio cassette is offered at £69.95 or by 6 monthly payments of £13.50. Find the extra charge by using monthly payments.

3 A music centre is on special offer at £94.95 or with a deposit of £15 and then 6 monthly payments of £15. Find the difference in cash price and the credit price.

4 A 16-inch colour television is on offer at £194.95 or with a deposit of £19 and then 12 monthly payments of £16. Find the saving by paying cash.

5 An electricity board offers a fridge–freezer for £179.99 cash or no deposit with 24 monthly payments of £8.98. How much extra do you pay by buying it over 24 months?

6 A remote control 22-inch colour television costs £369.95 cash or it can be bought with a deposit of £36 and then 24 monthly payments of £15.50. Find the difference between the cash price and the credit price.

7 A microwave oven, with turn table, is £249.95 cash or it can be bought by 12 monthly payments of £22.50. Find the saving by paying cash.

8 A gas fire is quoted at £144.95 cash. The total credit price for 12 monthly payments is quoted as £162.
   How much do you save by paying cash and how much a month do you pay in the credit agreement?

9 A gas cooker is on offer at £399.99 but it can be bought by a deposit of £40 and then 24 monthly payments of £17. What is the difference between the cash price and the credit price?

10 An electric cooker is £400 cash or it can be bought by a deposit of $\frac{1}{4}$ of the cash value plus 12 monthly payments of £28. Find the extra charge by using hire purchase.

11 A fridge–freezer can be bought by a deposit of $\frac{1}{5}$ of the cash price plus 6 monthly payments of £32.50. The cash price is £220. What is the saving by paying cash?

12 A secondhand car is on offer at £1000 cash or by a deposit of $\frac{1}{5}$ of the cash price plus 24 monthly payments of £40. Find the h.p. price.

13 A new car is on offer at £4400 cash. It can be bought with a deposit of $\frac{1}{4}$ cash price plus 36 monthly payments of £114. Find the credit price.

9.7   Bank Loans

If you have a bank account then your bank may be prepared to give you a personal loan to buy a cooker, a freezer, a car or any other expensive item.

Payment can be spread over 12 or 24 months just as with a hire purchase agreement. The bank puts the money into your account once you have signed the agreement with them.

Example 9.21

A woman sees a new car priced at £6400. The showroom asks for $\frac{1}{5}$ deposit and 24 monthly payments of £246. She goes to the bank and the bank offers her a loan of £6400 for 24 monthly payments of £290. Which overall payment is cheaper and by how much?

Hire purchase

Deposit $= \frac{1}{5}$ of cash price.
$\qquad\quad = \frac{1}{5} \times £6400$
$\qquad\quad = £1280.$
1 monthly payment $= £246.$
24 monthly payments $= £5904.$
Total amount $=$ deposit $+$ monthly payments
$\qquad\qquad\qquad = £1280 + £5904$
$\qquad\qquad\qquad = £7184.$

Bank

1 monthly payment $= £290.$
24 monthly payments $= 24 \times £290$
$\qquad\qquad\qquad\quad = £6960.$
Total amount $\qquad\quad = £6960.$
Answer   Bank payment is cheaper overall. (Difference $= £7184 - £6960 = £224.$)

Exercise 9.9

1 A bank offers a man a personal loan of £250. He has to pay it back in 12 monthly payments of £24. How much does the man pay extra for this agreement?
2 A mail order company has an outfit on offer at £56 but it can be bought by 12 weekly payments of £5.20. What extra charge is made for weekly payments?
3 A mail order company has a suit for £72 or by 12 weekly payments of £7.15. Find the difference between the cash price and the credit price.
4 A man sees his bank manager about a loan of £4000 to buy a secondhand car. The bank wants 24 monthly payments of £190. How much extra will the man have to pay to get his £4000 loan?
5 A woman sees a new car priced at £5000. The showroom asks for $\frac{1}{4}$ deposit and then 24 monthly payments of £192. Her bank offers her a loan of £5000 for 24 monthly payments of £235. Which overall payment is cheaper and by how much?
6 A motorbike is on offer at £480 cash but with a special offer of $\frac{1}{5}$ deposit and 24 monthly payments of £17. A man asks the bank and they offer a loan of £480 with 24 monthly payments of £22. Which overall payment is cheaper and by how much?

9.8 Gas and Electricity Bills

Both types of bill are calculated each quarter (3 months) as a charge for each unit used plus a fixed quarterly charge. (The unit for gas is a therm and that for electricity is a kilowatt-hour.)

A typical gas bill is shown in Fig. 9.4.

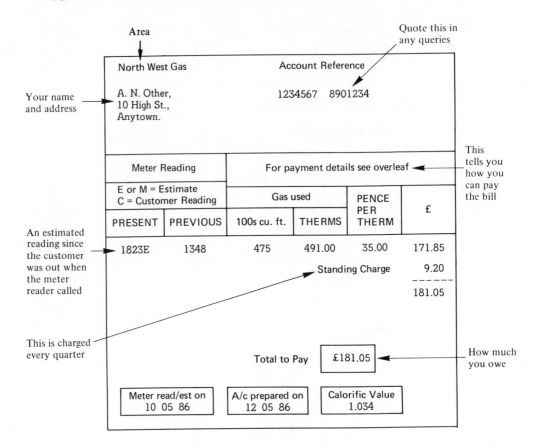

Figure 9.4   Typical gas bill

Note: Your gas meter measures how much gas you use in cubic feet but you are charged by the therm. The gas board works out how many therms are used because the actual heating value of each cubic foot of gas varies from one gas board to another.

Any items bought from the gas board on an h.p. agreement will also be charged on this bill.

A typical electricity bill is shown in Fig. 9.5.

Example 9.22

A gas bill shows 540 therms used in a quarter and the cost per therm as 38.10p. If the standing charge per quarter is £11.30 how much was the total bill?

Find the cost of the gas and then add on the standing charge and any other extras.

Gas costs 38.10p per therm.

540 therms cost 540 × 38.10p = 20574p.

= £205.74.

Standing charge = £11.30.
There are no other extra charges.
Total bill = £205.74 + £11.30
        = £207.04.
Answer   £207.04

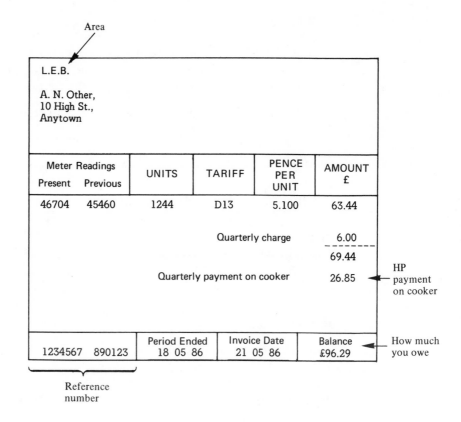

Area

L.E.B.

A. N. Other,
10 High St.,
Anytown

Meter Readings		UNITS	TARIFF	PENCE PER UNIT	AMOUNT £
Present	Previous				
46704	45460	1244	D13	5.100	63.44
				Quarterly charge	6.00
					69.44
				Quarterly payment on cooker	26.85
1234567	890123	Period Ended 18 05 86	Invoice Date 21 05 86	Balance £96.29	

HP payment on cooker

How much you owe

Reference number

Figure 9.5   Typical electricity bill

Example 9.23

An electricity bill shows a previous meter reading as 52 973 and the present reading as 54 253. The price per unit is 6.10p. The quarterly standing charge is £9.40 and the customer has a freezer on h.p. costing £11.25 a quarter and a colour television on h.p. costing £22.40 a quarter. How much is the quarterly bill?

Find how many units are used.
Meter reading is 54 253 and previously was 52 973.
Number of units used = 54 253 − 52 973
                    = 1280 units.
Cost per unit = 6.10p.
Cost for 1280 units = 1280 × 6.10p
                = 7808p = £78.08.
Standing charge = £9.40.
Extra charges are quarterly h.p. payments = £11.25 + £22.40
                                = £33.65.
Total bill = £78.08 + £9.40 + £33.65
        = £121.13.
Answer   £121.13

It is possible to pay gas and electricity bills by paying a fixed amount each month into a special account called a budget account. The gas and electricity boards estimate how much you will use over a year and this is then spread out over 12 months.

Example 9.24

A gas budget account is estimated at £35.00 a month. In the first quarter 220 therms are used at 39.0p a therm and the standing charge is £10.50. Is the account in credit or not at the end of the first quarter, and by how much?

Find the gas bill total and then how much is in credit in the budget account.

Gas Bill:

Gas is 39.0p a therm.
220 therms cost 220 × 39.0p = 8580p
                            = £85.80.
Standing charge is £10.50.
Gas bill total = £85.80 + £10.50
                = £96.30.

Budget Account:

£35 a month is paid.
In 3 months 3 × £35 is paid = £105.
Gas bill is £96.30.
Therefore, the account is in credit by £105 − £96.30 = £8.70.
Answer   £8.70 credit

Exercise 9.10

1 A gas bill showed that 90 therms were used in the summer quarter with the price per therm as 41.2p. If the standing charge was £10.80, how much was the gas bill?
2 210 therms of gas were used in a quarter when the price per therm was 40.6p. With the standing charge at £11.50 how much was the gas bill?
3 A householder bought a gas cooker on h.p. at £27.50 per quarter and this was put on her gas bill. She used 520 therms of gas at 40.3p a therm and the quarterly standing charge was £10.80. What was the total of her quarterly bill?
4 A man arranges to pay his gas bill by a budget account of £60 per month. For the first quarter (3 months) he uses 600 therms of gas at 40.8p a therm and the standing charge is £10.50. Is he in credit or not at the end of the first quarter, and by how much?
5 A gas bill totalled £138. The standing charge was £10 and the price per therm was 40p. How many therms were used?
6 An electricity bill shows the previous meter reading as 43 865 and the present reading as 48 965. If the price per unit was 5.9p and the standing charge £8.80 how much was the electricity bill?
7 An electricity meter reading showed 38 754 at the beginning of a quarter and 40 695 at the end. With a standing charge of £8.50 and electricity at 6.0p a unit how much should the bill be at the end of a quarter?

8 An electricity bill was £73.10. The standing charge was £10.50 and electricity was 5.0p a unit. The meter reading at the end of the quarter had been 37 250. What would have been the reading at the beginning of the quarter?

9 An electricity budget account is estimated as £42.00 a month. Over a quarter a household uses 2100 units of electricity at 5.0p a unit. If the standing charge is £10.50 how much is the householder in credit at the end of this quarter?

10 A man buys a cooker on h.p. at £28.50 a quarter and a freezer at £13.20 a quarter which is to go on his electricity bill. In a quarter the meter reading goes from 65 246 to 66 419. If the electricity is 6.0p a unit and the standing charge is £11.20, how much was the total electricity bill at the end of this quarter?

9.9   Insurance

If there is a risk involved then you can insure against it happening whether it is against fire, theft, damage, or even against being taken ill while on holiday or raining on the day of the summer fête.

The greater the risk the more it costs to insure against it happening. The insurance company weighs up the risk involved; for example, it costs more to insure a house in London than in Taunton, and it will cost more to insure a 17-year-old driver than a 35-year-old driver.

Example 9.25

Hi-fi equipment cost £600 and the insurance quote is 60p per £100 insured. What does it cost each year to insure the hi-fi?

The quote is for £100 insurance, so first find how many £100 there are in £600. Answer is 6.
£100 insurance costs 60p.
£600 insurance costs 6 × 60p = £3.60.
Answer   £3.60
This is not a lot to give peace of mind.

Example 9.26

A camera and some accessories cost £250. An insurance quote gives £2 per £100 insured. How much does it cost to insure the camera and accessories?

(Note: The insurance is likely to be higher for a camera because you carry it around and so it is more easily stolen or just lost.)

£100 insurance costs £2.
How many £100 in £250? the answer is $\frac{250}{100}$.
£250 insurance costs $\frac{250}{100} \times £2 = £\frac{500}{100} = £5$.
Answer   £5

Example 9.27

A house is insured for £30 000 and its contents for £10 000. The insurance for buildings is £1.60 per £1000 insured and for contents it is 60p per £100 insured. How much does it cost to insure the house and its contents?

It is usual to calculate the cost of insuring buildings and contents separately.

Buildings

£1000 insurance costs £1.60.
How many £1000 in £30 000? The answer is $\frac{30\,000}{1000}$.

£30 000 insurance costs $\dfrac{30\,000}{1000} \times £1.60 = 30 \times £1.60$

$$= £48.$$

Contents

£100 insurance costs 60p.
How many £100 in £10 000? the answer is $\frac{10\,000}{100}$.

£10 000 insurance costs $\dfrac{10\,000}{100} \times 60\text{p}$

$$= 100 \times 60\text{p.}$$
$$= £60.$$

Total insurance $= £48 + £60$
$$= £108.$$

Answer   £108

Example 9.28

A house is worth £54 000, the contents £14 000, and special items of jewellery, rings, cameras, etc., are worth £2800. What does it cost to insure everything if insurance for buildings is £1.70 per £1000, contents 50p per £100, and special items £1.20 per £100?

Again, calculate costs for each section separately.

Buildings

£1000 insurance costs £1.70.
£54 000 insurance costs $\frac{54\,000}{1000} \times £1.70 = 54 \times £1.70$
$$= £91.80.$$

Contents

£100 insurance costs 50p.
£14 000 insurance costs $\frac{14\,000}{100} \times 50\text{p} = 140 \times 50\text{p}$
$$= £70.$$

Special items

£100 insurance costs £1.20.

£2800 insurance costs $\frac{2800}{100}$ × £1.20 = 28 × £1.20

$$= £33.60.$$

Total insurance = £91.80 + £70 + £33.60

$$= £195.40.$$

Answer £195.40

Car and motorcycle insurance

The amount of insurance payable depends on the risk; the greater the risk the greater the payment. A twenty-year-old who has already been involved in three accidents is a greater risk than a thirty-year-old who has never been in an accident.

To compensate for this, car and motorcycle owners who have no accidents are allowed a percentage bonus for not making a claim against the insurance company, called a 'no-claim' bonus, and so they get a reduction in premium. The maximum bonus is usually 60 per cent of the full rate.

Example 9.29

The full insurance on a car is £460. The no-claim bonus is 10 per cent of this full amount for each year. (a) What is the annual premium after 1 year? (b) What is the annual premium after 4 years?

No-claim bonus after 1 year = 10 per cent of £460

$$= 0.1 × £460$$
$$= £46.$$

Premium after 1 year = £460 − £46

$$= £414.$$

(a) Answer £414

No-claim bonus after 4 years = 40 per cent of £460

$$= 0.4 × £460$$
$$= £184.$$

Premium after 4 years = £460 − £184

$$= £276.$$

(b) Answer £276

Exercise 9.11

1 A camera cost £200 and the insurance to take it abroad during a three week holiday is quoted at £4.50 per £100. What will it cost in insurance to take abroad?

2 Hi-fi equipment cost £700 and insurance costs £2.30 per £100. How much does it cost to insure the hi-fi?

3 A person insures the contents of her rented flat for £4500 at 70p per £100, while special items are insured for £1400 at £1.30 per £100. How much is her total insurance for contents and special items?

4 A house is worth £32 000. How much will it cost to insure the full value at £1.80 per £1000?

5 The rates for insuring a house in London or in Harrogate are quoted as £2.80 or £1.70 per £1000 respectively. How much extra does it cost in London to insure a house valued at £48 000?

6 A house is worth £35 000, the contents £11 000 and special items £1750. What does it cost to insure the lot if insurance for buildings is £1.70 per £1000, contents 60p per £100, and special items £1.30 per £100?

7 A house is said to be worth £22 000 and its contents £6500. What does a householder have to pay each year to insure the property and contents if the building insurance is £1.60 per £1000 insured and the contents 45p for every £100 insured?

8 Insurance for a holiday abroad is quoted as follows. It is free for children under 4 years and there is a reduced rate for children aged from 4 to 13.

	Adults	Children
Up to 3 days	£4.60	£3.10
Up to 6 days	£6.40	£4.20
Up to 9 days	£7.40	£4.90
Up to 17 days	£9.70	£6.50
Up to 24 days	£11.30	£7.50
Up to 31 days	£12.90	£8.60

(a) How much will it cost 2 adults with children aged 7 and 11 going abroad for 2 weeks?

(b) How much will it cost 2 adults with children aged 3 and 6 going abroad for 1 week?

(c) How much will it cost 2 adults with children aged 8, 11 and 15 going abroad for 3 weeks?

9 The insurance on a car for the first year is £300. If no claim is made in the first year then the cost for the second year reduces by $\frac{1}{5}$ and if no claim is made in the second year then the insurance cost reduces by a further tenth of the original cost. What is the insurance charge at the beginning of the third year, assuming no claims have been made against the company?

10 A flat is bought for £24 000 and it is insured at its full value at £1.90 per £1000. The contents worth £9500 are insured at 60p per £100.

(a) How much is the total insurance?

(b) The lady is told that if she installs a simple burglar alarm costing £171.00 then the insurance will be reduced by $\frac{1}{3}$. In how many years would she pay off the cost of the alarm by the saving on insurance?

9.10 Rates

Every property in the country – houses, shops, factories, schools and business premises – is given an assessment, or *rateable value* (RV). This rateable value depends on the property's size and location and whether it has central heating, garages, etc.

General rates and water rates are calculated on the rateable value. Since a local authority knows the sum total of all the rateable values in the district it covers it can calculate accurately how much money it will raise from each 1p rate levied.

Rates paid = RV × rate in the £

Example 9.30

A house has a rateable value (RV) of £300. If the rates are 90p in the £ how much is paid in rates?

Rates paid = RV × rate in the £
            = 300 × 90p
            = £270.
Answer   £270

Example 9.31

A house has a rateable value of £280. If the rates are £1.24 in the £, how much is paid in rates?

Rates paid = RV × rate in the £
            = 280 × £1.24
            = £347.20.
Answer   £347.20

Example 9.32

The water rate, in addition to a levy on the RV, also has a standing charge.
  A typical water rate demand will show the following:
RV £334

	Rate in £	Amount
Water — standing charge		14.50
— domestic property supply	11.50p	38.41
Sewage and environmental services	20.50p	68.47
	Total due	£121.38

Calculations: domestic = 334 × 11.50p = £38.41;
              sewage   = 334 × 20.50p = £68.47.
Answer   £121.38

9.11 Budgeting

How much do you earn? How do you spend it? Keep a check for a week and discover how money seems to disappear.

Such a check, preferably over a period of time but written down each week so as not to be forgotten, is called a budget. If you spend more than you earn, you will be dipping into savings or going into debt. Using a check over a period of time may show a pattern of spending, showing particularly the expensive periods.

Discuss whether a table like Table 9.6 on page 108 would help to show where the money goes.

Exercise 9.12

 1 A man earns £2.50 per hour for a 36-hour week. Overtime is calculated at time and a half. In a week he earns £112.50. How many hours overtime does he work?

   A 4 h   **B** 5 h   **C** 6 h   **D** 7 h

 2 A woman earns a total of £132.75 in a week. She pays £4.85 in NI and £8.20 in pension contributions, and she paid tax. Her nett pay was £90.75. Did she pay in tax

   A £13.05   **B** £42.00   **C** £32.75   **D** £28.95?

Table 9.6

Week ending	Notes	Food	Entertainment Drink/Eating out	Car/Bus/Train Transport	Clothing make-up/ toiletries	Newspapers Books Stationery	Rent Mortgage Rates	Gas Water Electricity	Savings	Miscellaneous
1986 4 Jan.	New Year's Eve Jan. sales	32.40	18.50	9.50	32.65	1.65	22.00		3.00	2.85
11 Jan.	Gas budget a/c	25.30	3.40	11.20		1.65	22.00	12.00	3.00	1.62
18 Jan	Electr. budget a/c	23.80		11.20	4.60	1.65 2.20	22.00	8.50	3.00	
25 Jan.		29.20	8.90	10.00		1.65	22.00		3.00	6.80 h.p.
Total	361.22	110.70	30.80	41.90	37.25	8.80	88.00	20.50	12.00	11.27
1 Feb.		38.50	13.25	8.65		1.65	22.00		3.00	3.46
8 Feb	Shoes	26.30	2.60	10.40	27.50	1.65	22.00	12.00	3.00	2.25
15 Feb.	TV repairs	28.00	5.20	10.90		1.65 50	22.00	8.50	3.00	43.65
22 Feb.		31.20	3.40	11.40	3.80	1.65	22.00		3.00	6.80 h.p.
Total	404.86	124.00	24.45	41.35	31.30	7.10	88.00	20.50	12.00	56.16

3 A woman exchanges £140 into French francs and the exchange rate is £1 = 11.75 francs. Does she receive

  A 11.91 francs   B 1645 francs   C 151.75 francs
  D 1400 francs?

4 A woman exchanges 475 German marks into £1 sterling when the exchange rate is £1 = 3.80 marks. Did she receive

  A £1805   B £478.8   C £125   D £150?

5 A cooker costing £200 is bought on h.p. over 24 months, each payment being £9.24. Is the extra charge

  A £21.76   B nil   C £16.00   D £18.94?

6 A radio costing £64 is bought over 12 months, the extra charge for credit being £6.20. Are the monthly payments

  A £5.85   B £6.20   C £5.33   D £4.81?

7 A bank arranges a loan for the purchase of a car costing £5200 and the extra charge made by the bank is £992. If the loan is spread over 24 months are the monthly payments

  A £216.66   B £41.33   C £175.00   D £258.00?

8 Gas is 40.3p a therm and the quarterly standing charge is £11.50. How much is the gas bill if 480 therms are used in a quarter?

  A £200   B £204.94   C £225.64   D £220

9 A gas bill totals £124 when the standing charge is £12 and the price per therm is 40p. Is the number of therms used

  A 400   B 350   C 280   D 260?

10 An electricity bill totals £82 when the standing charge is £10 and 1200 units are used. Is the price per unit

  A 6.0p   B 5.5p   C 6.5p   D 5.0p?

11 The rateable value of a house is £340. The rates are £1.15 in the £. How much is paid in rates?

  A £295.65   B £341.15   C £338.85   D £391.00

12 A council house annual rent is £650. The tenant must also pay rates of £260. How much is his combined weekly bill? (Take 1 year = 52 weeks.)

  A £17.50   B £21.00   C £18.50   D £19.00

10 Percentages

10.1 Introduction

Per cent means 'per hundred'. The symbol, %, is completely interchangeable with the words 'per cent'. A percentage is simply a fraction with 100 as denominator.

20% means $\frac{20}{100}$ or $\frac{1}{5}$.

35% means $\frac{35}{100}$ or $\frac{7}{20}$.

$8\% = \frac{8}{100} = \frac{2}{25}$.

$9\% = \frac{9}{100}$.

10.2 Percentage as a Fraction

To express a percentage as a fraction we write down the percentage as a fraction with denominator 100 and then reduce to its lowest terms.

Example 10.1

What is 25% as a fraction?

25% is $\frac{25}{100}$.

Now reduce to lowest terms (look at section 2.3):

$\frac{25}{100} = \frac{5}{20} = \frac{1}{4}$.

Answer $\quad \frac{1}{4}$

Example 10.2

Change 18% to a fraction.

18% is $\frac{18}{100} = \frac{9}{50}$.

Answer $\quad \frac{9}{50}$

Example 10.3

What is $17\frac{1}{2}\%$ as a fraction?

$$17\frac{1}{2}\% = \frac{17\frac{1}{2}}{100}$$

Eliminate fractions in the numerator by multiplying by the denominator of the fraction, in this case 2.

Then $17\frac{1}{2}\% = \dfrac{17\frac{1}{2}}{100} = \dfrac{35}{200}$ Multiplying denominator and numerator by 2.

$= \frac{7}{40}$.   Cancelling by 5.

Answer $\frac{7}{40}$

Example 10.4

What is $23\frac{1}{3}\%$ as a fraction?

$23\frac{1}{3}\% = \dfrac{23\frac{1}{3}}{100} = \dfrac{\overset{7}{\cancel{70}}}{\underset{30}{\cancel{300}}} = \dfrac{7}{30}$.   Multiplying numerator and denominator of

$\dfrac{23\frac{1}{3}}{100}$ by 3.

Answer $\frac{7}{30}$

Example 10.5

What is 140% as a fraction?

$140\% = \dfrac{\overset{7}{\cancel{140}}}{\underset{5}{\cancel{100}}} = \dfrac{7}{5} = 1\frac{2}{5}$.

Answer $1\frac{2}{5}$

Exercise 10.1

Change the following percentages to fractions, cancelling where possible.

1 50%	2 60%	3 75%	4 35%	5 80%	6 24%
7 72%	8 14%	9 11%	10 $12\frac{1}{2}\%$	11 $33\frac{1}{3}\%$	12 $62\frac{1}{2}\%$
13 160%	14 $22\frac{1}{2}\%$	15 18%	16 240%	17 $43\frac{1}{3}\%$	18 $52\frac{1}{2}\%$
19 63%	20 250%	21 $32\frac{1}{2}\%$	22 $46\frac{2}{3}\%$	23 17%	24 38%
25 $2\frac{1}{4}\%$	26 $72\frac{1}{2}\%$	27 51%	28 330%	29 66%	30 $66\frac{2}{3}\%$

10.3 Percentage as a Decimal

To change a percentage to a decimal just divide by 100, which means moving the decimal point 2 places.

Example 10.6

Change 15% to a decimal.

$15\% = \frac{15}{100} = 0.15$.   Moving decimal point 2 places.

Notice how the percentage is put over 100 to emphasise what is meant by percentage.

Answer   0.15

Example 10.7

Change 64% to a decimal.

$64\% = \frac{64}{100} = 0.64$.

Answer   0.64

Example 10.8

Change $32\frac{1}{2}\%$ to a decimal.

$$32\tfrac{1}{2}\% = \frac{32\frac{1}{2}}{100} = \frac{32.5}{100} = 0.325.$$

Answer   0.325

Example 10.9

Change 75.8% to a decimal.

$$75.8\% = \frac{75.8}{100} = 0.758.$$

Answer   0.758

Example 10.10

Change 145% to a decimal.

$$145\% = \frac{145}{100} = 1.45.$$

Answer   1.45

Example 10.11

Change 0.35% to a decimal.

$$0.35\% = \frac{0.35}{100} = 0.0035.$$

Answer   0.0035

Exercise 10.2

Change the following percentages to decimals.

1 50%	**2** 60%	**3** 75%	**4** 35%	**5** 80%
6 26%	**7** 41%	**8** 130%	**9** 18.4%	**10** 76.9%
11 2.5%	**12** 1.3%	**13** 220%	**14** 0.5%	**15** 0.82%
16 $3\frac{1}{2}\%$	**17** $82\frac{1}{2}\%$	**18** $65\frac{1}{4}\%$	**19** $29\frac{1}{4}\%$	**20** 2%
21 320%	**22** 28.4%	**23** 0.27%	**24** 1.07%	**25** 3.73%
26 0.4%	**27** 136%	**28** 11%	**29** $15\frac{1}{2}\%$	**30** $5\frac{1}{4}\%$

10.4   Changing Any Fraction or Decimal to a Percentage

To change any fraction or decimal to a percentage simply multiply by 100.

Example 10.12

Change $\frac{1}{4}$ to a percentage.

Multiply the fraction by 100.

$$\tfrac{1}{4} = \frac{1}{4} \times 100\% = \frac{100}{4}\% = 25\%.$$

Answer   25%

Example 10.13

Change $\frac{2}{5}$ to a percentage.

Multiply the fraction by 100.

$$\frac{2}{5} = \frac{2}{5} \times 100\% = \frac{200}{5}\% = 40\%.$$

Answer   40%

Example 10.14

Change $3\frac{1}{2}$ to a percentage.

$$3\frac{1}{2} = 3\frac{1}{2} \times 100\% = \frac{7}{2} \times 100\% = \frac{700}{2}\% = 350\%.$$

Answer   350%

Example 10.15

Change $\frac{7}{8}$ to a percentage.

$$\frac{7}{8} = \frac{7}{8} \times 100\% = \frac{700}{8} = 87\frac{1}{2}\%.$$

Answer $87\frac{1}{2}\%$

Example 10.16

Change 0.7 to a percentage.

Multiply the decimal by 100.
0.7 = 0.7 × 100% = 70%.   Move decimal point 2 places.
Answer   70%

Example 10.17

Change 0.28 to a percentage.

0.28 = 0.28 × 100% = 28%.
Answer   28%

Example 10.18

Change 6.47 to a percentage.

6.47 = 6.47 × 100% = 647%.
Answer   647%

Exercise 10.3

Change the following fractions to percentages.

1 $\frac{1}{2}$	2 $\frac{1}{10}$	3 $\frac{1}{5}$	4 $\frac{3}{4}$	5 $\frac{3}{5}$	6 $\frac{7}{10}$	7 $\frac{3}{10}$
8 $1\frac{3}{4}$	9 $\frac{3}{2}$	10 $\frac{4}{5}$	11 $\frac{9}{10}$	12 $\frac{1}{8}$	13 $\frac{3}{8}$	14 $\frac{27}{50}$
15 $\frac{29}{40}$	16 $\frac{7}{25}$	17 $\frac{9}{20}$	18 $2\frac{1}{4}$	19 $4\frac{1}{2}$	20 $\frac{9}{40}$	21 $\frac{12}{25}$

22 $\frac{5}{8}$	23 $\frac{13}{20}$	24 $\frac{2}{5}$	25 $1\frac{1}{4}$	26 $\frac{9}{8}$	27 $\frac{7}{15}$	28 $\frac{18}{25}$
29 $\frac{5}{4}$	30 $\frac{4}{15}$					

Exercise 10.4

Change the following decimals to percentages.

1 0.5	2 0.25	3 0.7	4 0.46	5 0.03
6 0.17	7 3.28	8 1.12	9 0.78	10 0.159
11 0.327	12 0.525	13 1.264	14 2.58	15 0.1
16 0.05	17 0.016	18 0.0725	19 0.6	20 0.92
21 2.03	22 0.104	23 0.057	24 1.021	25 3.502
26 0.36	27 0.004	28 1.523	29 0.501	30 0.0075

10.5 One Number as a Percentage of Another

In comparing two numbers a fraction is probably the natural answer but a percentage answer often makes comparisons easier. First, find as a fraction and then change to a percentage.

Example 10.19

I get 32 marks in an examination where the total marks are 80. What percentage mark is this?

32 marks out of 80 can be written as $\frac{32}{80}$.

$\frac{32}{80}$ as a percentage = $\frac{32}{80} \times 100\% = 40\%$

My percentage mark is 40%.

Example 10.20

An evening class has 24 adult students, of which 15 are women. What percentage of the class are men?

24 adult students are in the class.
If 15 are women, then 9 are men.

9 men out of 24 can be written as $\frac{9}{24}$ are men.

$\frac{9}{24}$ as a percentage = $\frac{\overset{3}{9}}{\underset{8}{24}\,_2} \times \overset{25}{100}\% = \frac{75}{2}\% = 37\frac{1}{2}\%.$

Answer $37\frac{1}{2}\%$ of the class are men

Exercise 10.5

1 What is 30 as a percentage of 60?
2 What is 15 as a percentage of 20?

3 A student gains 16 marks out of 25 in a test. What percentage is this?

4 There are 15 girls in a class of 40 children. What percentage are girls?

5 There are 12 minutes of adverts in an hour of television. What percentage is adverts?

6 A colour supplement of 48 pages has 15 pages of coloured adverts. What percentage is adverts?

7 A bookshelf has 6 books with red covers and 9 with blue covers. What percentage of books on the shelf has red covers?

8 An evening class has 24 adult students and 15 are women. What percentage of the class are women?

9 A student gains 34 marks out of 40 in an examination. What percentage is this?

10 A clothes rack in a shop has 6 pink dresses, 9 black and 5 light blue. What percentage of black dresses are there?

11 In a motorway car park there are 62 cars and 18 lorries. What percentage on the car park is lorries?

12 In making shortcrust pastry a person used 100 g of fat and 200 g of flour. What percentage of fat is in shortcrust pastry?

13 A cul-de-sac has 12 houses and 8 bungalows. What percentage is bungalows?

14 An orchard has 12 apple trees, 8 pear trees and 5 plum trees. What percentage of the orchard is apple trees?

15 A line is 10 cm long but in measuring it quickly a boy puts it down as 10.5 cm. What percentage error is this of the original line?

16 A purse contains six £1 coins, four 50p coins, eight 20p coins and two 10p coins. What percentage of coins (not value) does the £1 coins represent of the total in the purse.

17 On a football pool there are 15 draws. A man managed to get 4 draws. What percentage of draws has he got right?

18 A boy practising cricket bowls at the wickets without a batsman and finds he can hit the stumps with 7 bowls out of 12. What percentage success rate is this?

19 In a history exam a girl gets 90 marks out of 150, while in geography a boy gets 44 marks out of 80. Who gets the higher percentage of marks and by how much?

20 A survey in a class at college shows 12 people walk to college, 6 people go by bus, 2 by train, and 5 on motor bikes. What percentage travel by bus?

10.6 Percentages in Money

Percentages which refer to money will probably occur more often in our lives than any other type of percentage.

To do the following type of question, first change the percentage to a decimal or a fraction. Either method will do but since most questions deal with money and decimal currency it may be easier to concentrate on decimals. (Both methods will be shown initially.)

Example 10.21

Find 35% of £4.

Decimal Method

$$35\% = \frac{35}{100} = 0.35.$$

35% of £4 = 0.35 × £4
= £1.40.

<u>Answer £1.40</u>

Fraction Method

$35\% = \dfrac{35}{100}.$

$35\% \text{ of } £4 = \dfrac{35}{100} \times £4$

$= £\dfrac{140}{100}$

$= £1.40.$

<u>Answer 1.40</u>

Example 10.22

What is 30% of £60?

$30\% = \dfrac{30}{100} = 0.30.$

30% of £60 = 0.30 × £60
= £18.00.

<u>Answer £18.00</u>

Or $\qquad 30\% = \dfrac{30}{100}.$

$30\% \text{ of } £60 = \dfrac{30}{100} \times £60$

$= 3 \times £6$
$= £18.$

<u>Answer £18</u>

Example 10.23

A sale offers 15% off normal prices. What will be the sale price of a suit if the normal price is £80?

The sale offers a reduction of 15%.
First, find 15% of the normal price.

$15\% = \dfrac{15}{100} = 0.15.$

15% of £80 = 0.15 × £80 = £12.00.
Sale price = £80 − £12 = £68.

Or $15\% = \dfrac{15}{100}.$

15% of £80 = $\dfrac{\overset{3}{\cancel{15}}}{\underset{1}{\cancel{100}}} \times \overset{4}{\cancel{£80}} = £12.$

Sale price = £80 − £12 = £68.

Answer   £68

Example 10.24

A woman earns £90 a week but after wage talks is given an increase of 7%. What is her new wage?

Increase is 7%.

$7\% = \dfrac{7}{100} = 0.07.$

7% of £90 = 0.07 × £90 = £6.30.
New wage = £90 + £6.30 = £96.30.

Answer   £96.30

Exercise 10.6

Calculate the following:
 1 25% of £12   2 30% of £80   3 70% of £30   4 15% of £6
 5 45% of £14   6 20% of £7.50   7 22% of £15   8 120% of £20
 9 150% of £8.60   10 Increase £30 by 15%
11 Increase £15 by 12%   12 Decrease £80 by 14%
13 Decrease £50 by 8%
14 A woman earns £140 a week but then has a rise of 8%. What is her new wage?
15 All items in a sale are reduced by 15%. What is the sale price of a colour TV if the normal price is £360?
16 A man selling computers is paid by a 6% commission on all his sales. If sales total £125 000, what is his commission?
17 A young woman in a shop is paid £75 per week plus 4% commission on all sales. Last week she sold items totalling £320. How much did she earn altogether?
18 The Nationwide Building Society announced that house prices this year have gone up by 7.5%. How much is a house this year that cost £32 000 last year?
19 A firm has told its workers that, to keep them all on, the wages will have to be cut by 4%. If their present wage is £160, what will be their new wage?
20 The chairman of a very large company earned £150 000 last year. This year he has been given a rise of 22%. How much of a rise does he get?

10.7   Percentages of Other Quantities

Percentages can apply to any quantity, whatever the units, and not just money. The method used is the same as that for money.

Example 10.25

Find 15% of 6 km.

$15\% = \dfrac{15}{100} = 0.15.$

15% of 6 km = 0.15 × 6 km
            = 0.90 km.

Answer   0.90 km

Example 10.26

Find 8% of 12 ft.

$8\% = \dfrac{8}{100} = 0.08.$

8% of 12 ft = 0.08 × 12 ft
= 0.96 ft.

Answer   0.96 ft

If the answer is required in inches then multiply this answer by 12.

Example 10.27

A firm tells the union negotiator that the work force has to be cut by 12%. The firm employs 1400 men. How many men are likely to lose their jobs?

$12\% = \dfrac{12}{100} = 0.12.$

12% of 1400 men = 0.12 × 1400 men
= 168 men.

Answer   168 men

Example 10.28

A factory produces 3800 cars a week. Productivity has to increase by 3% next week. How many cars are being asked for next week?

$3\% = \dfrac{3}{100} = 0.03.$

3% of 3800 cars = 0.03 × 3800 cars
= 114 cars.

Number asked for = 3800 + 114 = 3914 cars.

Answer   3914 cars

Exercise 10.7

Find the following:
1 15% of 20 km   2 25% of 40 cm   3 35% of 150 kg
4 45% of 8 l   5 18% of 12 ft   6 20% of 30 lb
7 20% of 6 h   8 32% of 25 km   9 16% of 40 g
10 15% of 25 ml
11 A school of 900 pupils has 8% absent on one day. How many pupils were absent that day?
12 A motorway is laid in concrete strips of 50 m. A gap of 0.02% of the length of the strip is allowed for expansion. How much is allowed for expansion?
13 On a production line 2% of all parts are rejected by the supervisor. If 18 000 parts are produced in a day, how many are rejected?
14 A firm employs 650 women but due to increased orders the workforce is to be increased by 4%. How many women will the firm then employ?
15 In a new plantation the Forestry Commission thin out (remove) 30% of newly planted trees at the end of the year to allow the others to grow. 18 000 trees were planted. How many will there be after thinning out?
16 In a school there are 850 pupils. It is reckoned that 42% will go on to college at the end of the year. How many pupils go on to college?

17 A library has 25 600 books. It reckons on a loss of 1.5% of books during the year. How many books are lost?

18 Coal output in one year was 93 million tonnes. It dropped by 8% the following year. What was production in that year?

19 A firm guarantees 95% germination in a packet of seeds. A packet of lettuce seeds contains 4200 seeds. What is the minimum number of plants you can expect from a packet of lettuce seeds?

20 An ITV company is cutting the hours it is on the air by 5% because of increased costs. At present it broadcasts 110 hours a week. How many hours will there be after the cuts?

10.8 Percentage Increase or Decrease

A percentage increase or decrease is calculated on the original quantity, as shown in the following examples.

Example 10.29

A man has his working hours cut from 40 to 37 a week. What percentage decrease is this?

Original number of hours = 40 h
Decrease in hours = 3 h

Fractional decrease = $\dfrac{3 \text{ h}}{40 \text{ h}}$ (The decrease is always compared with the original amount.)

Percentage decrease = $\dfrac{3 \text{ h}}{40 \text{ h}} \times 100\%$

$= \frac{15}{2} = 7\frac{1}{2}\%.$

Answer $7\frac{1}{2}\%$

Example 10.30

A newsagent increased turnover from £50 000 a year to £65 000 the next year. What was the percentage increase in turnover?

Original turnover = £50 000.
Increase = £15 000.

Fractional increase = $\dfrac{£15\,000}{£50\,000}.$ (The increase is compared with the original amount.)

Percentage increase = $\dfrac{£15\,000}{£50\,000} \times 100\%$

$= 30\%.$

Answer 30%

Example 10.31

The rates bill for a house last year was £480 and this year is £520. What has been the percentage increase in rates?

Original rates charge = £480

Increase = £40

Percentage increase = $\dfrac{£40}{£480} \times 100\%$

$$= \frac{25}{3} = 8\tfrac{1}{3}\%$$

Answer $8\tfrac{1}{3}\%$

10.9 Value Added Tax

A tax is levied on all goods and services called value added tax (VAT); at present goods and services are either zero rated, no tax at all, or are charged at a rate of 15%. The tax goes to the government.

Assume in all examples that VAT is 15%.

Example 10.32

A photo copy of a drawing is 30p + VAT. Find the total cost of the copy.

First, VAT = 15%.
Find 15% of 30p to see how much VAT.
Then add the amount to 30p.

$15\% = \dfrac{15}{100} = 0.15.$

15% of 30p = 0.15 × 30p = 4.5p.
VAT = 4.5p.
Total cost = 30p + 4.5p = 34.5p.
Answer 34.5p

Example 10.33

Sunday lunch in a local restaurant is advertised as £5.60 + VAT. How much is the total?

Again, VAT = 15%.

$15\% = \dfrac{15}{100} = 0.15.$

15% of £5.60 = 0.15 × £5.60 = £0.84 = 84p.
Total charge = £5.60 + 84p
              = £6.44p.
Answer £6.44

Example 10.34

A sun roof for a car is advertised at £90 + VAT. Find the total cost.

VAT = 15%.

$15\% = \dfrac{15}{100} = 0.15.$

15% of £90 = 0.15 × £90 = £13.50.
Total = £90 + £13.50
      = £103.50.
Answer £103.50

120

Example 10.35

A quarterly telephone bill may look like this:

Quarterly rental	20.00
1350 units at 4.80p	64.80
Total	84.80
VAT at 15%	12.72
Total payable	97.52

Answer   £97.52

Exercise 10.8   (Assume VAT is 15%.)

1 A piece of guttering in a DIY shop is priced at £8 + VAT. What is the total price paid?

2 A double glazing firm gives a quote for new windows in a house as £1800 + VAT. What would be the total bill?

3 A garage advertises a car service as £40 plus parts plus VAT. If no parts are required what is the cost of a service?

4 If a customer uses this garage and in addition to the service is charged for an oil filter (£5) and new plugs (£6), what is the total bill inclusive of VAT?

5 A new car tyre is advertised as £30 + VAT. What would it cost to have four new tyres?

6 A quarterly telephone bill shows a fixed charge of £20 and 1200 units at 5p a unit. VAT has to be added on to this. What is the total amount payable?

7 A tennis club annual subscription is £40 + VAT. What is the cost to each member?

8 Floor tiles are quoted as £5.60 per square metre excluding VAT. What is the price inclusive of VAT?

9 A conference hotel gives a quote to a firm for its Christmas party as £6 per person excluding VAT. The firm has 72 employees. What will it cost the firm if all the employees go?

10 A coat is sold for £115 including VAT. How much was paid in VAT?
(If you find this difficult to work out look at example 10.40.)

10.10   Profit and Loss

It is important to know when we sell anything whether we have made a profit (a gain) or a loss. We have a buying price, what it costs us to buy the object, and a selling price, what we sold the object for.

Example 10.36

A radio is bought for £58 and sold for £46. What is the profit or loss?

If it is sold for less than what was paid for it then we have made a *loss*.
Loss = £58 − £46 = £12.

Usually the profit or loss is asked for as a percentage.

Example 10.37

A shop buys radios at £16 and sells them for £20. What is the percentage profit?

The method of working is as follows:

(a) find the actual cash profit or loss;
(b) express this as a fraction of the buying price;
(c) work out this fraction as a percentage.

Selling price = £20
Buying price = £16
Profit   = £ 4

This is a profit of £4 on the buying price of £16.

$$\frac{\text{Profit}}{\text{Buying price}} = \frac{£4}{£16}.$$

Percentage profit = $\dfrac{£4}{£16} \times 100\%$

$$= 25\%.$$

Answer   25%

Unless instructed to the contrary always give the percentage profit or loss as a percentage of the buying price.

Example 10.38

An item is bought for £40 and sold for £43. Find the percentage profit.

Selling price = £43
Buying price = £40

Profit   = £ 3

$$\frac{\text{Profit}}{\text{Buying price}} = \frac{£3}{£40}.$$

Both parts of the fraction *must* be in the same units but since top and bottom of the fraction are in the same units these can be cancelled:

Percentage profit = $\dfrac{3}{40} \times 100\% = \dfrac{15\%}{2}$

$$= 7\tfrac{1}{2}\%.$$

Answer $7\tfrac{1}{2}\%$

Example 10.39

Biro pens are bought in a box of 100 costing £5. They are sold at 7p each. What is the percentage profit?

How much do you get when you sell all the pens?
1 pen is sold for 7p
100 pens are sold for $100 \times 7p = £7$.
Selling price = £7
Buying price = £5
Profit   = £2

$$\frac{\text{Profit}}{\text{Buying price}} = \frac{£2}{£5}.$$

Percentage profit $= \dfrac{2}{5} \times 100\% .$

$$= 40\% .$$

Answer   40%

Example 10.40

A dress is bought for £36 and sold one month later for £22.50. What is the percentage loss?

Buying price = £36.00
Selling price = £22.50
Loss   = £13.50

$$\frac{\text{Loss}}{\text{Buying price}} = \frac{£13.50}{£36} = \frac{£13\frac{1}{2}}{£36} = \frac{27}{72}.$$

Percentage loss $= \dfrac{27}{72} \times 100\% = \dfrac{75}{2}\%$

$$= 37\tfrac{1}{2}\% .$$

Answer $37\frac{1}{2}\%$

Example 10.41

A 25 lb box of apples is bought for £4 and sold for 28p a lb. At the bottom of the box it was found that 2 lb of apples were bruised and could not be sold. What is the percentage profit?

Only 23 lb of apples can be sold.
23 lb at 28p a lb = 23 × 28p
            = £6.44.
Selling price = £6.44
Buying price = £4.00
Profit   = £2.44

$$\frac{\text{Profit}}{\text{Buying price}} = \frac{£2.44}{£4} = \frac{244}{400}.$$

Percentage profit $= \dfrac{244}{400} \times 100\%$

$$= 61\% .$$

Answer   61%

Example 10.42

An old car was bought for £350 and after a respray was sold at a profit of 20%. How much was it sold for?

Buying price = £350
Profit is calculated on the buying price.

$$20\% = \frac{20}{100} = 0.2.$$

123

Profit = 20% of £350 = 0.2 × £350
                              = £70.
Selling price = £350 + £70
                    = £420.

Answer   £420

How do you find the cost price if the selling price and profit (loss) are given?
An article is sold for £60, giving a profit of 50%. What was the buying price?

Example 10.43

The percentage profit is always worked out on the buying price.
The buying price = 100% (the original whole one).
Profit = 50%.
Then selling price = 150%.
Now relate these percentages to the question:
Selling price 150% = £60

which means $1\% = \dfrac{£60}{150}$.

Buying price = 100%.

$$100\% = \overset{20}{\cancel{100}} \times \dfrac{\overset{2}{\cancel{£60}}}{\underset{\underset{1}{3}}{\cancel{150}}}$$

        = £40.
Buying price = £40.
Answer   £40

Example 10.44

An article is sold for £60 giving a loss of 20%. What was the buying price?

Buying price = 100%.
Loss   = 20%.
Selling price = 80%.
Selling price 80% = £60

$$1\% = \dfrac{£60}{80}.$$

Buying price = 100% = $100 \times \dfrac{\overset{3}{\cancel{£60}}}{\underset{4}{\cancel{80}}}$

                = £75.
Answer   £75

Exercise 10.9

Find the selling price.
1	Buying price = £80	Profit = 20%
2	Buying price = 60p	Profit = 10%
3	Buying price = £20	Profit = 15%
4	Buying price = 50p	Profit = 40%
5	Buying price = £8.50	Profit = 30%
6	Buying price = £220	Loss = 25%
7	Buying price = £120	Loss = 18%
8	Buying price = £50	Loss = 12%

9 Buying price = £64   Loss = 32%
10 Buying price = £26   Loss = 9%

Exercise 10.10

Find the percentage profit or loss.
1 Buying price = £10   Selling price = £8
2 Buying price = £32   Selling price = £40
3 Buying price = 25p   Selling price = 16p
4 Buying price = £7.50   Selling price = £10
5 Buying price = £12   Selling price = £14.40
6 Buying price = £16   Selling price = £18.40
7 Buying price = 30p   Selling price = 39p
8 Buying price = £250   Selling price = £280
9 Buying price = £400   Selling price = £472
10 Buying price = £90   Selling price = £105

Exercise 10.11

Find the cost price.
1 Selling price = £25   Profit = 25%
2 Selling price = £66   Profit = 10%
3 Selling price = £138   Profit = 15%
4 Selling price = £96   Profit = 20%
5 Selling price = £325   Profit = 30%
6 Selling price = £120   Loss = 25%
7 Selling price = £40   Loss = 20%
8 Selling price = £14.40   Loss = 10%
9 Selling price = £34   Loss = 15%
10 Selling price = £42   Loss = 30%

Exercise 10.12

1 Ballpoint pens are bought at £6 per 100. They are sold at 8p each. What is the percentage profit?
2 A car was bought for £250 and after doing it up the owner sold it and made a profit of 15%. How much was it sold for?
3 Pears are bought in 25 lb boxes for £5 and sold at 30p a lb. What is the percentage profit?
4 A case of mandarin oranges containing 36 tins is bought at £8 and sold at 30p a tin. What is the percentage profit?
5 A market trader buys a job lot of 40 sweaters costing £200. He sells half at £7.50 and half at £6.50. What profit does he make and what is the percentage profit?
6 A box of 72 Kit Kat can be bought for £9.00. If each one is sold for 16p each what is the percentage profit?
7 A 100 box of peaches is bought for £15. 5% are found to be bad and unsaleable. The rest are sold at 23p each. What is the percentage profit?
8 A man buys some pullovers and decides he will make 30% profit if they are sold at £13.65. How much were they bought at?

9 A sale advertises all clothes at a discount of 15% off normal prices. The normal price of a dress is £40.
  (a) What is the discount price?
  (b) Even then the shopkeeper makes a profit of 36%. What was the dress bought for in the first place?
10 By selling an article for £20 a dealer made a profit of 25%. At what price should it be sold to make a profit of 50%?

10.11 Interest

Interest is money paid for use of money lent or money borrowed. The rate at which you are paid or have to pay the interest is given as a percentage.

An interest rate is quoted per annum (p.a.), that is per year.

You will be paid interest for saving with a building society or in a Post Office savings account or a bank deposit account or as savings certificates.

Example 10.45

I save £200 with a building society for 1 year with interest at 7% p.a. How much interest is paid to me at the end of the year?

$7\% = \dfrac{7}{100} = 0.07.$

7% of £200 = $0.07 \times £200$
$\qquad\qquad\quad = £14.$

Interest is £14.

Answer   £14

Note that the interest after 6 months would have been $\dfrac{£14}{2} = £7.$

For 3 months it would have been $\dfrac{£14}{4} = £3.50.$

Example 10.46

What is the interest after a year on £540 at an interest rate of 8% p.a.?

$8\% = \dfrac{8}{100} = 0.08.$

8% of £540 = $0.08 \times £540$
$\qquad\qquad\quad = £43.20.$

Answer   £43.20.

10.12 Simple Interest

This is interest reckoned on the original capital only. It is most likely to be used when money is borrowed.

Expect to pay a higher interest charge to borrow money than when lending it.

Example 10.47

A bank quotes an interest rate of 15% to borrow money. I need £5000 to buy a car. How much does it cost to borrow money over 2 years?

First, find the interest for one year.

$$15\% = \frac{15}{100} = 0.15.$$

Interest = 15% of £5000 = 0.15 × £5000
$$= £750.$$
Interest for one year = £750.
Interest for two years = 2 × £750
$$= £1500.$$

Answer   £1500

This is called simple interest; the interest remains the same in every year.

Example 10.48

Find the simple interest on £400 for 3 years at 6% p.a.

$$6\% = \frac{6}{100} = 0.06.$$

Interest for one year = 6% of £400 = 0.06 × £400
$$= £24.$$
Simple interest for 3 years = 3 × £24
$$= £72.$$

Answer   £72

Example 10.49

Find the simple interest on £600 for $2\frac{1}{2}$ years at $8\frac{1}{2}\%$ p.a.

$$8\tfrac{1}{2}\% = \frac{8.5}{100} = 0.085.$$

Interest for one year = $8\frac{1}{2}\%$ of £600 = 0.085 × £600
$$= £51.$$
Simple interest for $2\frac{1}{2}$ years = $2\frac{1}{2}$ × £51
$$= £127.50.$$

Answer   £127.50

10.13   Compound Interest

Savings are often for more than a year and the calculation of interest is likely to be compound interest; the interest at the end of the year is added on to the savings and this itself earns interest.

This is the method adopted in most savings schemes.

Example 10.50

Find the compound interest on £2000 being saved for 2 years at 5% p.a.

First, find the interest after one year.

$5\% = \dfrac{5}{100} = 0.05.$

5% of £2000 $= 0.05 \times 2000$
$\qquad\qquad\quad = £100.$
After one year we have original capital of £2000 plus £100 interest
$= £2100.$
Now find the interest for the 2nd year.
5% of £2100 $= 0.05 \times £2100$
$\qquad\qquad\quad = £105.$
After two years we have £2100 + £105 = £2205.
Compound interest $= £2205 - £2000$
$\qquad\qquad\qquad\quad = £205.$

Answer   £205

Example 10.51

Find the compound interest on £500 for 2 years at 8% p.a.

The setting out can be made more compact than in the example above.

$8\% = \dfrac{8}{100} = 0.08.$

1st Year	Original capital	£500	
	Interest	40	$(0.08 \times £500)$
2nd Year	New capital	540	
	Interest	43.20	$(0.08 \times £540)$
	New capital	£583.20	

Interest $= £583.20 - £500$
$\qquad\quad\; = £83.20.$

Answer   £83.20

Example 10.52

£5000 is placed with a building society for 3 years. To how much does it grow if the interest rate is 10% p.a.?

$10\% = \dfrac{10}{100} = 0.10.$

1st Year	Original capital	£5000	
	Interest	500	$(0.10 \times £5000)$
2nd Year	New capital	5500	
	Interest	550	$(0.10 \times £5500)$
3rd Year	New capital	6050	
	Interest	605	$(0.10 \times £6050)$
	After three years	£6655	

Answer   £6655

All savings schemes work on the compound interest principle.

Exercise 10.13

1 How much interest is earned on £200 in one year at 8% p.a.?
2 What is the interest earned in one year on £300 at $6\frac{1}{2}$% p.a.?
3 What is the interest earned in one year on £350 at 5% p.a.?
4 How much interest is earned on £350 in one year at $7\frac{1}{2}$% p.a.?
5 How much interest is earned in 6 months on £400 at 6% p.a.?
6 How much interest is earned in 3 months on £1200 invested at 8% p.a.?
7 What is the interest earned on £850 if it is placed in a building society account for 6 months at 8% p.a.?
8 I borrow £2500 from a bank, to be repaid in one year, when the interest charged is 14%. How much interest do I have to pay on the money borrowed?
9 I borrow £2000 from the bank when the interest rate for borrowers is 20%. The loan is for one year. How much do I pay to the bank every month in order to pay off the loan and the interest in one year?
10 A man has a legacy left him of £36 000. While he decides what to do with it he puts it in a building society account for 1 month at 8% p.a. How much interest has accrued when he takes out the money at the end of the month?

Exercise 10.14

Find the compound interest on the following:
1 £1000 invested for 2 years at 8% p.a.   2 £500 for 2 years at 6% p.a.
3 £400 for 2 years at 4% p.a.   4 £600 for 2 years at 5% p.a.
5 £800 for 2 years at 7% p.a.   6 £10 000 for 3 years at 4% p.a.
7 £400 for 3 years at 10% p.a.   8 £800 for 3 years at 5% p.a.
9 One building society advertises a rate of 8% p.a. with interest calculated yearly; another society advertises a rate of 8% p.a. with interest calculated six-monthly. For an investment of £1000 what is the difference in interest at the end of one year?
10 I invest £3000 in a building society for 2 years at 7%. What can I expect to have at the end of this time if the interest rate does not change?

Exercise 10.15

Find the simple interest on the following:
1 £200 for 2 years at 5% p.a.   2 £300 for 2 years at 7% p.a.
3 £500 for 3 years at 4% p.a.   4 £120 for 2 years at 4% p.a.
5 £1000 for $2\frac{1}{2}$ years at 4% p.a.   6 £50 for 4 years at 8% p.a.
7 £250 for 3 years at 6% p.a.
8 A bank charges simple interest on its loans. What will be the interest charged on a loan of £2000 for 2 years at 12% p.a.?
9 Find the simple interest charged by a bank on a loan of £3500 for 2 years at 14% p.a.
10 A man buys a car with a loan of £5000 from a bank. The loan is for 2 years at 15% p.a. How much per month does he have to pay, to the nearest £, in order to pay the loan and interest charges?

10.14 Income Tax

Income tax is a tax on a person's earnings after certain allowances have been made — as a rule the greater the earnings the greater the tax.

After allowances are deducted all the income left is taxed. This tax goes to the government.

For 1985/86 income tax rates were as follows; a tax year is from 5 April in one year until 4 April the following year.

Rate of tax	Income after allowances have been deducted
30%	Up to £16 200
40%	£16 201–£19 200
45%	£19 201–£24 400
50%	£24 401–£32 320
55%	£32 321–£40 200
60%	Above £40 201

The 30% rate is called the standard rate.

Example 10.53

A woman has taxable income after allowances have been deducted of £8200. How much does she pay in income tax?

$$30\% = \frac{30}{100} = 0.30.$$

Tax payable = 30% of £8200
= 0.30 × £8200
= £2460.

(This is nearly £50 a week.)

Answer   £2460

Example 10.54

A man earns £14 000 a year and has allowances of £3455. How much tax does he pay in the year?

First, find the *taxable income* by deducting all the allowances from the earned income.

Taxable income = earned income − allowances.
Taxable income = £14 000 − £3455
= £10 545.
Tax payable = 30% of £10 545
= 0.30 × £10 545
= £3163.50.

Answer   £3163.50

Example 10.55

A man earns £185 a week. How much, to the nearest £, does he pay in tax each week if his allowances are £2200 a year (52 weeks)?

First, find how much he earns per year.

He earns £185 a week.

Earnings per year = 52 × £185

= £9620.

Allowances = £2200.

Tax income = £9620 − £2200

= £7420.

Tax payable = 30% of £7420

= 0.30 × £7420

= £2226.

This is the tax per year.

Tax per week = £2226 ÷ 52

= £42.80.

Answer (to the nearest £) £43

Example 10.56

A woman has an income of £25 000 a year and a personal allowance of £2200. How much does she pay in income tax?

Taxable income = £25 000 − £2200

= £22 800.

This income gives above the 30% tax rate (which is up to £16 200) and above the 40% rate (which is from £16 201 to £19 200) and into the 45% rate (£19 201 to £24 400).

Work out how much taxable income there is in each tax band:

All up to £16 200 is taxed at 30%.

All from £16 201 to £19 200 is taxed at 40%. Notice this is £3000 at 40% because both figures are inclusive.

All from £19 201 to £22 800, which is £3600, is taxed at 45%.

Total tax payable = 30% of £16 200 + 40% of £3000 + 45% of £3600

= 0.30 × £16 200 + 0.40 × £3000 + 0.45 × £3600

= £4860 + £1200 + £1620

= £7680.

Exercise 10.16

Use the tax rates given in section 10.14 for the following questions.

1 Find the income tax on a taxable income of £8000.

2 Find the income tax on a taxable income of £12 500.

3 Find the income tax on a taxable income of £7255.

4 A woman earns £14 000 a year and has a personal allowance of £2200. How much does she pay in tax per year?

5 A married man earns £200 per week and has allowances of £3455. How much, to the nearest £, does he pay in tax per week?

6 A barrister is said to earn £40 000 per year. If his allowances amount to £7500 how much does he pay in income tax per year?

7 The chairman of one of the large companies has a taxable income, after allowances, of £100 000 p.a. How much tax does he pay in a year?

8 A man earns £6000 a year and his wife £7500. The allowances for such a couple are £3455 plus £2200. The joint income is used for tax purposes. What is the total income tax paid in one year?

Exercise 10.17

1 What is 48% as a fraction?

   A 4.8   **B** $\frac{3}{4}$ **C** $\frac{12}{25}$ **D** $\frac{1}{2}$

2 What is 5.25% as a decimal?

   A 0.0525   **B** 5.25   **C** 525   **D** 0.525

3 How much is $\frac{2}{5}$ as a percentage?

   A 20%   **B** 10%   **C** 200%   **D** 40%

4 To pass an exam means getting 40 marks out of a possible 80. Is this

   A 40%   **B** 50%   **C** 60%   **D** $\frac{1}{2}$%?

5 A dealer wants a 15% deposit on a motor bike. Is the deposit on a motor bike costing £640

   A £64   **B** £625   **C** £96   **D** £9.60?

6 A shop put the price of a dress up from £40 to £50. Is the percentage increase

   A 25%   **B** 10%   **C** 20%   **D** 80%?

7 A salesman gets 8% commission on all sales. The sales amount to £15 000. How much does the salesman receive?

   A £1500   **B** £1875   **C** £1200   **D** £1000

8 The Post Office puts up the charges of a parcel from 32p to 36p. Is the percentage increase

   A $11\frac{1}{9}$%   **B** 4%   **C** 10%   **D** $12\frac{1}{2}$%

9 During the summer months the number of units of gas used in a household dropped from 1200 units to 900 units. Is this a decrease of

   A 25%   **B** 300%   **C** $33\frac{1}{3}$%   **D** 30%?

10 A car service is £60 + VAT (15%). Is the charge

   A £75   **B** £45   **C** £69   **D** £67.50?

11 An insurance company raises its charges on house insurance by $7\frac{1}{2}$%. A household previously paid £240 p.a. Is the new insurance cost to be

   A £247.50   **B** £255   **C** £258   **D** £262?

12 An article bought for £80 is sold for £100. Is the profit

   A 20%   **B** 200%   **C** 25%   **D** $33\frac{1}{3}$%?

13 A secondhand car bought for £800 is sold for £400. Is the loss

   A 50%   **B** 100%   **C** 200%   **D** 400%?

14 An article sold at £20 makes a profit of 25%. Was it bought at

   A £15   **B** £17.50   **C** £25   **D** £16?

15 A tie sold at £6 makes a profit of 20%. To make a 40% profit should it be sold at

   A £12   **B** £8   **C** £7   **D** £6.50?

16 I invest £500 in a building society at 10% p.a. compound interest. How much is in the account after 2 years?

A £600 **B** £520 **C** £605 **D** £585.50

17 A bank charges 12% simple interest on a £3000 loan over 2 years. Is the interest charge

A £720 **B** £600 **C** £360 **D** £240?

18 The price of a book goes up from £4.95 to £5.95. Is the percentage increase approximately (to nearest whole number)

A 14% **B** 20% **C** 16% **D** 25%?

19 On taxable income of £10 000 is the tax payable

A £300 **B** £7000 **C** £3000 **D** £700?

20 A woman earns £8000 a year and has a personal allowance of £2200. Is the income after tax

A £1740 **B** £6260 **C** £5800 **D** £4060?

21 A woman earns £30 000 a year and has allowances of £5000. Does she pay in tax per week (to the nearest £)

A £167 **B** £500 **C** £144 **D** £151?

11 Signs, Symbols and Graphs

11.1 Introduction

This chapter looks at all the forms of diagrams which give information; these include

(a) signs and symbols used to instruct, advise or warn;
(b) graphs and charts;
(c) diagrams used to represent planned sequences (flowcharts);
(d) three-dimensional representation.

11.2 Signs and Symbols

Certain shapes and colours are all-important.

(a) Prohibition Signs (mostly circular with red circles)

No vehicles

No smoking

(b) Warning Signs (mostly triangular)

**Warning:
Steep hill downwards**

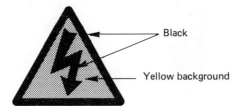

Warning:
Risk of electric shock

(c) **Mandatory Signs** (must be obeyed; background colour is blue, with white symbol)

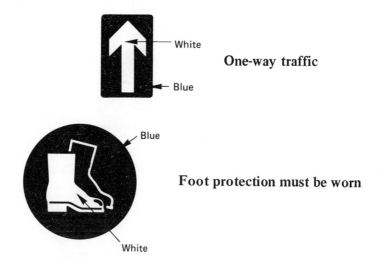

One-way traffic

Foot protection must be worn

(d) **Information Signs**

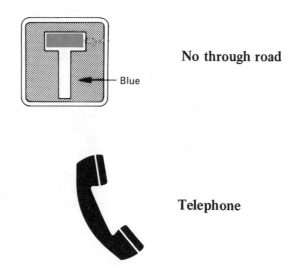

No through road

Telephone

Washing instructions
Maximum temperature of wash 40°C.
The figure above the wavy line (5) refers to the maximum mechanical action of the wash, on a scale from 1 to 9 (1 being the highest and 9 the lowest).

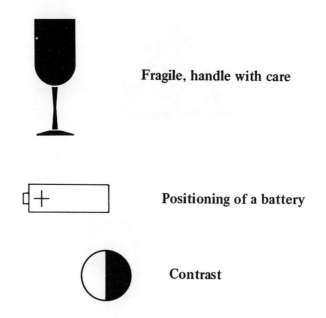

Fragile, handle with care

Positioning of a battery

Contrast

For a comprehensive list of symbols consult the Highway Code and publication PP7307 of the British Standards Institution.

Exercise 11.1

Find out what the following symbols mean.

11.3 Graphs

A graph is a diagram showing the relationship between two quantities. To draw or plot a graph two reference lines, called axes, are drawn at right angles to each other. A scale is then marked along each axis sufficient to cover the variation in each of the two quantities.

A graph is a good way (as with signs and symbols) of communicating information.

11.4 Simple Graphs

Note: Any reference to a suitable scale in this chapter assumes the graph paper to be 230 mm × 180 mm.

Example 11.1

Draw a line graph to represent the average monthly rainfall for the United Kingdom in 1982:

mm of rain	Jan.	Feb.	Mar.	Apr.	May	June	July	Aug.	Sept.	Oct.	Nov.	Dec.
	70	44	102	22	46	128	40	88	72	126	84	65

It is usual, when a graph is drawn, for the axes and the graph to be in pencil, and for figures and writing to be in ink.

First Draw two axes at right angles to each other about 1 or 2 cm from the bottom and left-hand side of the paper; this leaves room for you to write the names of the quantities represented.

Second Look at the range of values for each quantity and then choose a suitable scale. The scale does not have to be the same on each axis but the scales should normally be as large as the paper will allow, unless a scale has been given already. Scales must be evenly spaced.

In Example 11.1 we have to represent up to 12 months and rainfall up to 128 mm. A suitable scale would be 1 cm = 1 month, horizontally, taking up 12 cm and 1 cm = 10 mm of rain, vertically, taking up 13 cm. Any scale chosen must continue along the same axis at the same rate.

Third Plot the graph. Beginning at Jan. put in a rainfall of 70 mm (indicated by a small pencilled dot or cross), for Feb. a rainfall of 44 mm, for Mar. a rainfall of 102 mm, and so on. Join successive dots by a straight pencil line.

Fourth Name the graph at the top or bottom of the graph paper; in other words state what the graph is representing.

The completed graph is shown in Fig. 11.1.

Example 11.2

A scale does not have to begin at 0 (nought) since this might give a graph appearing at the top or bottom of a page.

Draw a line graph to represent the number of people killed on the roads in Great Britain in 1984:

	Jan.	Feb.	Mar.	Apr.	May	June	July	Aug.	Sept.	Oct.	Nov.	Dec.
Number of people killed	411	364	369	418	433	444	464	490	525	495	556	545

Again, there are 12 months and 1 cm = 1 month would be suitable for the horizontal scale.

The *range* of people killed goes from 364 to 556 so if the graph ranges from 300 to 600 it will cover all possible values.

Suggested scale: horizontally 1 cm = 1 month;
        vertically 1 cm = 20 people killed.

The completed graph is shown as Fig. 11.2.

With the scale starting at 0 the same graph would have looked like Fig. 11.3.

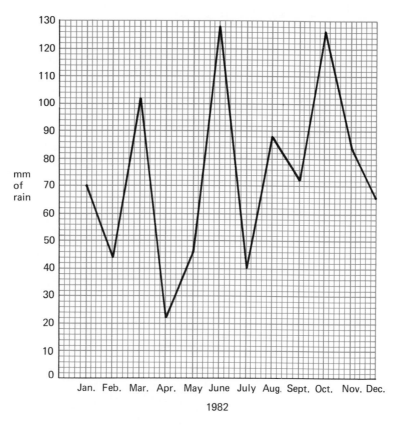

Figure 11.1 Average monthly rainfall for the UK in 1982

These two graphs are representing the same figures and show why great care must be taken when interpreting a graph.

Example 11.3

The number of fraud/forgery offences notified to the police in 1981 and 1982 were as follows:

Number of	1981				1982			
fraud/forgery	1st qr	2nd qr	3rd qr	4th qr	1st qr	2nd qr	3rd qr	4th qr
offences	23.5	26.4	27.1	29.7	28.5	30.3	31.4	32.9
(thousands)								

The information has been put on to two graphs, Fig. 11.4 and Fig. 11.5, one to show there was apparently little increase between the first quarter of 1981 and the fourth quarter of 1982, and the other to show there was a dramatic increase.

From the same data you can produce a representation to suit your needs.

Example 11.4

Sometimes it is a help to put two graphs on the same piece of paper for the purpose of comparison. Make sure you can distinguish between them, by for example drawing one with broken lines.

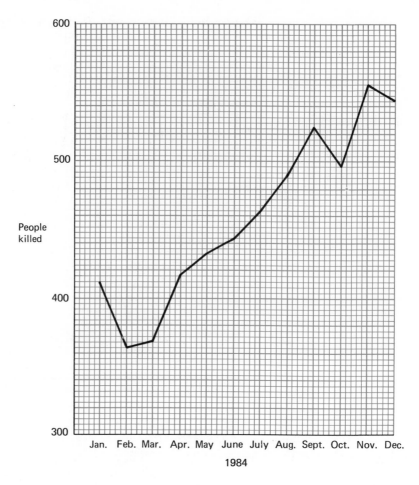

Figure 11.2 Graph of number of people killed on the roads in Great Britain in 1984

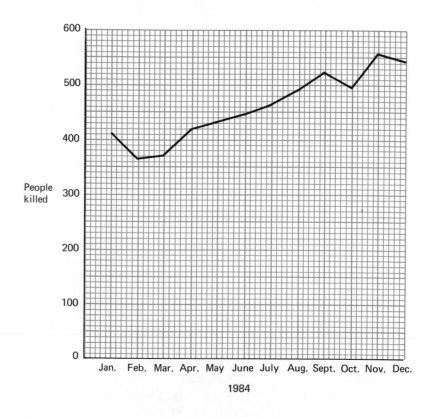

Figure 11.3 Graph of number of people killed on the roads in Great Britain in 1984

140

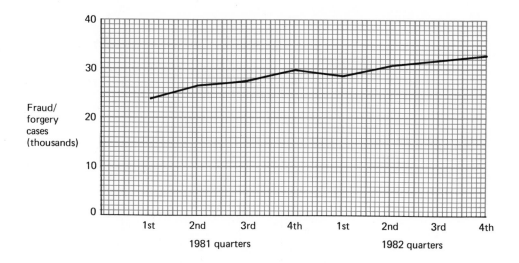

Figure 11.4 Graph of fraud/forgery cases in 1981 and 1982

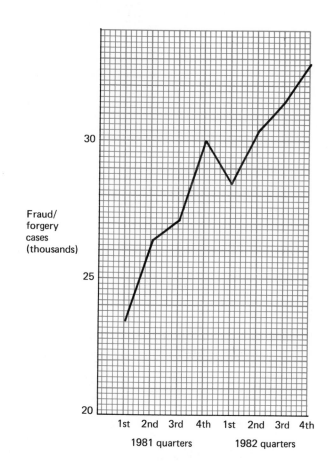

Figure 11.5 Graph of fraud/forgery cases in 1981 and 1982

Monthly sales for 1984 and 1985 of a clothing firm were as follows:

	Jan.	Feb.	Mar.	Apr.	May	June
1984 (£000)	50.0	40.6	45.4	51.8	63.2	54.0
1985 (£000)	58.7	46.4	42.3	49.0	66.4	58.2

Suggested scales: 2 cm = 1 month horizontally;
  1 cm = £2000 sales vertically. Begin at £40 000.
The completed graph is shown as Fig. 11.6.

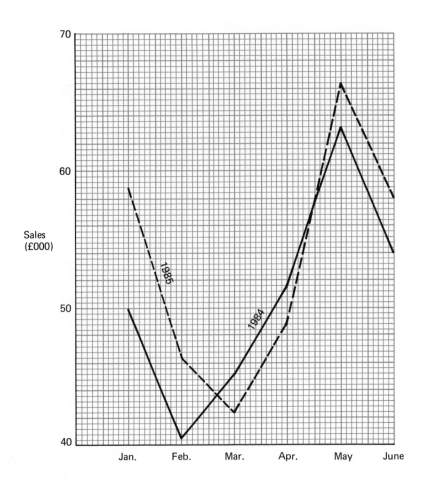

Figure 11.6 Graph of monthly sales for 1984 and 1985

Where graphs cross one another make sure you can distinguish one from another.

Exercise 11.2

The answers to the following questions are meant to be drawn as line graphs.
  1 Draw a graph to show the average monthly rainfall for the UK in 1984:

mm of rain	Jan.	Feb.	Mar.	Apr.	May	June	July	Aug.	Sept.	Oct.	Nov.	Dec.
	144	57	59	11	59	43	27	57	116	100	145	80

Suggested scales: horizontally 1 cm represents 1 month;
                              vertically   1 cm represents 10 mm of rain.
  2 Draw a graph to show the average hours of sunshine for the UK in 1984:

Hours of sunshine	Jan.	Feb.	Mar.	Apr.	May	June	July	Aug.	Sept.	Oct.	Nov.	Dec.
	2.2	2.1	2.1	7.3	5.5	6.9	7.8	6.5	3.8	3.3	1.8	1.8

Suggested scales: horizontally 1 cm represents 1 month;
                              vertically   2 cm represents 1 hour sunshine.
  3 Plot a graph to show the number of cars sold by a manufacturer in 1984:

	Jan.	Feb.	Mar.	Apr.	May	June
Thousands of cars	14.1	10.0	12.6	13.7	12.8	11.9
	July	Aug.	Sept.	Oct.	Nov.	Dec.
Thousands of cars	6.2	15.2	13.3	12.0	13.6	10.3

Why is there a sudden jump in sales in August and January?

4 Draw two graphs on one pair of axes to show live births and deaths for the following years in the UK:

	1977	1978	1979	1980	1981	1982	1983	1984
Live births (thousands)	657	687	735	754	731	719	721	730
Deaths (thousands)	655	667	676	662	658	663	659	645

5 Draw a graph to show the annual figures for the number of cases of criminal damage notified to the police in England and Wales:

	1980	1981	1982	1983	1984
Criminal damage (thousands)	360	387	418	443	498

6 Draw two graphs on one pair of axes to show the average daily hours of sunshine of two places for the months given:

	Oct.	Nov.	Dec.	Jan.	Feb.	Mar.	Apr.
Algarve	7.4	5.8	5.1	5.1	6.4	6.8	8.8
London	3.5	2.0	1.6	1.8	2.0	4.0	5.6

7 Draw two line graphs on one pair of axes to show the number of people killed on the roads for corresponding months of 1981 and 1982:

	Jan.	Feb.	Mar.	Apr.	May	June
Number killed 1981	445	407	459	319	468	464
Number killed 1982	404	397	492	439	435	465

Are the figures for 1984, example 11.2, better or worse than these two years?

8 Draw a line graph to show the amount of gas supplied, in millions of therms, in the following months:

	1984							
	May	June	July	Aug.	Sept.	Oct.	Nov.	Dec.
Millions of therms of gas	286	210	170	161	220	318	399	469

	1985			
	Jan.	Feb.	Mar.	Apr.
Millions of therms of gas	583	556	508	377

9 Draw two graphs on one pair of axes to show the monthly sales of a small pottery firm over the two years given:

	Jan.	Feb.	Mar.	Apr.	May	June	July
1984 (£000)	22.6	18.5	20.8	24.5	25.9	32.3	29.6
1985 (£000)	28.5	16.7	24.2	28.7	31.0	35.6	28.4

Make sure you can distinguish one graph from the other.

10 Draw a line graph to show the number of billions of cigarettes smoked in the months of 1984:

1 billion = 1000 million.

	Jan.	Feb.	Mar.	Apr.	May	June
Cigarettes smoked (billions)	11.3	8.5	11.1	3.6	7.5	7.3
	July	Aug.	Sept.	Oct.	Nov.	Dec.
Cigarettes smoked (billions)	7.6	8.8	11.6	5.2	7.9	7.8

11.5 Bar Graphs (Bar Charts)

A bar graph (or bar chart) is often used when the horizontal scale is simply a list of categories, for example countries, holidays, transport, etc., whereas a line graph is often used when the horizontal axis has some kind of timescale (hours, days, months, etc.). It is possible, of course, to draw a bar graph or a line graph for each of these lists of data.

The quantities are represented by the heights of the bars. The bars are of equal width.

Example 11.5

Draw a bar graph to represent the number of houses and flats built in the United Kingdom in five successive years as follows:

	1980	1981	1982	1983	1984
Houses and flats completed (thousands)	213	177	154	171	181

Make sure the horizontal scale points are sufficiently far apart to allow for the drawing of a bar, with the vertical scale evenly spaced.

Suggested scales: horizontally 2 cm represents 1 year;
vertically 1 cm represents 20 000 houses.
The completed graph is shown in two forms in Fig. 11.7, with the bars apart and with them touching. It is a matter of taste as to which is the preferable method.

Example 11.6

Bar charts are a useful representation when percentages are given. Draw a bar graph to represent the countries stayed in by UK residents on holidays abroad in 1984:

	Spain/Majorca	France	W. Germany	Italy	Greece	USA	Other countries
Percentage of total	36	10	5	6	6	2	35

Suggested scales: horizontally 2 cm represents each country;
vertically 2 cm represents 10% of total.
The completed graph is shown as Fig. 11.8.

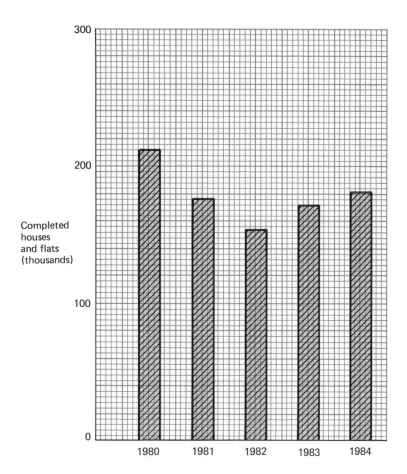

Figure 11.7   Number of houses and flats completed in the United Kingdom

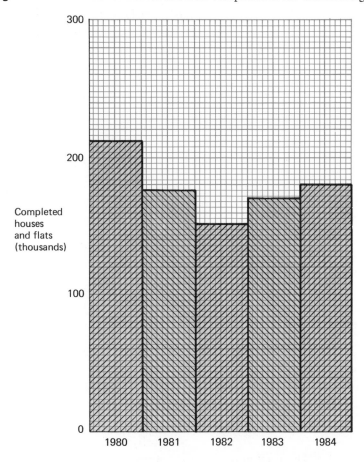

Figure 11.7   Number of houses and flats completed in the United Kingdom

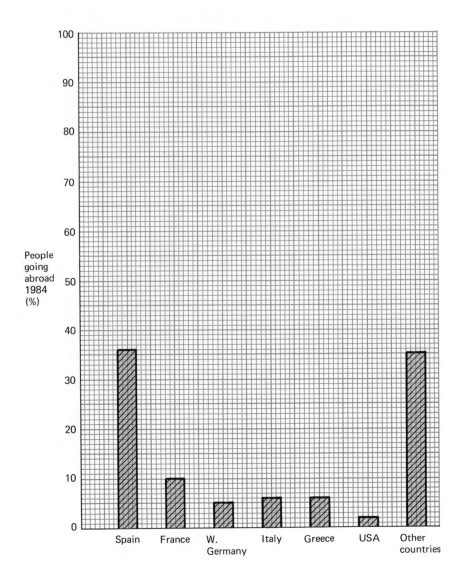

Figure 11.8 Countries stayed in on holidays abroad by UK residents in 1984

Example 11.7

Perhaps the most useful value of bar graphs is in comparison of two or three quantities.

Draw a bar graph to show the June 1984 UK population census of percentages of males/females in various age groups (out of a total population of 56.38m).

Age (years)	0–4	5–14	15–29	30–44	45–59	60+
Males (%)	6.7	14.2	24.3	20.3	16.9	17.5
Females (%)	6.0	12.7	22.3	19.2	16.4	23.5

Since there are two different bars for each age group turn the paper so that the long side is horizontal.

Suggested scales: horizontally 3 cm for each age group;
vertically 2 cm represents 5% of total.

The completed graph is shown as Fig. 11.9.

146

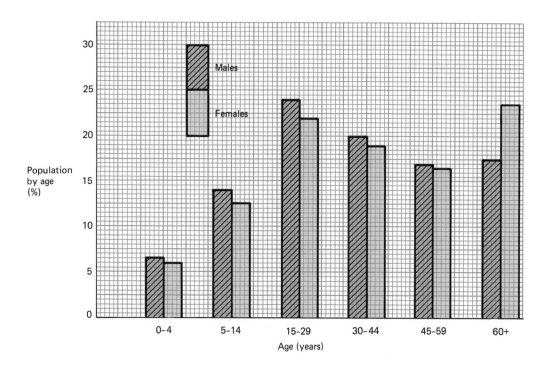

Figure 11.9 Percentage of male/female population by age in June 1984

Exercise 11.3

All the questions in Exercise 11.2 can also be used as questions for the drawing of bar graphs.

1 Draw a bar graph to show the average daily maximum Fahrenheit temperature in London for 1984–85:

	Oct.	Nov.	Dec.	Jan.	Feb.	Mar.	Apr.
London (°F)	56	50	45	38	45	50	56

2 Draw a bar graph to show the overall mileage per gallon of petrol for the cars given:

Overall mileage per gal	Aston-Martin V8 Saloon	Mini Metro 1.0	Daimler Sovereign	Ford Escort 1.6GL	Rolls-Royce Corniche	Vauxhall Cavalier 1.3
	10.7	38.8	15.7	30.9	11.6	31.7

3 Represent by a bar graph the manufacturing output for the UK for the years given, if 1970 is represented by 100.

Year	1973	1974	1975	1976	1977	1978	1979	1980	1981	1982	1983
Output	108.8	107.5	100	102.0	103.9	104.5	104.6	95.1	89.0	85.2	78.4

4 Draw a bar graph to show the percentages of male/female cigarette smokers aged 16 and over.

	1972	1974	1976	1978	1980	1982	1984
Males 16+	52	51	46	45	42	38	36
Females 16+	41	41	38	37	37	33	32

147

5 Draw a bar graph to show the percentage of people without jobs in various regions as at May 1985.

	North	Yorks and Humberside	East Midlands	East Anglia	S. East	S. West	West Midlands	North West	Wales	Scotland	N.Ireland
% Jobless	18.8	14.9	12.7	10.6	9.8	11.8	15.4	16.2	16.8	15.4	20.8

6 Draw a bar graph to show unemployment in the United Kingdom in successive years, percentages of total employable population as at June of each year.

	1981	1982	1983	1984	1985
% Unemployed	11.2	11.6	12.7	12.8	13.4

7 Draw bar graphs to show the increase in prices of the following items if 15 Jan 1974 = 100.

	1974	1976	1978	1980	1982	1984
All items	108.5	157.1	197.1	263.7	320.4	351.8
Food	106.1	159.9	203.8	255.9	299.3	326.1
Durable household goods	107.9	144.2	182.1	226.3	243.8	256.7

8 Draw a bar graph to show the number of passengers carried by air in the UK for 1984.

	Jan.	Feb.	Mar.	Apr.	May	June	July	Aug.	Sept.	Oct.	Nov.	Dec.
Thousands of passengers	1442	1359	1622	1818	1951	2105	2242	2256	2287	2079	1738	1650

9 Draw bar graphs to show the changing pattern of home ownership since 1914.

	1914	1938	1960	1971	1983
% Owner-occupied	10	32	43	53	62
% Private rented	90	58	32	29	27
% Public rented	0	10	25	18	11

10 The Halifax Building Society said that average house prices for areas of the country in July 1985 were

	Scotland	Northern Ireland	North East England	North West England	Yorks and Humberside	East Midlands
Average house price	£30 400	£26 300	£24 800	£25 000	£23 800	£27 200

	West Midlands	East Anglia	Wales	Greater London	South East	South West
Average house price	£28 600	£33 400	£25 500	£48 200	£44 600	£35 600

Draw a bar graph to illustrate these prices.

11.6 Pie Charts

A pie chart is a diagram in which a circle is divided into sectors. The size of each sector represents the proportion of the whole.

Example 11.8

Draw a pie chart to show a liquid containing 25% carbon, 40% hydrogen and 35% oxygen.

Carbon = 25%,   hydrogen = 40%,   oxygen = 35%.   Total = 100%.

First, draw a circle of any radius between, say, 3 and 4 cm.

25% of this circle is to represent carbon.

In a circle there are 360°.

1% of the circle = $\frac{360}{100}$°.

25% of the circle = $\frac{360}{100}$ × 25 = 90°.

40% of the circle (hydrogen) = $\frac{360}{100}$ × 40 = 144°.

35% of the circle (oxygen)   = $\frac{360}{100}$ × 35 = 126°.

As a check, add up these figures to make sure the total comes to 360°. Draw a reference line from the centre of the circle to the circumference OX as in Fig. 11.10. With OX as base line draw an angle of 90°, XOY. With OY as base line now draw an angle of 144°, YOZ. Check that the remaining angle, XOZ, is 126°. Label the chart. The completed pie chart is drawn as Fig. 11.10.

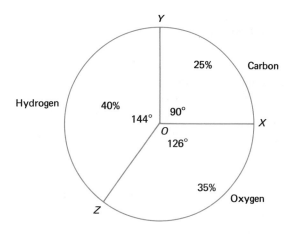

Figure 11.10   Elements contained in a liquid

Example 11.9

A small orchard has 10 apple trees, 8 pear trees, 4 cherry trees and 2 plum trees. Illustrate this on a pie chart.

Whole orchard = 24 trees (10 + 8 + 4 + 2).

The 24 trees have to be represented by a circle, 360°.

24 trees = 360°.

1 tree = $\frac{360}{24}$° = 15°.

10 trees = 150°.

8 trees = 8 × 15° = 120°, 4 trees = 60°, 2 trees = 30°.

Draw the pie chart divided into angles of 150°, 120°, 60°, 30°. The chart is shown as Fig. 11.11.

Alternatively, the angles could have been calculated by a proportion sum.

Whole orchard = 24 trees.

Proportion of apple trees = $\frac{10}{24}$.

Proportion of circle = $\frac{10}{24}$ × 360° = 150°.

The angles to represent the other trees could have been calculated in a similar way.

149

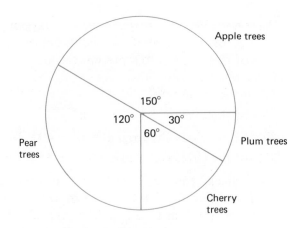

Figure 11.11 Trees in an orchard

Example 11.10

Where figures are given, add them up to find the whole, and then find individual proportions.

The amount of money out on hire purchase and other credit for 1980 was £7000m, 1981 £8000m, 1982 £9000m, 1983 £12 000m and 1984 £14 000m. Show this on a pie chart.

Total amount = £50 000m.

Proportion for 1980 = $\frac{£7000m}{£50\,000m}$ = $\frac{7}{50}$.

Proportion of the circle = $\frac{7}{50} \times 360°$ = $50.4°$.

Proportion for 1981 = $\frac{£8000m}{£50\,000m}$ = $\frac{8}{50}$.

Angle = $\frac{8}{50} \times 360°$ = $57.6°$.

Angle for 1982 = $\frac{9}{50} \times 360°$ = $64.8°$.
Angle for 1983 = $86.4°$. Angle for 1984 = $100.8°$.
Check that all these angles add up to 360°.
The pie chart is drawn as Fig. 11.12.

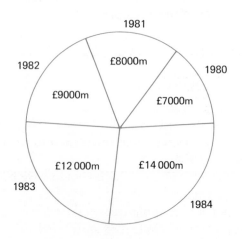

Figure 11.2 Amount of money out on h.p. and other credit

Exercise 11.4

1 Draw a pie chart to represent a class having 14 girls and 11 boys.
2 Draw a pie chart to show a liquid having 2 parts hydrogen and 1 part oxygen.
3 Draw a pie chart to illustrate a metal having 45% copper, 30% zinc and 25% aluminium.
4 A school has 700 pupils, 52 teaching staff and 48 ancillary staff. Show this on a pie chart.
5 Illustrate by a pie chart a compound having 15% calcium, 25% carbon and 60% oxygen.
6 Represent by a pie chart the percentage of goods imported into Britain in 1981:
  Food, drink and tobacco 30%; crude oil and lubricants 12%; raw materials and metal ore 17%; finished goods 16%; partly manufactured 25%.
7 Draw a pie chart to illustrate how paint was sold through various types of shop in 1984:
  Wallpaper and paint specialists 28%; DIY stores 25%; supermarkets 12%; Woolworths 10%; department stores 5%; builders merchants 5%; hardware stores 5%; other retail outlets 10%.
8 Draw a pie chart to show the percentage of toilet tissues sold by brand name in 1983 in UK:
  Andrex 28%; Kleenex 10%; Dixcel 6%; own label 35%; others 21%.
9 These toilet tissues were sold in the following shops (% of all tissues sold):
  Sainsbury 13%; Tesco 13%; Asda 7%; other multiple chains 23%; independent grocers 16%; Co-ops 13%; chemists 9%; others 6%.
  Draw a pie chart to show these figures.
10 Draw a pie chart to show the numbers of calculators sold in 1984, expressed as a percentage:
  Casio 35%; Sharp 19%; Texas 15%; Cannon 10%; others 21%.

11.7   Pictograms

A pictogram is similar to a bar graph except that the bar is replaced by a simple drawing of the quantities being represented and each drawing represents a stated amount.

Example 11.11

The figures below show the number of cigarettes smoked in Great Britain in the first seven months of 1982:

Month	Jan.	Feb.	Mar.	Apr.	May	June	July
Billions of cigarettes	11.1	13.1	10.0	6.4	4.8	6.6	7.7

(1 billion = 1000 million)

A pictogram of this data could be shown as in Fig. 11.13 with a drawing of 1 cigarette representing 2 billion cigarettes.

Pictograms such as this are often seen in daily newspapers; note that the 'pictures' usually go horizontally. It is not easy to draw small fractions of the picture, whether it is cigarettes, cars, ships, trees or whatever, and the actual values can be written alongside the pictures. Comparisons can be seen as easily as a bar graph.

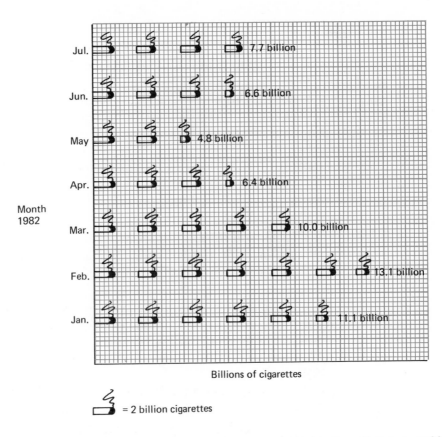

Month 1982

Jul. 7.7 billion

Jun. 6.6 billion

May 4.8 billion

Apr. 6.4 billion

Mar. 10.0 billion

Feb. 13.1 billion

Jan. 11.1 billion

Billions of cigarettes

= 2 billion cigarettes

Figure 11.13 Pictogram of cigarettes smoked in Great Britain in 1982

11.8 Straight-line graphs

A straight-line graph results when there is a definite fixed relationship between two quantities.

Example 11.12

Draw a graph to show the relationship between pounds and dollars if £100 = $138.

Suitable scale: 1 cm = £10 horizontally;
                 1 cm = $10 vertically.

An important fact for this type of graph is that you will receive no dollars for no pounds.
Start the scales at 0.
Put in the point for £100 = $138.
Join this point by a straight line to 0, 0. The point 0, 0 is called the origin.

The type of graph may be called a conversion graph because it can be used for converting pounds to dollars and vice versa.

The completed graph is shown as Fig. 11.14.

From the graph you can read off how many dollars for £30. How many for £70? How many for £45?

How many £s for 120 dollars? 90 dollars? 25 dollars?

A similar type of graph could be drawn for such things as 500 ballpoint pens cost £15 (remember 0 ballpoints = 0 charge), 1 metre = 39.3 in (0 metres = 0 in).

152

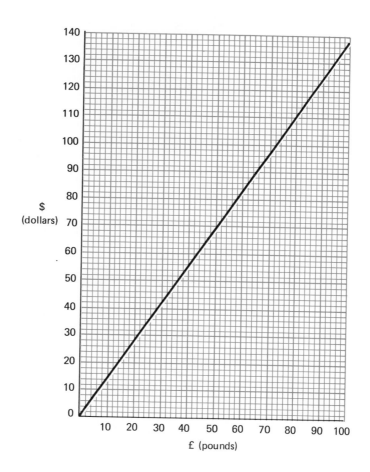

Figure 11.14   Relationship between pounds and dollars when £100 = $138

Example 11.13

Not all straight-line graphs go through the point 0, 0 (origin). A supplier offers to make metal brackets at a cost of 1000 for £250, on a pro rata basis, plus a fixed charge of £50. Draw a graph to show the costs of up to 1000 brackets.

Cost of 1000 brackets = £250 + £50 fixed charge = £300.
Cost of no brackets = £50 fixed charge.
These are the two points needed in order to draw the graph.
Scale: 1 cm = 100 brackets horizontally;
         1 cm = £25 vertically.
The completed graph is shown as Fig. 11.15 (page 154).

Notice from the graph that 500 brackets cost more than half the cost of 1000 brackets.

11.9   Curved Graphs

When the points of a graph have been plotted, as in example 11.1, it may be that joining by straight lines is not the best solution — some graphs suggest a smooth curve can be drawn through the points.

153

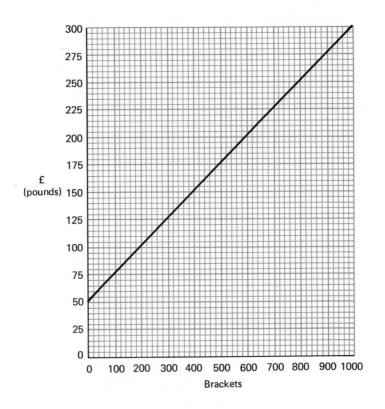

Figure 11.15 Cost of brackets with fixed charge of £50

Example 11.14

A Leylandii tree was 2 ft high when planted and its height was measured every 5 years. Draw a smooth curved graph to show the relationship between its height and age.

Years after planting	0	5	10	15	20	25	30
Height in ft	2	21	39	53	64	71	76

Scale: 2 cm = 5 yr horizontally;
          2 cm = 10 ft vertically.

The completed graph is shown in Fig. 11.16. From this graph you can estimate what the height was after 8 yr, 17 yr, 22 yr, etc., or how long it took to reach 30 ft, 50 ft, 70 ft, and so on.

Example 11.15

A moving car needs a certain braking distance for it to stop. Plot a curved graph to show the relationship between speed and braking distance.

Speed (mile/h)	0	10	20	30	40	50	60
Braking distance (ft)	0	5	18	44	80	126	176

The completed graph is shown in Fig. 11.17.
Scale: 2 cm = 10 mile/h horizontally;
          2 cm = 20 ft vertically.

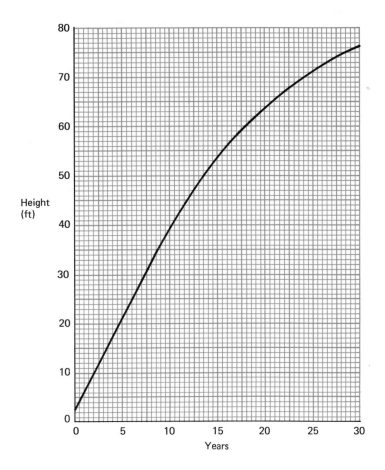

Figure 11.16 Growth of a tree

Exercise 11.5

1 Draw a straight-line graph to show the relationship between miles and kilo-metres if 31 miles = 50 km. From the graph change (a) 22 miles into km (b) 20 km into miles.

2 Draw a graph using the fact that 1 gallon (8 pints) = 4.57 litres so that the graph can be used to show up to 10 gallons (80 pints). From the graph find (a) how many litres in 7.5 gallons, (b) how many gallons in 30 litres.

3 1 lb = 454 g. Draw a graph so that it can be used up to 100 lb. From the graph find (a) how many lb in 3000 g, (b) how many g in 45 lb.

4 If in August 1985 £500 = 900 Canadian dollars, draw a graph to show the relationship. From the graph find (a) how many £ you would receive for 400 dollars, (b) how many Canadian dollars for £280.

5 In August 1985 £500 was worth 11 000 Spanish pesetas. Draw a graph to show this. From the graph find (a) how many Spanish pesetas for £180, (b) how many £ for 8000 pesetas.

6 In an experiment of hanging weights on the end of a coiled spring the results were as follows:

Weight attached (g)	0	50	100	150	200	250	300
Length of spring (cm)	15	17	19	21	23	25	27

Draw a graph to show the results.

7 A supplier offers to make cardboard boxes at a cost of 1000 for £80, on a pro rata basis, plus a fixed charge of £20. Draw a graph to show the costs of up to 1000 boxes. How much would (a) 500 cost, (b) 150 cost?

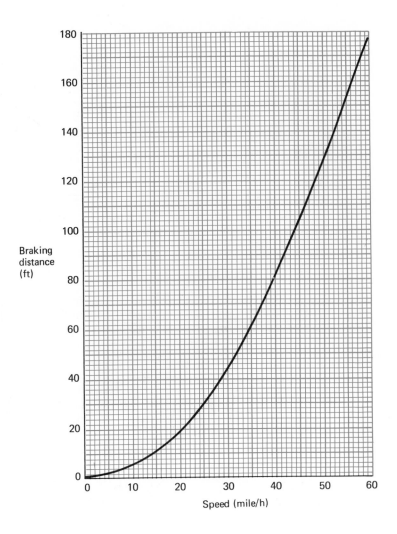

Figure 11.17 Graph of speed vs. braking distance

8 Before an article is made there are costs of £40. When 250 articles have been made the total cost of making them is £200. Draw a graph to show these facts. From the graph estimate the cost of making (a) 150 articles, (b) 75 articles.

9 When a number is multiplied by itself the results are as follows:

Number	0	1	2	3	4	5	6	7	8	9	10
Number multiplied by itself	0	1	4	9	16	25	36	49	64	81	100

Draw a smooth curved graph to show the results. From the graph estimate how much is (a) 5.5 multiplied by itself, (b) 7.7 multiplied by itself.

10 A tree was measured in height every 3 years with the following results:

Age of tree (years)	3	6	9	12	15	18	21	24
Height of tree (metres)	1.2	2.2	2.9	3.5	4.0	4.4	4.7	4.9

Draw a smooth curved graph to show the results.

11.10 Substitution

Later in this chapter we will be looking at simple algebraic graphs. First, we will consider some simple algebra.

Symbols or letters can be used sometimes in place of numbers. Even when you have letters, they still follow the pattern of arithmetic.

$a + b$ means a plus b; $\dfrac{a}{b}$ means $a \div b$.

$a - b$ means a minus b.

$a \times b$ means a multiplied by b and this is usually written ab.

$4b$ means $4 \times b$.

Using these facts it is possible to substitute given numbers in place of symbols.

Example 11.16

Find the value of $a + b$ if $a = 7$ and $b = 6$.
To find the value we substitute the value 7 wherever we see a and substitute 6 wherever we see b.

$a + b = 7 + 6 = 13$.
Answer   13

Example 11.17

If $a = 7$ and $b = 6$ find the value of $2a + 3b$.

In $2a + 3b$ write down what each term means:

$$2a \text{ means } 2 \times a, \qquad 3b \text{ means } 3 \times b.$$

Now substitute the values $a = 7$ and $b = 6$:

$$2a + 3b = 2 \times a + 3 \times b$$
$$= 2 \times 7 + 3 \times 6$$
$$= 14 + 18$$
$$= 32.$$

Answer   32

Example 11.18

Find the value of the following expressions if $r = 2, s = 3, t = 4$:

(a) $3r + 5s - 2t$; (b) $\dfrac{3r + 5t}{2}$.

(a) $3r + 5s - 2t = 3 \times r + 5 \times s - 2 \times t$

Now substitute the values given:

$$= 3 \times 2 + 5 \times 3 - 2 \times 4$$
$$= 6 + 15 - 8$$
$$= 13.$$

Answer   13

(b) $\dfrac{3r + 5t}{2} = \dfrac{3 \times r + 5 \times t}{2}$

Substitute the values given:

$$= \dfrac{3 \times 2 + 5 \times 4}{2}$$

$$= \dfrac{6 + 20}{2}$$

Answer   13

Exercise 11.6

If $a = 4$, $b = 5$, $c = 6$, find the value of the following:

1 $3a$	2 $6b$	3 $3a + 4b$	4 $2a + 3b$
5 $4a + b + 2c$	6 $a + 3b - 2c$	7 $3a - 2b + c$	8 $6a - b - c$
9 $\dfrac{3a + 4b}{4}$	10 $\dfrac{3a + 6b}{c}$		

11.11   Further Substitution

$a \times b$ can be written as ab.

$a \times b \times c$ can be written as abc.

Where the letter (symbol) is multiplied by itself such as $a \times a$ it can be written a^2, (*a* squared).

Similarly, $b \times b = b^2$ (*b* squared)

The substitution of values is made easy if you remember what is meant by each expression. For example, $2x^2$ means $2 \times x^2$.

Example 11.19

Find the value of the following expressions if $x = 3$, $y = 2$:
(a) $4y$; (b) x^2; (c) $2x + y^2$; (d) $2x^2$; (e) $3x^2 - 2y^2$.

In each case write down what each term means:

(a) $4y = 4 \times y$

Substitute the value $y = 2$; then

$4y = 4 \times y = 4 \times 2 = 8.$

Answer   8

(b) $x^2 = x \times x$ Now substitute $x = 3$.

$= 3 \times 3 = 9.$

Answer   9

(c) $2x + y^2 = 2 \times x + y \times y$ Substitute $x = 3$, $y = 2$

$= 2 \times 3 + 2 \times 2$

$= 6 + 4 = 10.$

Answer   10

(d) $2x^2 = 2 \times x^2 = 2 \times x \times x$

$\qquad = 2 \times 3 \times 3 \qquad$ Since $x = 3$.

$\qquad = 18$.

Answer   18

(e) $3x^2 - 2y^2 = 3 \times x \times x - 2 \times y \times y$

$\qquad = 3 \times 3 \times 3 - 2 \times 2 \times 2 \qquad x = 3, y = 2$

$\qquad = 27 - 8$

$\qquad = 19$.

Answer   19

Example 11.20

Find the value of the following expressions if $r = 4$, $s = 3$, $t = 2$.

(a) $3r + 5s - 2t$;   (b) $\dfrac{3r + 2s}{3}$;   (c) $\dfrac{3r^2}{2t}$;   (d) rs^2;   (e) $\dfrac{2r^2 + 8s}{t + 2}$.

(a) $3r + 5s - 2t = 3 \times r + 5 \times s - 2 \times t$

$\qquad = 3 \times 4 + 5 \times 3 - 2 \times 2$

$\qquad = 12 + 15 - 4$

$\qquad = 23$.

Answer   23

(b) $\dfrac{3r + 2s}{3} = \dfrac{3 \times r + 2 \times s}{3} = \dfrac{3 \times 4 + 2 \times 3}{3}$

$\qquad = \dfrac{12 + 6}{3} = \dfrac{18}{3} = 6$.

Answer   6

(c) $\dfrac{3r^2}{2t} = \dfrac{3 \times r \times r}{2 \times t} = \dfrac{3 \times 4 \times 4}{2 \times 2} = \dfrac{48}{4} = 12$.

Answer   12

(d) $rs^2 = r \times s \times s \qquad$ *Note:* Only the s is squared.

$\qquad = 4 \times 3 \times 3 = 36$.

Answer   36

(e) $\dfrac{2r^2 + 8s}{t + 2} = \dfrac{2 \times r \times r + 8 \times s}{t + 2}$

$\qquad = \dfrac{2 \times 4 \times 4 + 8 \times 3}{2 + 2}$

$\qquad = \dfrac{32 + 24}{4} = 14$.

Answer   14

Exercise 11.7

1 If $a = 4$, $b = 3$, $c = 5$ find the value of
   (a) $3a + b$;   (b) $a + 4b$;   (c) $4a + 2b - 2c$;   (d) $3c - 2a + 4b$;
   (e) $6a - b - 2c$.

2 If $x = 4$, $y = 3$, $z = 2$ find the value of
   (a) y^2;   (b) $2x^2$;   (c) $4x + 2y^2$;   (d) $4z - x + 3y^2$;   (e) xyz.

3 If $r = 5$, $s = 2$, $t = 6$ find the value of

   (a) $4r + \dfrac{3t}{s}$;   (b) $\dfrac{6r + t}{3s}$;   (c) $\dfrac{3s^2}{t}$;   (d) $2rs + st$;   (e) $2ts + 5rt - 3s$.

159

4 If $v = 2$, $w = 5$, $x = 3$, $y = 4$ find the value of
(a) $xw + 2vy + 4wy$;   (b) $wxy - 3vx + vy$;   (c) $xy^2 + w^2 - 3wy$;
(d) $x^2 w + vyx - 3vx$;   (e) $2xy + 3wy + xwv - 3wx$.

11.12   Formulae and Equations

ab is an expression but if we put $R = ab$ (R equals ab) then we have an equation. This could be called a formula.

Example 11.21

The cost of a gas bill is as follows:
Cost of gas = standing charge plus (the price of a therm times the number of therms used)
= standing charge + price of a therm × number of therms.
If c = cost of gas, s = standing charge (£), t = price of a therm (£) and n = number of therms used, then $c = s + tn$, and this formula can be used in future for working out all gas bills.

Similarly, the cost of electricity can be expressed as $E = s + np$, where E = cost of electricity, s = standing charge (£), p = cost per unit (£) and n = number of units used.

Example 11.22

Find a formula if the salary of a salesman is a basic salary plus 20% commission of all sales.

Salary = basic salary + 20% commission of all sales.

$S = B + 20\% \ C$ where S = salary (£)
$S = B + 0.2 \ C$. B = basic salary (£)
                                C = all sales (£);

Answer $S = B + 0.2C$

Example 11.23

Find a formula for temperature in Fahrenheit, if Fahrenheit temperature is $\frac{9}{5}$ of Celsius temperature plus 32.

Fahrenheit temperature = $\frac{9}{5}$ of Celsius temperature + 32

$F = \frac{9}{5}$ of $C + 32$ where F = Fahrenheit temperature
                                C = Celsius temperature

Answer $F = \frac{9}{5}C + 32$.

Example 11.24

Given a formula it is easy to substitute values into that formula.

If $F = \frac{9}{5}C + 32$ find F when $C = 20$.

$$F = \frac{9 \times 20}{5} + 32$$

$$= 36 + 32$$

$$= 68.$$

Answer $F = 68$ when $C = 20$.

Example 11.25

If $S = \left(\dfrac{U + V}{2}\right) \times t$ find S when $U = 8$, $V = 12$, $t = 6$.

As for arithmetic, first work out the brackets when the values have been substituted.

$$S = \left(\frac{8 + 12}{2}\right) \times 6$$

$$= \left(\frac{20}{2}\right) \times 6$$

$$= 10 \times 6$$

$$= 60.$$

Answer $S = 60$

Exercise 11.8

1 Find a formula for the salary of a salesman if he gets a basic salary plus 25% commission on all sales.
2 Find a formula for the cost of production if it is equal to twice the cost of labour plus the cost of materials.
3 Find a formula for the perimeter of a rectangle if it is equal to twice the length of the long side plus twice the length of the short side.
4 Find a formula for distance travelled if it is equal to time multiplied by the average speed.
5 If $V = C \times R$ find V when $C = 4$, $R = 3$.
6 If $V = U + ft$ find V when $U = 6$, $f = 3$, $t = 2$.
7 If $I = \dfrac{PRT}{100}$ find I when $P = 200$, $R = 3$, $T = 5$.
8 If $C = \dfrac{A \times D}{A + 12}$ find C when $A = 6$, $D = 12$.
9 If $A = 4r^2 + 3rh$ find A when $r = 3$, $h = 4$.
10 If $S = ut + \frac{1}{2}ft^2$ find S when $u = 3$, $t = 4$ and $f = 3$.

11.13   Simple Algebraic Graphs

These graphs stem from an expression using symbols where certain values have to be substituted into the expression.

Example 11.26

Using values of x from 1 to 10, plot a graph of $y = 2x$.

$y = 2x$ is called an equation (y equals $2x$) and will always be true.
First, if $x = 1$ what does y equal?

$y = 2x$ so when $x = 1$, $y = 2 \times x = 2 \times 1 = 2$.

When $x = 2$, $y = 2x = 2 \times x = 2 \times 2 = 4$

$x = 3$, $y = 2 \times 3 = 6$ and so on.

Notice that if $x = 0$, then $y = 2 \times 0 = 0$.

You may find it easier to put the results in the form of a table as follows:

Value of x	0	1	2	3	4	5	6	7	8	9	10
$y = 2x$	0	2	4	6	8	10	12	14	16	18	20

The graph is drawn by always putting values of x horizontally, and values of y vertically.

Scale: 1 cm = 1 unit for x, horizontally

1 cm = 1 unit for y, vertically.

The completed graph is shown as Fig. 11.18.

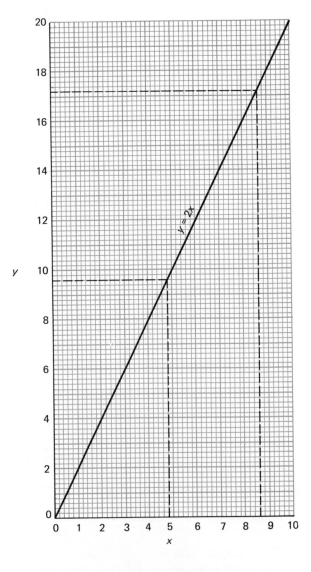

Figure 11.18   Graph of $y = 2x$

When the points are plotted it is easy to see that they are all in a straight line. Compare it with Fig. 11.12. Notice that, having drawn the graph, the graph can now be used to read off the value of y for any value of x, and vice versa.

For example, what is y when $x = 8.6$?   Answer $y = 17.2$ when $x = 8.6$ (the dotted lines show the 'reading off').

What is the value of x when $y = 9.6$?   Answer $x = 4.8$ when $y = 9.6$.

Example 11.27

A relationship will often involve a number as well as x and y. Using values of x from 1 to 10, draw the graph of $y = 2x + 7$. Give values to x of 1, 2, 3, 4, etc.

For $x = 1$, $y = 2x + 7 = 2 \times 1 + 7 = 2 + 7 = 9$
$x = 2$, $y = 2x + 7 = 2 \times 2 + 7 = 4 + 7 = 11$
$x = 3$, $y = 2x + 7 = 2 \times 3 + 7 = 6 + 7 = 13$.

Note, when $x = 0$ then $y = 7$.

Continuing the values of x produces the following table:

Value of x	0	1	2	3	4	5	6	7	8	9	10
$y = 2x$	0	2	4	6	8	10	12	14	16	18	20
+ 7	+7	+7	+7	+7	+7	+7	+7	+7	+7	+7	+7
$y = 2x + 7$	7	9	11	13	15	17	19	21	23	25	27

Try and keep the number separate in the table because it does not alter no matter what the value of x.

Scale: 1 cm = 1 unit for x horizontally;
         1 cm = 2 units for y vertically.

The completed graph is shown as Fig. 11.19. Notice the close resemblance of this graph to Fig. 11.18.

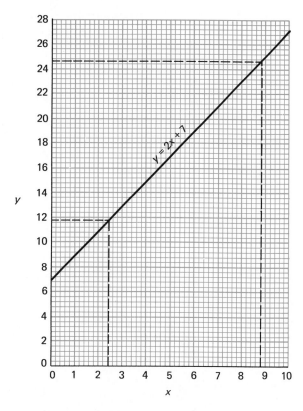

Figure 11.19   Graph of $y = 2x + 7$

What is the value of y when $x = 2.4$?
Answer: $y = 11.8$ when $x = 2.4$.
What is the value of x when $y = 24.6$?
Answer: $x = 8.8$ when $y = 24.6$.

Example 11.28

There are negative numbers as well as positive numbers.
Draw the graph of $y = 2x - 10$ from $x = 0$ to $x = 10$.

Values of x from $x = 0$ to $x = 10$ produces the following table for $y = 2x - 10$.

Value of x	0	1	2	3	4	5	6	7	8	9	10
$y = 2x$	0	2	4	6	8	10	12	14	16	18	20
-10	-10	-10	-10	-10	-10	-10	-10	-10	-10	-10	-10
$y = 2x - 10$	-10	-8	-6	-4	-2	0	$+2$	$+4$	$+6$	$+8$	$+10$

Scale: 1 cm = 1 unit for x horizontally;
1 cm = 1 unit for y vertically.
The completed graph is shown as Fig. 11.20.

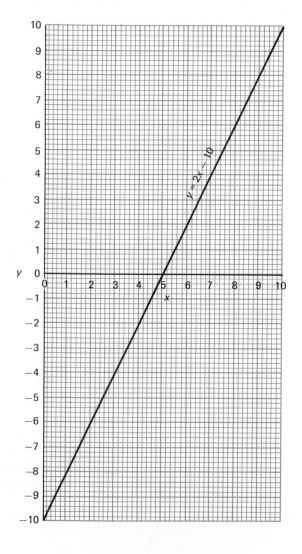

Figure 11.20   Graph of $y = 2x - 10$

To accommodate the value of y going from -10 to $+10$ the x-axis is drawn in the middle of the paper.

Example 11.29

Draw the graph of $y = 15 - 3x$ from $x = 0$ to $x = 10$.

Using the values of x given produces the following table of results for $y = 15 - 3x$:

Value of x	0	1	2	3	4	5	6	7	8	9	10
$y = 15$	15	15	15	15	15	15	15	15	15	15	15
$-3x$	0	-3	-6	-9	-12	-15	-18	-21	-24	-27	-30
$y = 15 - 3x$	15	12	9	6	3	0	-3	-6	-9	-12	-15

The completed graph is shown as Fig. 11.21.

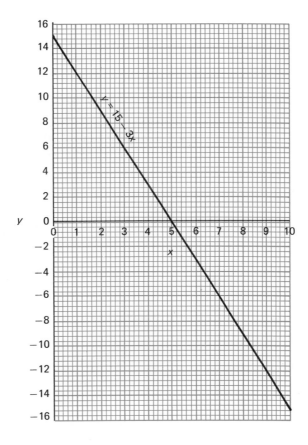

Figure 11.21   Graph of $y = 15 - 3x$

Note how the graph 'slopes' the other way.

Exercise 11.9

1 Draw the graph of $y = x$ for values of $x = 0$ to $x = 10$. From the graph find the values of y when $x = 3.5$, 6.6, 2.3 and 7.9.
2 Draw the graph of $y = 3x$ for values of x from $x = 0$ to $x = 10$. From the graph find the values of y when $x = 0.7$, 5.3 and 7.4.

3 Draw the graph of $y = x + 6$ from $x = 0$ to $x = 10$. From the graph find y when $x = 7.1, 0.9, 5.7$ and 6.8.

4 Draw the graph of $y = 3x + 7$ from $x = 0$ to $x = 10$. From the graph find x when $y = 9.4, 15.7, 22.0, 25.6$ and 31.0.

5 Draw the graph of $y = 4x - 12$ from $x = 0$ to $x = 8$. From the graph find the value of y when $x = 2.5, 3.9$ and 6.3.

6 Draw the graph of $y = 3x - 15$ from $x = 0$ to $x = 10$. From the graph find the values of x when $y = -10, -2.6$ and 12.4.

7 Draw the graph of $y = 25 - 3x$ from $x = 0$ to $x = 10$. From the graph find the values of x when $y = 6.4, 13.8$ and -4.

8 Draw the graph of $y = 12 - x$ from $x = 0$ to $x = 10$. From the graph find y when $x = 1.8, 3.7, 5.4$ and 7.5.

9 Draw the graph of $y = 3x - 5$ from $x = 0$ to $x = 12$. From the graph find x when $y = -3.6, 0.8, 14.4$ and 24.8.

10 Draw the graph of $a = 3b + 4$ from $b = 0$ to $b = 6$. From the graph find the value of a when $b = 1.9, 3.5$ and 5.2.

11.14   Flowcharts

A simple flowchart is a series of small diagrams showing the order of operations and decisions to be made for a process to be completed.

The shape of a diagram has a particular meaning. A minimum of words is used. The main diagram shapes are as follows:

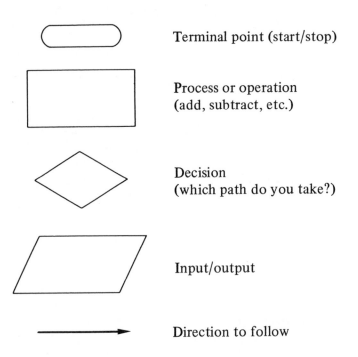

Terminal point (start/stop)

Process or operation (add, subtract, etc.)

Decision (which path do you take?)

Input/output

Direction to follow

Example 11.30

What methods can I use to deal with savings of a large amount of money? The beginning of a flowchart to set me thinking might be as follows:

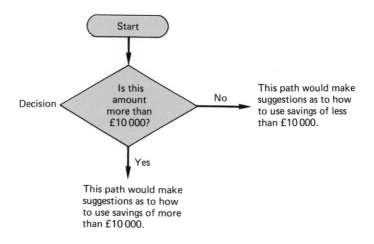

Example 11.31

To have a drink of water might be shown as follows:

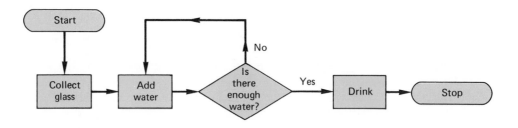

Example 11.32

The flowchart gives the answer to a calculation carried out on a series of numbers.

Number   0 1 2 3 4 5 6
Answer

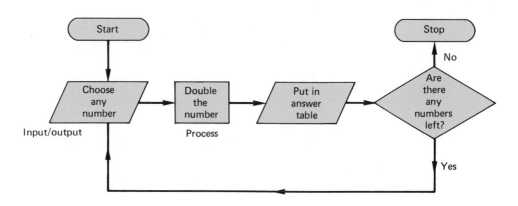

Follow the arrows and instructions as given on the flowchart.
Start.
Choose any number, say 3.
Double the number, making 6.
Write 6 in the answer table.
Are there any numbers left? Yes.
Choose any number, say 4.
Repeat the process until all numbers have been used.

Exercise 11.10

1 The flowchart shows how to calculate an answer from a given number.
   What is the answer, (a) given a number 3; (b) given a number 5?

Number   1 2 3 4 5 6
Answer

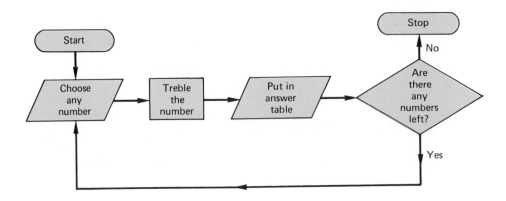

2 The flowchart shows how to calculate an answer from a given number.
   Complete the answers for the numbers given.

Number   1 2 3 4 5 6
Answer

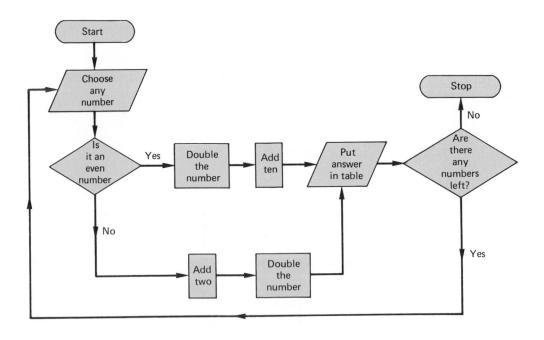

168

3 The flowchart shows how to sort a letter.
Into which coloured bag does a letter weighing 30 g go?

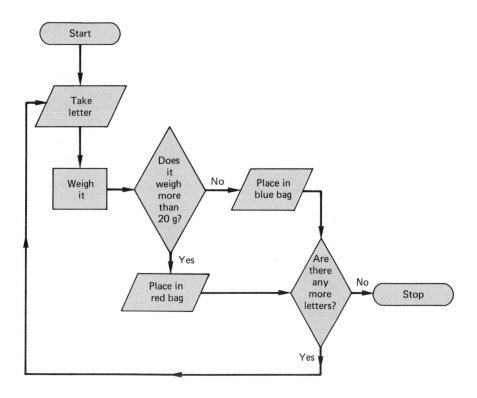

4 The stages of preparing an orange drink, not in order, are drink, add orange, collect glass, taste, add water.
Write in the various instructions on the flowchart.

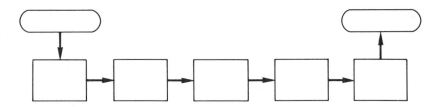

5 Where in the flowchart of question 4 would you place the following decision?

> Is
> the
> mixture
> correct
> ?

6 Try to draw a simple flowchart for a vending machine selling coffee only, with or without milk and with or without sugar.

7 Try to draw a simple flowchart for a vending machine selling coffee, tea, and fruit drink with no other choices.

8 The flowchart is for sorting parcels. Into which bag will go a parcel weighing
(a) 45 kg (b) 8.5 kg (c) 17 kg (d) 15 kg (e) 23.5 kg?

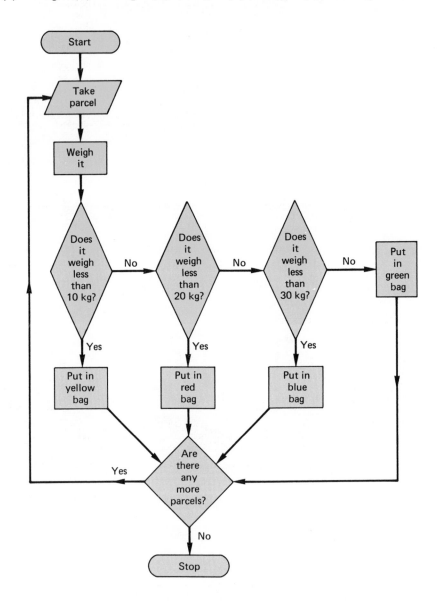

12 Plane Shapes

12.1 Common Shapes

The most common shapes are lines, angles, triangles, rectangles, squares, and circles. We shall consider some of the main facts associated with these shapes.

12.2 Straight Lines and Angles

An angle is the rotation of a straight line fixed at one end to a point. A complete rotation (a circle) represents 360 degrees, written 360°.

A unit of angular measure is a degree.

A simple instrument for measuring angles is a protractor.

Example 12.1

Measuring an angle:

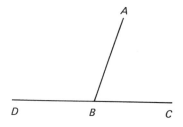

Angle *ABC* is the angle between line *AB* and line *BC*; imagine that *BC* has rotated anticlockwise until it reached *BA*.

Similarly, angle *ABD* is the angle between line *DB* and *BA*; imagine *DB* rotating clockwise until it reaches *BA*.

Place the base line of a protractor (0–180) so that it coincides with line *DC* and the centre of the protractor coincides with point *B*, as shown in Fig. 12.1.

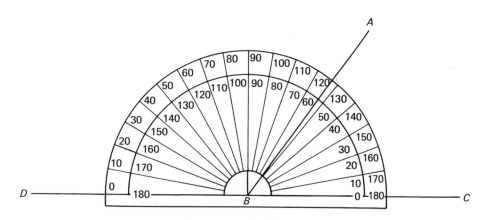

Figure 12.1   Measuring an angle with a protractor

Read off the angle: angle $ABC = 53°$,
angle $ABD = 127°$.
Note that a straight line is equivalent to $180°$.
An angle of $90°$ is called a right angle.

Example 12.2

How big is angle XOZ?

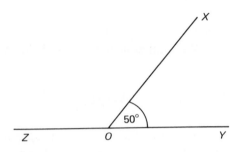

Angle XOY is shown as $50°$.
The straight line ZOY is equivalent to $180°$.
So angle $XOZ = 180° - 50° = 130°$.
Answer $130°$

Example 12.3

When two straight lines cross then opposite angles are equal.

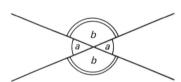

Example 12.4

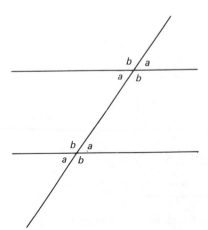

These are parallel lines, i.e. they continue for ever without crossing one another.

Equal angles are shown, using the same letter.

172

12.3   Bearings

A bearing indicates how to reach one point (place) from another one by using an angle and a fixed reference line. The fixed reference line is due north and an angle is given from this reference line in a clockwise direction using the full 360° of a circle.

Example 12.5

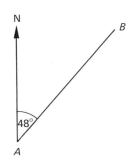

The bearing of *B* from *A* is said to be 048°, that is, starting at the fixed reference line you have to go along a course which is at an angle of 48° in a clockwise direction.

Sometimes the direction is given with reference to the points of a compass north, south, east and west.

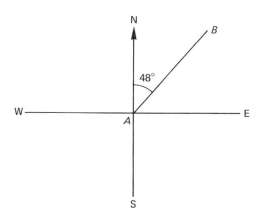

The direction of *B* from *A* is 48° east of north.

In this book we will use the fixed reference line and the full 360°.

Example 12.6

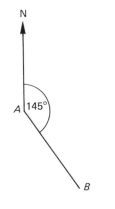

Bearing of *B* from *A* is 145°.

Example 12.7

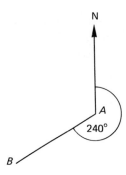

Bearing of B from A is $240°$.

Example 12.8

What is the bearing of an aircraft flying *from B to A* as shown in the diagram?

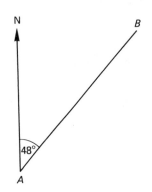

Note how important it is to say which way you are going — compare this with example 12.5.

To do this example put in a dotted line, through B, and parallel to the fixed reference line. Call it XY.

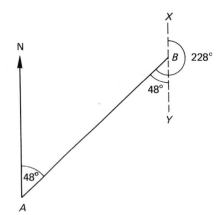

Angle $XBY = 180°$ (straight line).
Angle $ABY = 48°$ (parallel lines).
So that going in a clockwise direction the angle $XBA = 228°$ ($180° + 48°$).
Bearing of A from $B = 228°$.

Answer $228°$

1 Measure the angles given below.

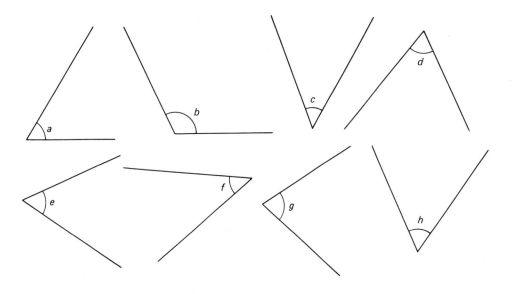

2 Draw the following angles:
   (a) 42°   (b) 75°   (c) 90°   (d) 140°   (e) 172°   (f) 210°   (g) 240°
   (h) 290°.

3 How big are angles *a*, *b*, and *c*?

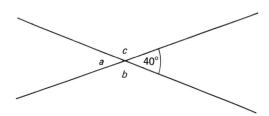

4 Find the size of the angles denoted by letters.

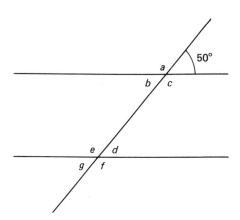

5 What is the bearing of *B* from *A*?

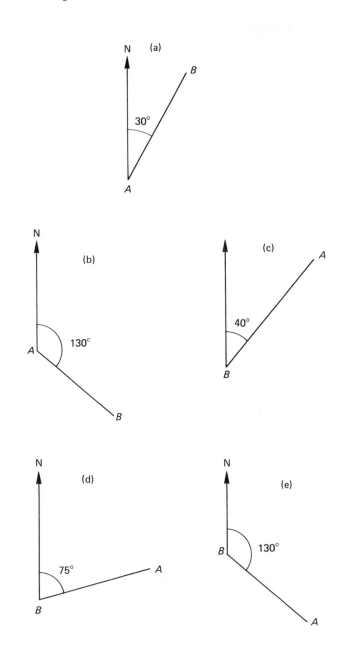

6 Find the size of the angles denoted by letters.

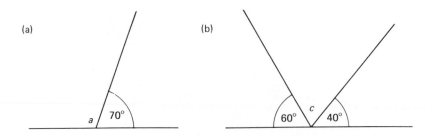

12.4   Rectangles and Squares

A rectangle is a four-sided figure with its opposite sides equal and all four angles equal. The angles are each 90°.

A square is a special rectangle in which all four sides are equal.

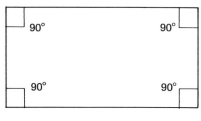

Rectangle

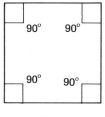

Square

12.5   Perimeters

The perimeter is the distance all round the sides of a shape.

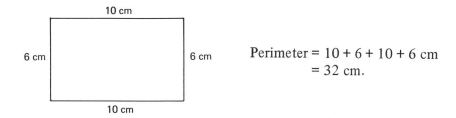

Perimeter = 10 + 6 + 10 + 6 cm
            = 32 cm.

A diagram often helps in working out a problem.

Example 12.9

A rectangle has one side 15 cm and a perimeter of 80 cm. Find the length of a side of different length.

15 cm

If one side is 15 cm then the side opposite is also 15 cm. The two sides total 30 cm.

Perimeter = 80 cm.
Total length of the other two equal sides = 80 cm − 30 cm
                                          = 50 cm.
Length of one other side = $\frac{50}{2}$ cm   = 25 cm.

Answer   25 cm

Example 12.10

A rectangle has sides of 14 cm and 8 cm. What would be the length of side of a square having the same perimeter?

177

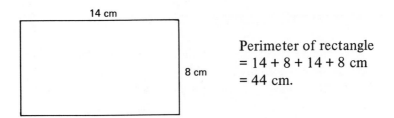

Perimeter of rectangle
= 14 + 8 + 14 + 8 cm
= 44 cm.

A square has four equal sides and its perimeter has to be 44 cm (equal to the rectangle).

Length of side of square = $\frac{44}{4}$ cm = 11 cm.

Answer 11 cm

12.6 Area of Rectangles

Area is measured in square units.

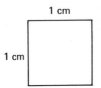

Area within this perimeter is 1 square cm (1 sq cm or 1 cm²).

For any rectangle, therefore, imagine it to be divided into squares.

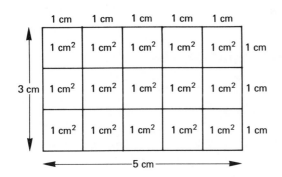

Add the squares together.
Area = 15 cm².
There are five rows with three squares in each row.
5 cm x 3 cm = 15 cm².

The area of any rectangle is found by multiplying length by breadth.

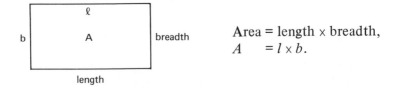

Area = length x breadth,
A = $l \times b$.

Important: The length and breadth must be in the same units and the answer will then be in square units of the same name.

Example 12.11

A rectangular sheet of paper is 12 cm x 15 cm. Find its area.

First, get into the habit of drawing a diagram.

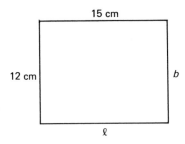

Area = length x breadth
     = 15 cm x 12 cm
     = 180 cm².

Example 12.12

A square has a side of 8 cm 5 mm. What is its area?

Note: Before multiplying, measurements must be in the same units.

8 cm 5 mm is 8.5 cm or 85 mm.

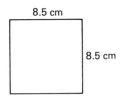

Area = length x breadth
     = 8.5 cm x 8.5 cm
     = 72.25 cm².

Area = length x breadth
     = 85 mm x 85 mm
     = 7225 mm².

Example 12.13

Find the area of the shape below.

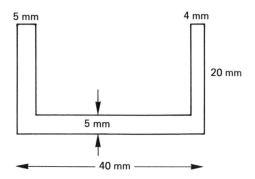

A shape like this is made up of rectangles.

Put in dotted lines to show the rectangles, label each one and find the area of each.

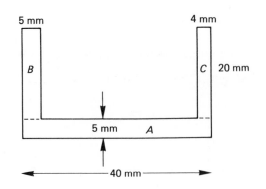

Area of rectangle A = 40 mm x 5 mm = 200 mm^2.

Area of rectangle B = 15 mm x 5 mm = 75 mm^2.

Area of rectangle C = 15 mm x 4 mm = 60 mm^2.

Total area = 200 mm^2 + 75 mm^2 + 60mm^2

$\qquad$ = 335 mm^2.

Exercise 12.2

1 A square has a side of 8 cm 4 mm. What is the perimeter?
2 A rectangle has sides of 10 cm and 14 cm. What would be the length of side of a square having the same perimeter?
3 A rectangle has one side 14 cm long and a perimeter of 40 cm. What is the length of the shorter side?
4 The perimeter of a square is 132 cm. What is the length of a side?
5 A square has a side of 15 cm. A rectangle of the same perimeter has a short side of 12 cm. What is the length of the long side?

Exercise 12.3

Find the areas of the following figures.

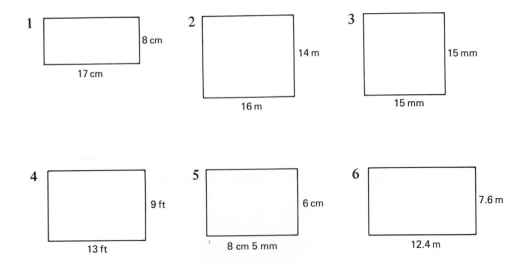

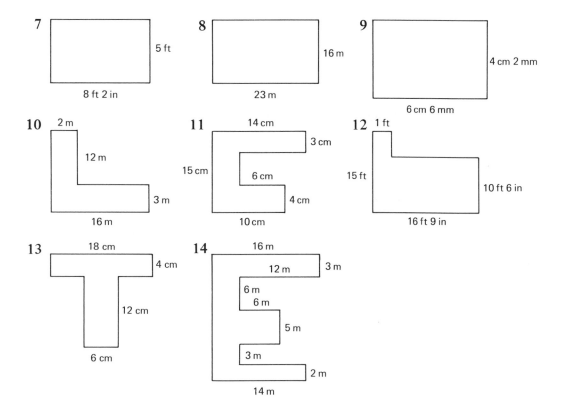

7 5 ft / 8 ft 2 in

8 16 m / 23 m

9 4 cm 2 mm / 6 cm 6 mm

10 2 m / 12 m / 3 m / 16 m

11 14 cm / 3 cm / 15 cm / 6 cm / 4 cm / 10 cm

12 1 ft / 15 ft / 10 ft 6 in / 16 ft 9 in

13 18 cm / 4 cm / 12 cm / 6 cm

14 16 m / 12 m / 3 m / 6 m / 6 m / 5 m / 3 m / 2 m / 14 m

Find the area of the shaded parts in the following four figures.

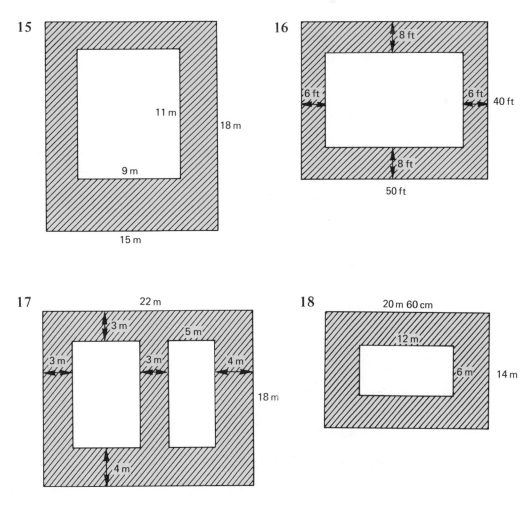

15 11 m / 18 m / 9 m / 15 m

16 8 ft / 6 ft / 6 ft / 40 ft / 8 ft / 50 ft

17 22 m / 3 m / 5 m / 3 m / 3 m / 4 m / 18 m / 4 m

18 20 m 60 cm / 12 m / 6 m / 14 m

181

12.7 Costing

Area is often involved with costs; for example, how much does it cost to paint a surface, how much to sow a lawn, how much to carpet a floor, how much to put glass in window frames, how much to wallpaper a room, how much to tile a wall, how much to make a dress, and so on.

Example 12.14

An area 12 m by 4 m has to be painted. The instructions on the paint tin say that 1 litre should cover 8 m^2. If one litre of paint costs £2.25 what will it cost to paint the whole surface?

What is the area of the surface?

Area = length × breadth

$\quad\quad$ = 12 m × 4 m

$\quad\quad$ = 48 m^2.

1 litre of paint covers 8 m^2. How many tins of paint are needed?

Number of tins = $\dfrac{48 \text{ m}^2}{8 \text{ m}^2}$ = 6.

One tin costs £2.25,

6 tins cost 6 × £2.25 = £13.50.

Answer $\quad$ £13.50

Example 12.15

A garden 10 m × 6 m is to be grassed. Best lawn seed costs £2.40 for 500 g and the recommended sowing is 50 g (3 handfuls) per m^2.

Turf is £1 per m^2. Find the cost of making a lawn in each case.

Area of garden = length × breadth

$\quad\quad\quad\quad\quad\quad$ = 10 m × 6 m = 60 m^2.

Cost of turf at £1 per m^2 = £60.

Cost of using seed:

50 g cover 1 m^2.

To cover 60 m^2 needs 60 × 50 g of seed

$\quad\quad\quad\quad$ = 3000 g.

500 g cost £2.40.

3000 g will cost $\dfrac{\overset{6}{\cancel{3000}}}{\underset{1}{\cancel{500}}}$ × £2.40 = £14.40

Cost of using seed = £14.40.

Answer $\quad$ Cost of turf £60; cost of seed £14.40

Example 12.16

A kitchen 3 m x 4.5 m is to have quarry tiles on the floor. Each tile is 15 cm square. How many tiles are required?

Method 1

Find the area of the floor and divide by the area of each tile.

Area of floor = 3 m x 4.5 m

$\qquad$ = 300 cm x 450 cm

$\qquad$ = 135 000 cm² .

Area of one tile = 15 cm x 15 cm

$\qquad$ = 225 cm² .

Number of tiles required = $\dfrac{\text{area of floor}}{\text{area of 1 tile}}$ = $\dfrac{135\,000 \text{ cm}^2}{225 \text{ cm}^2}$ = 600.

Answer   600

Method 2

Find how many tiles are required on each side of the kitchen.

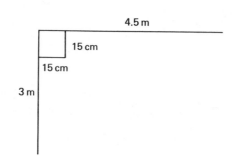

How many tiles (15 cm) are required to go along 4.5 m?

Answer = $\dfrac{4.5 \text{ m}}{15 \text{ cm}}$ = $\dfrac{450 \text{ cm}}{15 \text{ cm}}$ = 30.

How many tiles (15 cm) are required to go along 3 m?

Answer = $\dfrac{3 \text{ m}}{15 \text{ cm}}$ = $\dfrac{300 \text{ cm}}{15 \text{ cm}}$ = 20.

Number of tiles required = 30 x 20 = 600.
Answer   600

Sometimes it is easier to work on 'length runs' such as in floorboards or wallpaper.

Example 12.17

A wall is 4.68 m long by 2.20 m high. What length of wallpaper is needed to cover the wall if wallpaper is 52 cm wide?

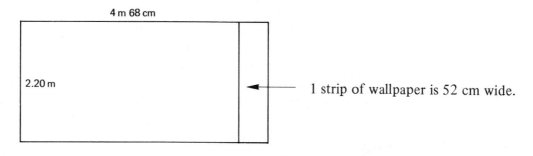

1 strip of wallpaper is 52 cm wide.

How many strips of wallpaper will cover 4.68 m?

Number of strips = $\dfrac{4.68 \text{ m}}{52 \text{ cm}}$ = $\dfrac{468 \text{ cm}}{52 \text{ cm}}$ = 9.

Each strip is 2.20 m long.

Therefore, 9 strips will be 9 × 2.20 m long = 19.80 m.

Length of wallpaper needed = 19.80 m.

Normally, of course, wallpaper is bought as a roll which is just over 10 m long. To cover the wall would need 2 rolls.

Answer   2 rolls

Example 12.18

A small bungalow is L-shaped with basic floor measurements as shown. How many floorboards 2.5 m × 12 cm are needed to cover the floor (assume no waste)? What is the cost if a floorboard is £1.35?

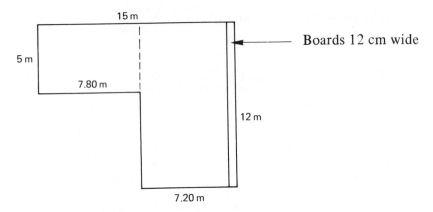

How many boards, side by side, will be needed to go across 7.20 m and then 7.80 m?

Number of boards, side by side, in 7.20 m = $\dfrac{7.20 \text{ m}}{12 \text{ cm}} = \dfrac{720 \text{ cm}}{12 \text{ cm}} = 60$.

Length of board required in 12 m side = 60 × 12 m = 720 m.

Number of boards, side by side, in 7.80 m = $\dfrac{7.80 \text{ m}}{12 \text{ cm}} = \dfrac{780 \text{ cm}}{12 \text{ cm}} = 65$.

Length of board required in 5 m side = 65 × 5 m = 325 m.

Total length of board required = 720 m + 325 m = 1045 m.

A floorboard is 2.5 m long.

Number of floorboards required = $\dfrac{1045 \text{ m}}{2.5 \text{ m}} = 418$.

Each board costs £1.35.

Total cost = £1.35 × 418

         = £564.30.

Answer   £564.30

In practice, there is waste and a certain percentage is added on to allow for waste.

Exercise 12.4

1 What length of carpet 300 cm wide is required to cover a floor 9 m × 9 m?
2 What is the cost of covering a floor 3 m × 2 m with carpet costing £7.95 per m² ?

3 A rectangular room 4 m × 3 m has a carpet $3\frac{1}{2}$ m × $2\frac{1}{2}$ m. What area is not carpeted?

4 Carpet tiles are to be laid to cover a rectangular room 9 ft by 12 ft. The tiles are 9 in square. How many tiles are needed?

5 A $2\frac{1}{2}$ litre can of paint costs £7.95 and should cover a surface area of 60 m². How much would it cost to cover a surface 45 m by 12 m?

6 What length of wallpaper is required to cover a wall 3 m 64 cm long by 2 m high if the wallpaper is 52 cm wide and is put on vertically?

7 Concrete flagstones are 3 ft by 2 ft and cost £2.95. What is the cost of flagging a patio which is 12 ft by 15 ft?

8 A roll of wallpaper is 10 m by 52 cm wide. How many rolls are required to wallpaper a room 5 m 20 cm square and 2 m high, if there is no waste and windows and doors are equivalent to one roll?

9 Glass, when cut to size, is charged at £4 per m². What is the cost of putting in a window 80 cm × 60 cm when the glass is cut to size?

10 Ranch type fencing is 15 cm wide and 2 cm thick and costs £2 per metre run. What is the cost of putting this type of fencing down one side of a garden 10 m long if three widths of fencing are to be used together with 8 supports costing £3.50 each?

12.8 Triangles

A triangle is a three-sided figure.

A triangle with two sides of equal length (or two equal angles) is called an isosceles triangle.

A triangle with three sides equal (or three equal angles) is called an equilateral triangle.

The three angles of any triangle add up to 180°.

12.9 Perimeter of Triangles

The perimeter is the distance round all the sides of the triangle.

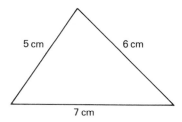

Perimeter = 5 cm + 6 cm + 7 cm = 18 cm.

12.10 Area of Triangles

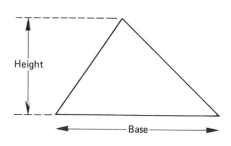

Let the base be the side drawn horizontally.

Height is the vertical height of the triangle.

$$\text{Area of triangle} = \frac{\text{base} \times \text{height}}{2};$$

$$A = \frac{b \times h}{2}.$$

Example 12.19

Find the area of a triangle of base 25 mm and perpendicular height 40 mm.

(Usually the word perpendicular is missed out.)

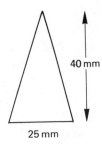

40 mm

25 mm

$$\text{Area} = \frac{\text{base} \times \text{height}}{2}$$

$$= \frac{25 \text{ mm} \times 40 \text{ mm}}{2}$$

$$= 500 \text{ mm}^2 .$$

Example 12.20

Find the area of a triangle of base 1 m 20 cm and height 40 cm. Before beginning the question make sure all measurements are in the same units.

	1 m 20 cm = 1.20 m;	40 cm = 0.40 m;
or	1 m 20 cm = 120 cm	40 cm = 40 cm.

$$\text{Area} = \frac{\text{base} \times \text{height}}{2} \qquad \text{or} \quad \text{Area} = \frac{\text{base} \times \text{height}}{2}$$

$$= \frac{1.20 \text{ m} \times 0.40 \text{ m}}{2} \qquad\qquad = \frac{120 \text{ cm} \times 40 \text{ cm}}{2}$$

$$= \frac{0.48 \text{ m}^2}{2} \qquad\qquad\qquad = \frac{4800 \text{ cm}^2}{2}$$

$$= 0.24 \text{ m}^2 . \qquad\qquad\qquad = 2400 \text{ cm}^2$$

Answer   0.24 m²   Answer   2400 cm²

Example 12.21

A triangle has an area of 120 cm². If the height is 20 cm how long is the base?

$$\text{Area} = \frac{\text{base} \times \text{height}}{2}$$

$$120 = \frac{\text{base} \times 20}{2}$$

$$120 = \text{base} \times 10$$

$$\frac{120}{10} = \text{base}$$

$$12 \text{ cm} = \text{base}.$$

Answer   12 cm

Exercise 12.5

1 Find the perimeter of a triangle whose sides are 9 cm, 7 cm and 6 cm.
2 Find the perimeter of a triangle whose sides are 6 cm 4 mm, 9.3 cm, and 11 cm 5 mm.

3 An isosceles triangle has a perimeter of 20 cm. If the length of one of the equal sides is 7 cm 4 mm, what is the length of the unequal side?

4 An equilateral triangle has a perimeter of 28 cm 8 mm. What is the length of one side?

5 Find the area of the following triangles:
   (a) base = 8 cm, height = 4 cm;   (b) base = 10 cm, height = 6 cm;
   (c) base = 14 mm, height = 8 mm;   (d) base = 7 m, height = 8 m.

6 Find the area of the following triangles:
   (a) base = 2 m 60 cm, height = 4 m; (b) base = 4 cm 8 mm, height = 2 cm;
   (c) base = 2 ft, height = 1 ft 6 in;   (d) base = 16 cm, height = 8 cm 4 mm.

7 Find the base or height measurement in the following triangles:
   (a) area = 112 cm², height = 16 cm;
   (b) area = 72 mm², height = 16 mm;
   (c) area = 45 m², height = 18 m;
   (d) area = 98 ft², base = 14 ft;
   (e) area = 216 cm², base = 12 cm;
   (f) area = 96.8 cm², base = 8.0 cm.

8 Find the area of the following figures. (*Hint:* Where a shape looks awkward split it up into triangles and rectangles.)

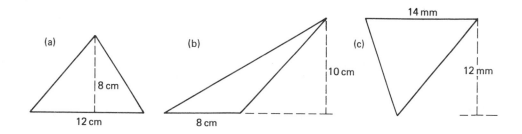

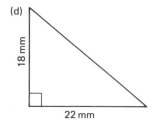

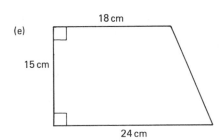

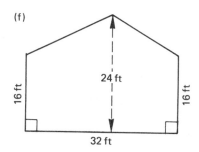

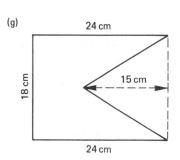

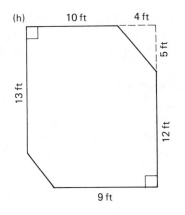

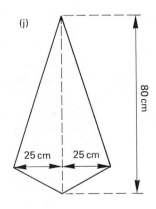

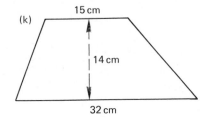

12.11 Circles

The most common terms in connection with a circle are as follows:

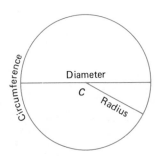

The circumference of the circle is the distance all the way round it, i.e. it is the perimeter.

The diameter is the distance from circumference to circumference through the centre of the circle, C.

The radius is the distance from the circumference to the centre.

Diameter = twice the radius: if D = diameter and R = radius then $D = 2 \times R = 2R$.

12.12 Circumference of Circles

Circumference = $\pi \times D$ or $\pi \times 2R$.

What is π? It is the number of times the diameter will divide into the circumference of a circle; no matter what the size of the circle the value is always the same. The value of π to be used will be given for any question. It is usually given as $\frac{22}{7}$ ($3\frac{1}{7}$) or as 3.14.

Example 12.22

Find the circumference of a circle whose diameter is 21 cm. (Take $\pi = \frac{22}{7}$.)

Circumference = $\pi \times$ diameter

$$= \frac{22}{\cancel{7}_1} \times \cancel{21}^3 \, cm$$

$$= 66 \, cm.$$

Example 12.23

Find the circumference of a circle of radius 4 cm. (Take $\pi = \frac{22}{7}$.)

Circumference = $\pi \times$ diameter (diameter = 2 $\times$ radius)

$$= \frac{22}{7} \times 2 \times 4 \, cm$$

$$= \frac{176}{7} \, cm$$

$$= 25\frac{1}{7} \, cm.$$

When you have written down the relationship between circumference and diameter often enough, it becomes a habit to write

$$C = \pi \times D \quad \text{or} \quad C = 2 \times \pi \times R.$$

Example 12.24

Find the circumference of a circle of radius $5\frac{1}{4}$ in. (Take $\pi = \frac{22}{7}$.)

$$C = 2 \times \pi \times R$$

$$= 2 \times \frac{22}{7} \times 5\frac{1}{4} \, in$$

$$= \cancel{2}^1 \times \frac{\cancel{22}^{11}}{\cancel{7}_1} \times \frac{\cancel{21}^3}{\cancel{4}_{\cancel{2}_1}} \, in$$

$$= 33 \, in.$$

Example 12.25

Find the circumference of a circle of diameter 80 cm. (Take $\pi = 3.14$.)

$$C = \pi \times D$$

$$= 3.14 \times 80 \, cm$$

$$= 251.2 \, cm.$$

Example 12.26

Find the diameter of a circle if the circumference is 99 cm. (Take $\pi = \frac{22}{7}$.)

$C = \pi \times D$.

Substitute the values given:

$$99 = \frac{22}{7} \times D$$

To remove fractions multiply both sides of the equation by 7:

$$99 \times 7 = \not{7}^{1} \times \frac{22}{\not{7}_{1}} \times D$$

$$693 = 22D.$$

To find D, now divide by 22:

$$\frac{\not{693}^{63}}{\not{22}_{2}} = D$$

$$31\tfrac{1}{2} \text{ cm} = D.$$

Example 12.27

Find the radius of a circle if the circumference is 132 cm. (Take $\pi = \frac{22}{7}$.)

$C = 2 \times \pi \times R$;

$$132 = 2 \times \frac{22}{7} \times R;$$

$7 \times 132 = 2 \times 22 \times R;$ (Multiplying both sides by 7.)

$$924 = 44R;$$

$$\frac{\not{924}^{84\,21}}{\not{44}_{\not{4}_{1}}} = R.$$

<u>Answer   21 cm</u>

Exercise 12.6

1 Find the circumference of the following circles (take $\pi = \frac{22}{7}$):
  (a) where diameter = 35 cm;   (b) diameter = 63 cm;
  (c) diameter = 42 in;   (d) diameter = 105 m.

2 Find the circumference of the following circles (take $\pi = \frac{22}{7}$):
  (a) where radius = 21 cm;   (b) radius = 7 ft;
  (c) radius = 28 m;   (d) radius = 49 cm.

3 Find the circumference of the following circles (take $\pi = \frac{22}{7}$):
  (a) where radius = 10 cm;   (b) radius = 16 cm;
  (c) diameter = 6 m;   (d) diameter = 2 ft.

4 Find the circumference of the following circles (take $\pi = 3.14$):
  (a) where diameter = 10 cm;   (b) diameter = 6 cm;
  (c) radius = 100 cm;   (d) radius = 4 cm.

5 Find the diameter of the following circles (take $\pi = \frac{22}{7}$):
  (a) where circumference = 66 in;   (b) circumference = 176 cm;
  (c) circumference = 220 cm;   (d) circumference = 242 mm.

6 Find the radius of the following circles (take $\pi = \frac{22}{7}$):
  (a) where circumference = 88 cm;   (b) circumference = 33 ft;
  (c) circumference = 121 cm;   (d) circumference = 440 mm.

7 A piece of wire is 22 cm long. It is bent to form a circle. What is the diameter of the circle ($\pi = \frac{22}{7}$)?

8 A piece of metal is a circle of diameter 21 cm. It is hammered into a square shape. What is the size of one side of the square ($\pi = \frac{22}{7}$)?

9 Find the perimeter of the following shape ($\pi = \frac{22}{7}$):

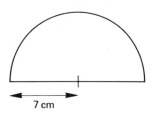

7 cm

10 Find the perimeter of the running track shown ($\pi = \frac{22}{7}$):

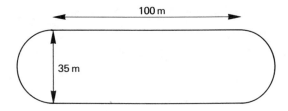

100 m

35 m

12.13 Area of Circles

The formula for calculating the area of a circle is $\pi \times R^2$.

π is the same symbol as used to find the circumference.

R^2 ('R squared') means $R \times R$; see section 11.11.

It will probably help your working out if you write down the meaning each time.

Example 12.28

Find the area of a circle whose radius is 14 cm. (Take $\pi = \frac{22}{7}$.)

Area of circle $= \pi R^2$

$$= \pi \times R \times R$$

$$= \frac{22}{7} \times 14 \times 14 \text{ cm}^2$$

$$= 616 \text{ cm}^2.$$

Answer   616 cm²

Note the units of area are square units.

Example 12.29

Find the area of a circle of radius 4 cm. (Take $\pi = \frac{22}{7}$.)

Area of circle $= \pi R^2$

$$= \pi \times R \times R$$

$$= \frac{22}{7} \times 4 \times 4 \text{ cm}^2$$

$$= \frac{352}{7} \text{ cm}^2$$

$$= 50\frac{2}{7} \text{ cm}^2.$$

Answer $50\frac{2}{7}$ cm².

Example 12.30

Find the area of a circle of diameter 20 cm. (Take $\pi = 3.14$.)

If the diameter is given then divide it by 2 in order to find the radius.

$D = 20; \ R = 10$.

Area of circle $= \pi R^2$

$$= \pi \times R \times R$$

$$= 3.14 \times 10 \times 10 \text{ cm}^2$$

$$= 3.14 \times 100 \text{ cm}^2$$

$$= 314 \text{ cm}^2.$$

Answer   314 cm²

Example 12.31

Find the area of the following shape, which is a semicircle ($\pi = \frac{22}{7}$).

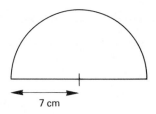

7 cm

First, find the area of the whole circle, then divide by 2 to find the area of the semicircle.

Area of circle $= \pi R^2$

$$= \pi \times R \times R$$

$$= \frac{22}{7} \times 7 \times 7 \text{ cm}^2$$

$$= 154 \text{ cm}^2.$$

This is the area of the whole circle, therefore,

Area of semicircle $= \dfrac{154}{2} = 77 \text{ cm}^2$.

Answer   77 cm²

Example 12.32

Find the area of the shape below. (Take $\pi = \frac{22}{7}$.)

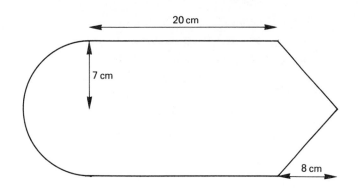

Split the shape into shapes you already know:

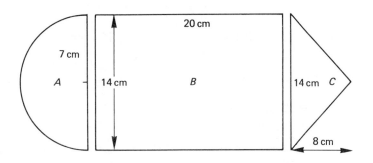

A is a semicircle, B a rectangle, C a triangle.

Area of triangle C $= \frac{1}{2}$ base × height

$= \frac{1}{2} \times 14 \times 8$ cm²

$= 56$ cm².

Area of rectangle B = length × breadth

$= 20 \times 14$ cm²

$= 280$ cm².

Area of semicircle A $= \frac{1}{2}$ area of whole circle

$= \frac{1}{2} \times \pi R^2$

$= \frac{1}{2} \times \pi \times R \times R$

$= \frac{1}{\cancel{2}_1} \times \frac{\cancel{22}^{11}}{\cancel{7}_1} \times \cancel{7}^1 \times 7$ cm²

$= 77$ cm².

Area of whole shape $= 56$ cm² $+ 280$ cm² $+ 77$ cm²

$= 413$ cm².

Answer   413 cm²

Example 12.33

Find the area of the shaded portion if it is 7 cm wide ($\pi = \frac{22}{7}$).

Treat the figure as 2 circles and take the area of the small circle away from the area of the large circle.

Area of small circle $= \pi R^2$

$$= \pi \times R \times R$$

$$= \frac{22}{\cancel{7}} \times 7 \times \cancel{7} \text{ cm}^2$$

$$= 154 \text{ cm}^2.$$

Area of large circle $= \pi R^2$

$$= \pi \times R \times R$$

$$= \frac{22}{\cancel{7}} \times 14 \times \cancel{14}^{2} \text{ cm}^2$$

$$= 616 \text{ cm}^2.$$

Area of shaded portion $= 616 - 154 \text{ cm}^2$

$$= 462 \text{ cm}^2.$$

Answer   462 cm²

Exercise 12.7

1 Find the area of the following circles (take $\pi = \frac{22}{7}$):
   (a) where radius $= 7$ cm;   (b) radius $= 21$ m;
   (c) radius $= 14$ in;   (d) radius $= 35$ m.
2 Find the area of the following circles (take $\pi = \frac{22}{7}$):
   (a) where diameter $= 4$ cm;   (b) diameter $= 10$ in;
   (c) diameter $= 21$ cm;   (d) diameter $= 7$ cm.
3 Find the area of the following circles (take $\pi = \frac{22}{7}$):
   (a) radius $= 3$ cm;   (b) radius $= 3\frac{1}{2}$ m;
   (c) diameter $= 5\frac{1}{4}$ cm;   (d) diameter $= 10\frac{1}{2}$ cm.
4 Find the area of the following circles (take $\pi = 3.14$)
   (a) radius $= 10$ m;   (b) radius $= 2$ m;
   (c) diameter $= 6$ cm;   (d) diameter $= 2$ m.
5 A circle has a circumference of 66 cm. What is its area? ($\pi = \frac{22}{7}$.)

Exercise 12.8

Find the areas of the figures given ($\pi = \frac{22}{7}$):

1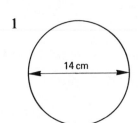

14 cm

2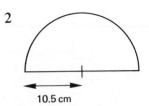

10.5 cm

3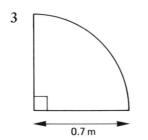

0.7 m

4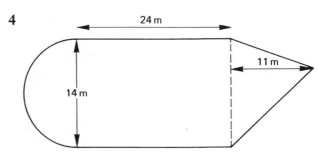

24 m

14 m

11 m

5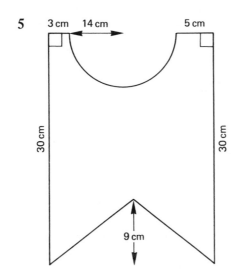

3 cm 14 cm 5 cm

30 cm 30 cm

9 cm

6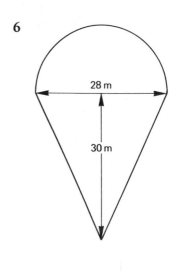

28 m

30 m

7 Find the area of the shaded part if it is 3.5 m wide.

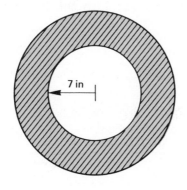

7 in

8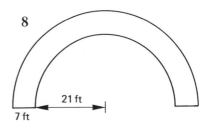

21 ft

7 ft

10 Find the area of the actual running track (shaded) if it is 7 m wide.

9 Find the area of the unshaded portion.

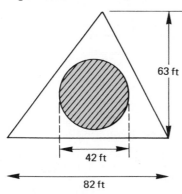

63 ft

42 ft

82 ft

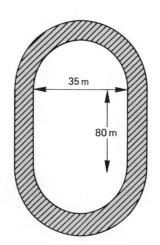

35 m

80 m

Exercise 12.9 (Where required take $\pi = \frac{22}{7}$.)

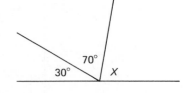

1 Is angle X equal to

    A 100°   **B** 80°   **C** 70°

    D 50°?

2 Using a protractor, angle ABC
   measures

    A 37°   **B** 53°   **C** 127°

    D 133°

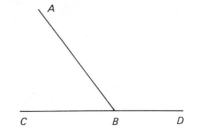

3 Is the bearing of an aircraft flying
   from X to Y

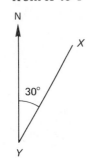

    A 030°   **B** 060°   **C** 150°   **D** 210°?

4 A rectangle has sides of 10 cm and 18 cm. Is the side of a square of equal
   perimeter

    A 7 cm   **B** 56 cm   **C** 14 cm   **D** 28 cm?

5 A rectangle of sides 8 cm and 12 cm has a piece cut away equivalent to 5 cm².
   Is the area left

    A 15 cm²   **B** 35 cm²   **C** 91 cm²   **D** 56 cm²?

6 Kitchen tiles 6 in by 6 in are laid on a floor 8 ft by 10 ft 6 in. The floor will
   need

    A 37 tiles   **B** 74 tiles   **C** 336 tiles   **D** 154 tiles.

7 A triangle has an area of 48 cm². The height is 8 cm. Is the base

    A 12 cm   **B** 6 cm   **C** 8 cm   **D** 10 cm?

8 The perimeter of a square is 32 cm. Is the area

    A 128 cm²   **B** 8 cm²   **C** 64 cm²   **D** 32 cm²?

9 A circle has a radius of 7 cm. Is the circumference

    A 49 cm   **B** 77 cm   **C** 44 cm   **D** 14 cm?

10 A circle has an area of 616 cm². Is the diameter

    A 14 cm   **B** 28 cm   **C** 24.8 cm   **D** 30 cm?

11 Is the area of the unshaded portion in the diagram

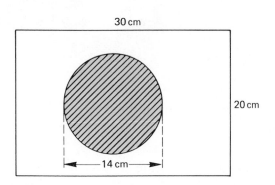

  A 600 cm² **B** 154 cm² **C** 446 cm² **D** 586 cm²?

12 A mosaic tile is 2 cm square and costs 5p. What is the cost to tile the floor of a cloakroom which is 2 m by 1 m 20 cm?

  A £30 **B** £120 **C** £150 **D** £300

13 Space Shapes

13.1 Volume

Volume is a measure of space taken up.

Space is taken up or occupied by houses, bricks, factories, footballs, buses, rivers, mountains, planets, and so on. All have a certain volume.

13.2 Measurement of Volume

Volume is measured in cubic units.

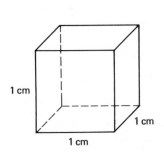

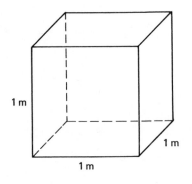

This would be 1 cubic cm (1 cm^3).   1 cubic metre (1 m^3).

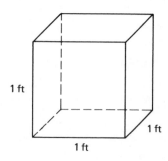

1 cubic ft (1 ft^3).

This book is concerned only with finding the volumes of regular shapes called right prisms.

13.3 Volumes of Right Prisms

A right prism has all its sides vertical to the base and they are all the same length.

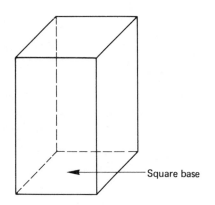

Square prism

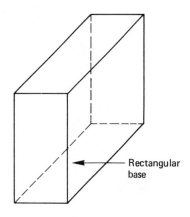

Rectangular prism

The two shapes above are often called cuboids or simply box shapes.

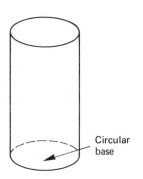

Circular prism
(cylinder)

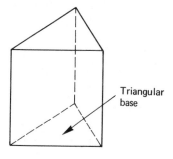

Triangular prism

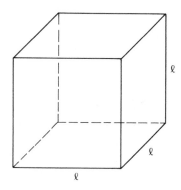

Cube

A cube is a square prism but its height is equal to the length of one of the sides of the base.

In every case of a right prism

volume = area of base × height.

All measurements must be in the same units.

Example 13.1

Find the volume of a small box 10 cm × 8 cm × 6 cm.

Get into the habit of drawing a diagram of what you think the box looks like.

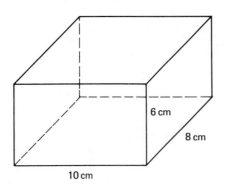

Volume = area of base × height.
Area of base = length × breadth
           = 10 cm × 8 cm
           = 80 cm².
Volume = area of base × height
       = 80 cm² × 6 cm
       = 480 cm³.
Answer   480 cm³

Example 13.2

Find the volume of a trinket box which measures 12 cm × 8 cm 5 mm × 6 cm 5 mm.

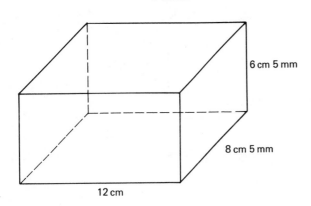

Measurements must be in the same units:
8 cm 5 mm = 8.5 cm;
6 cm 5 mm = 6.5 cm.
Volume = area of base × height
Area of base = length × breadth
           = 12 cm × 8.5 cm
           = 102 cm².
Volume = area of base × height
       = 102 cm² × 6.5 cm
       = 663 cm³.
Answer   663 cm³

Example 13.3

Find the volume of a cardboard box 3 ft × 2 ft 6 in by 1 ft 3 in.

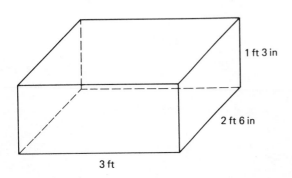

Measurements must be in the same units:
3 ft   = 36 in;
2 ft 6 in = 30 in;
1 ft 3 in = 15 in.
Volume = area of base × height.
Area of base = length × breadth
           = 36 in × 30 in
           = 1080 in².
Volume = area of base × height
       = 1080 in² × 15 in
       = 16 200 in³.
Answer   16 200 in³

Example 13.4

Find the volume of a circular prism (cylinder) of radius 7 cm and height 20 cm ($\pi = \frac{22}{7}$.)

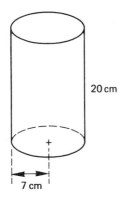

Volume = area of base × height.
Area of base $= \pi R^2$
$\qquad = \pi \times R \times R$
$\qquad = \frac{22}{7} \times 7 \text{ cm} \times 7 \text{ cm}$
$\qquad = 154 \text{ cm}^2$.
Volume = area of base × height
$\qquad = 154 \text{ cm}^2 \times 20 \text{ cm}$
$\qquad = 3080 \text{ cm}^3$.
Answer   3080 cm³

Example 13.5

Find the volume of a cylinder of radius 2 cm and height 10 cm ($\pi = 3.14$).

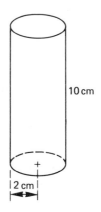

Volume = area of base × height.
Area of base $= \pi R^2$
$\qquad = \pi \times R \times R$
$\qquad = 3.14 \times 2 \text{ cm} \times 2 \text{ cm}$
$\qquad = 12.56 \text{ cm}^2$.
Volume = area of base × height
$\qquad = 12.56 \text{ cm}^2 \times 10 \text{ cm}$
$\qquad = 125.6 \text{ cm}^3$.
Answer   125.6 cm³

Example 13.6

Find the volume of the piece of steel shown:

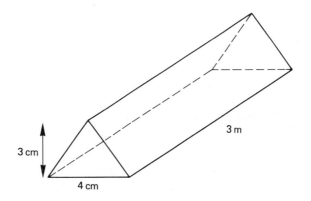

The sides do not go up vertically from the base but by standing it on the triangular side they will.

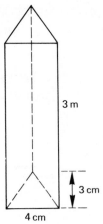

Volume = area of base × height.

$$\text{Area of base} = \frac{\text{length} \times \text{height}}{2}$$

$$= \frac{4 \text{ cm} \times 3 \text{ cm}}{2}.$$

$$= 6 \text{ cm}^2.$$

Volume = area of base × height

$$= 6 \text{ cm}^2 \times 3 \text{ m}$$

$$= 6 \text{ cm}^2 \times 300 \text{ cm}$$

$$= 1800 \text{ cm}^3.$$

Answer 1800 cm^3

Example 13.7

The method of example 13.6 can apply to any shape that has the same cross section along the whole length.

Find the volume of an angle iron having the following measurements:

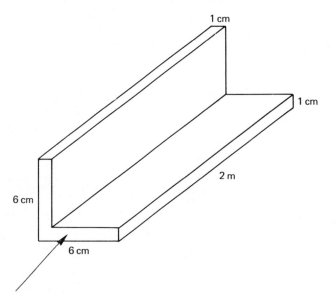

Use this as the base.

Volume = area of base × height.

Base is really two rectangles:

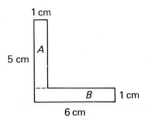

Area = area of A + area of B

$$= 1 \text{ cm} \times 5 \text{ cm} + 1 \text{ cm} \times 6 \text{ cm}$$

$$= 5 \text{ cm}^2 + 6 \text{ cm}^2$$

$$= 11 \text{ cm}^2.$$

Volume of angle iron = area of base × height

$$= 11 \text{ cm}^2 \times 2 \text{ m}$$

$$= 11 \text{ cm}^2 \times 200 \text{ cm}$$

$$= 2200 \text{ cm}^3.$$

Answer 2200 cm^3

Example 13.8

A swimming pool is 15 m long by 8 m wide. The shallow end is 1 m deep and it slopes gradually to the deep end which is 2 m deep. What volume of water does the pool hold?

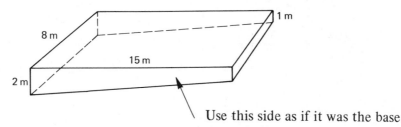

Use this side as if it was the base

Volume of the pool = area of side shown × width.

To calculate the area of the side split it into two simple shapes, a rectangle A and a triangle B:

Area of rectangle = length × breadth
$$= 15 \text{ m} \times 1 \text{ m}$$
$$= 15 \text{ m}^2.$$

Area of triangle $= \dfrac{\text{base} \times \text{height}}{2}$

$$= \dfrac{1 \text{ m} \times 15 \text{ m}}{2}$$

$$= 7\tfrac{1}{2} \text{ m}^2.$$

Total area of side $= 15 \text{ m}^2 + 7\tfrac{1}{2} \text{ m}^2$
$$= 22\tfrac{1}{2} \text{ m}^2.$$

Volume of pool = area of side × width
$$= 22\tfrac{1}{2} \text{ m}^2 \times 8 \text{ m}$$
$$= 180 \text{ m}^3.$$

Answer   180 m³

Example 13.9

A garden shed has a shape and measurements as shown. What is its volume?

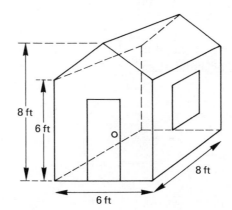

The front end of the shed continues in this shape throughout its length.
Volume of shed = area of end × length.
Area of end:

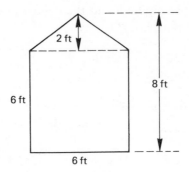

The shape consists of a rectangle and a triangle.

Area of end = 6 ft × 6 ft + $\dfrac{6 \text{ ft} \times 2 \text{ ft}}{2}$

$$= 36 \text{ ft}^2 + 6 \text{ ft}^2$$
$$= 42 \text{ ft}^2.$$

Volume of shed = area of end × length
$$= 42 \text{ ft}^2 \times 8 \text{ ft}$$
$$= 336 \text{ ft}^3.$$

Answer   336 ft³

Example 13.10

The same type of working applies to shapes such as pipes. A metal pipe has an internal diameter of 20 mm and an external diameter of 40 mm. Find the volume of metal in a pipe 3 m long ($\pi = 3.14$).

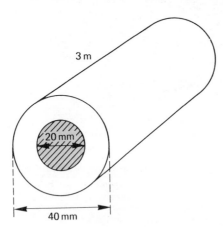

In this case find the area of metal at the end and then multiply by the length.

Volume of metal in pipe = area of metal at end × length.
Area of metal at end:

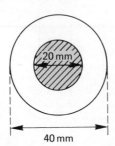

If $D = 20$ mm, $R = 10$ mm
$= 1$ cm.
$D = 40$ mm, $R = 20$ mm
$= 2$ cm.

To find the area of the end, unshaded part, first find the area of the outer circle and subtract from it the area of the inner circle.

Area of outer circle $= \pi R^2$
$$= \pi \times R \times R$$
$$= 3.14 \times 2 \text{ cm} \times 2 \text{ cm}$$
$$= 12.56 \text{ cm}^2.$$

Area of inner circle $= \pi R^2$
$$= 3.14 \times 1 \text{ cm} \times 1 \text{ cm}$$
$$= 3.14 \text{ cm}^2.$$

Area of end $= 12.56 \text{ cm}^2 - 3.14 \text{ cm}^2$
$$= 9.42 \text{ cm}^2.$$

Volume of metal in pipe $=$ area of end $\times$ length
$$= 9.42 \text{ cm}^2 \times 3 \text{ m}$$
$$= 9.42 \text{ cm}^2 \times 300 \text{ cm}$$
$$= 2826 \text{ cm}^3.$$

Answer   2826 cm³

13.4 Surface Area

Each of the prisms considered so far, whether solid or hollow, also has a surface area. It is this surface area which encloses the space, so giving a volume.

It will help to draw a diagram and then try and imagine what the object would look like if it was flattened out.

Example 13.11

A cube has a side of 5 cm. Find the total surface area of the cube.

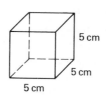

Imagine the cube to be cut open and then flattened.
It would look like this:

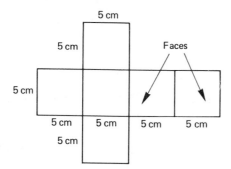

There are six faces altogether, all of equal size.

Area of one face $= 5 \text{ cm} \times 5 \text{ cm}$
$$= 25 \text{ cm}^2.$$

Total surface area $= 25 \text{ cm}^2 \times 6$
$$= 150 \text{ cm}^2.$$

Answer   150 cm²

13.5 Importance of Surface Area

Most containers for storage and packing are made from sheet cardboard, sheet wood, or sheet metal. These are used to make 'box' shapes, cylinder shapes, or pipe shapes and so buying the material in sheets enables a costing to be done for making a container.

In other words, costs are usually calculated from surface area and not volume.

Example 13.12

A house is heated by oil contained in a metal tank which is 2 m by 1.5 m by 1 m. The sheet metal from which the tank was made cost £10 per m². What was the cost of the metal needed to make the tank?

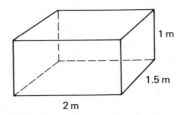

Without flattening it out you may be able to see that

the top and bottom will be of equal size
the two sides will be of equal size
and   the two ends will be of equal size.

Area of bottom = 2 m × 1.5 m = 3 m².
Area of top and bottom = 6 m².
Area of one side = 2 m × 1 m = 2 m².
Area of two sides = 4 m².
Area of one end = 1.5 m × 1 m = 1.5 m².
Area of two ends = 3 m².
Total surface area = 6 m² + 4 m² + 3 m²
$$= 13 \text{ m}^2.$$
Cost is £10 per m².
Cost of 13 m² = £10 × 13
= £130.

Answer   £130

Example 13.13

A large tin of Heinz baked beans is 110 mm tall and has a diameter of 74 mm. What area of sheet tin goes into the making of one tin? (Take π = 3.14.)

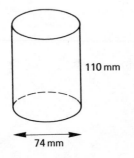

Imagine the two ends to be lifted up and the remaining part of the tin cut and then flattened.

It will look like this:

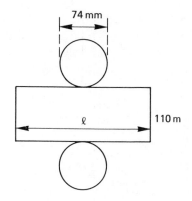

The flattened-out part of the tin will be the same length as the circumference of the top or bottom lid.

Area of top lid $= \pi R^2$

$\quad = 3.14 \times 3.7$ cm $\times 3.7$ cm

$\quad = 3.14 \times 13.69$ cm^2

$\quad = 42.99$ cm^2.

Area of bottom lid is also 42.99 cm^2.

Area of flattened metal $= \ell \times 11$ cm

$\quad = \pi D \times 11$ cm

$\quad = 3.14 \times 7.4$ cm $\times 11$ cm

$\quad = 255.60$ cm^2.

Total area $= 42.99$ cm^2 $+ 42.99$ cm^2 $+ 255.60$ cm^2

$\quad = 341.58$ cm^2.

Answer   341.58 cm^2 of sheet tin

Exercise 13.1

Find the volumes of the following shapes ($\pi = \frac{22}{7}$):

1
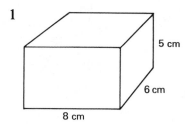

2
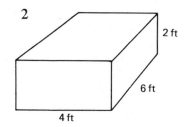

3
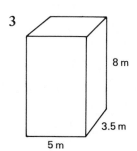

4
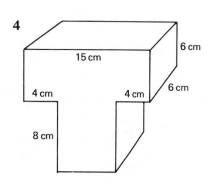

5

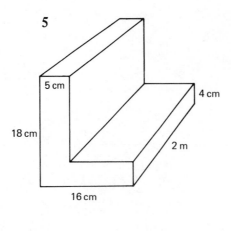

5 cm

4 cm

18 cm

2 m

16 cm

6

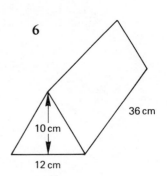

10 cm

36 cm

12 cm

7

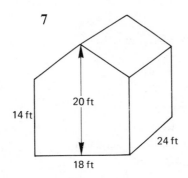

20 ft

14 ft

24 ft

18 ft

8

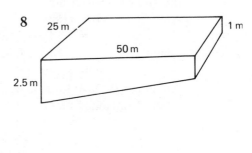

25 m

1 m

50 m

2.5 m

9

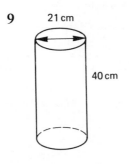

21 cm

40 cm

10

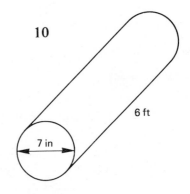

6 ft

7 in

11

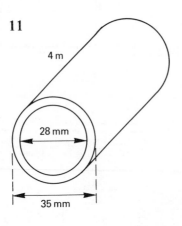

4 m

28 mm

35 mm

12

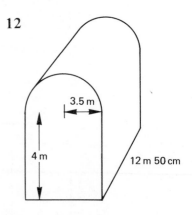

3.5 m

4 m

12 m 50 cm

208

13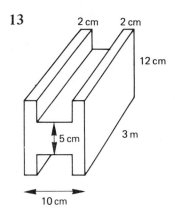

14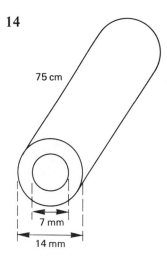

Exercise 13.2

1 Find the volume of a trinket box which measures 8 cm by 6 cm by 4 cm.
2 Find the volume of a cardboard box which measures 15 cm by 20 cm by 10 cm.
3 Find the volume of a water tank which has a base of 3 ft × 2 ft and is 1 ft 6 in high.
4 A rectangular prism has a base area of 12 cm². The volume of the prism is 132 cm³. What is the height of the prism?
5 A circular prism (cylinder) has a base area of 15 cm². What is its volume if it is 6 cm high?
6 A tent is in the form of a triangular prism. The rectangular base is 8 ft by 6 ft. If the height to the ridge is 5 ft what is the volume occupied by the tent?
7 Find the volume of a cylinder 10 cm high if the radius of the base is 7 cm. ($\pi = \frac{22}{7}$.)
8 Find the volume of a cylinder 8 cm high which has a diameter of 8 cm. ($\pi = 3.14$.)
9 A bar of gold is 30 cm × 10 cm × 6 cm. Find (a) its volume, (b) its weight in kg if each cm³ weighs 19 g.
10 Which has the bigger volume and by how much, a cylinder of diameter 7 cm and 7 cm high or a cube of side 7 cm? ($\pi = \frac{22}{7}$.)
11 Find the volume of a cube of side 3 cm.
12 A water tank is 3 ft × 3 ft by 2 ft high. How many gallons of water will it hold if 1 ft³ holds $6\frac{1}{4}$ gallons?
13 In 1985 it was estimated that 1 in of rain fell on the centre court at Wimbledon on one afternoon. If the court area is 120 ft by 60 ft what volume (ft³) of water fell on the court?
14 An oil tank, with top, is 2 m × 2 m × 1.5 m. What area of sheet metal was required to make the tank?
15 An oil tanker carries oil in a cylindrical tank. How much sheet metal is used to make the cylinder if it is 20 ft long and of diameter 7 ft? ($\pi = \frac{22}{7}$.)

Exercise 13.3

1 A cube has a side of length 4 cm. Is its volume

   A 16 cm³   **B** 12 cm³   **C** 64 cm³   **D** 96 cm³ ?

2 A box is 3 m by 4 m by 5 m. Is its volume

$\quad$ **A** $\quad 60\,\text{m}^3$ $\quad$ **B** $\quad 20\,\text{m}^3$ $\quad$ **C** $\quad 80\,\text{m}^3$ $\quad$ **D** $\quad 15\,\text{m}^3$?

3 A box is 30 cm by 20 cm by 3 m. Is its volume

$\quad$ **A** $\quad 1800\,\text{cm}^3$ $\quad$ **B** $\quad 1.8\,\text{m}^3$ $\quad$ **C** $\quad 18\,\text{m}^3$ $\quad$ **D** $\quad 180\,000\,\text{cm}^3$?

4 A cube has a volume of $27\,\text{cm}^3$. Is the length of one side

$\quad$ **A** $\quad 9\,\text{cm}$ $\quad$ **B** $\quad 2.5\,\text{cm}$ $\quad$ **C** $\quad 3\,\text{cm}$ $\quad$ **D** $\quad 13.5\,\text{cm}$?

5 A child's building cube has a side of 3 cm. How many will go into a box measuring 18 cm x 12 cm x 9 cm?

$\quad$ **A** $\quad 648$ $\quad$ **B** $\quad 216$ $\quad$ **C** $\quad 48$ $\quad$ **D** $\quad 72$

6 A cylinder has a volume of $200\,\text{cm}^3$. The circular base has an area of $40\,\text{cm}^2$. Is the height

$\quad$ **A** $\quad 5\,\text{cm}$ $\quad$ **B** $\quad 8000\,\text{cm}$ $\quad$ **C** $\quad 0.5\,\text{cm}$ $\quad$ **D** $\quad 10\,\text{cm}$?

7 Lead weighs 11 g for every cm^3. What is the weight of a lead ingot 20 cm x 15 cm x 5 cm?

$\quad$ **A** $\quad 2\,\text{kg}$ $\quad$ **B** $\quad 16.5\,\text{kg}$ $\quad$ **C** $\quad 10\,\text{kg}$ $\quad$ **D** $\quad 1.65\,\text{kg}$

8 A cornflake packet measures 32 cm x 22 cm x 7 cm. How many can be packed into a cardboard box which measures 70 cm x 66 cm x 64 cm?

$\quad$ **A** $\quad 36$ $\quad$ **B** $\quad 60$ $\quad$ **C** $\quad 42$ $\quad$ **D** $\quad 40$

9 A cylindrical tin has a height of 20 cm and a diameter of 14 cm. How much sheet tin is needed to make one such tin? ($\pi = \frac{22}{7}$.)

$\quad$ **A** $\quad 1188\,\text{cm}^2$ $\quad$ **B** $\quad 280\,\text{cm}^2$ $\quad$ **C** $\quad 2968\,\text{cm}^2$ $\quad$ **D** $\quad 3080\,\text{cm}^2$?

10 A tent is in the shape of a triangular prism. The floor is 2 m by 1 m and the height to the ridge is 1.5 m. What volume does the tent occupy?

$\quad$ **A** $\quad 3\,\text{m}^3$ $\quad$ **B** $\quad 0.5\,\text{m}^3$ $\quad$ **C** $\quad 1.5\,\text{m}^3$ $\quad$ **D** $\quad 2\,\text{m}^3$

11 A water tank in the roof space of a house is 2 m x 1.5 m x 1.5 m. If $1\,\text{cm}^3$ of water weighs 1 g, what weight of water is in a full tank?

$\quad$ **A** $\quad 45\,\text{kg}$ $\quad$ **B** $\quad 450\,\text{kg}$ $\quad$ **C** $\quad 4500\,\text{kg}$ $\quad$ **D** $\quad 45\,000\,\text{kg}$

12 Cylindrical tins 8 cm in diameter and 10 cm high are packed into a box which is 30 cm x 24 cm x 24 cm. How many tins can be packed in the box?

$\quad$ **A** $\quad 25$ $\quad$ **B** $\quad 27$ $\quad$ **C** $\quad 30$ $\quad$ **D** $\quad 24$

14 Electronic Calculators

14.1 Introduction

The diagram (Fig. 14.1) shows the figures and symbols that are likely to be on a simple, cheap, electronic calculator.

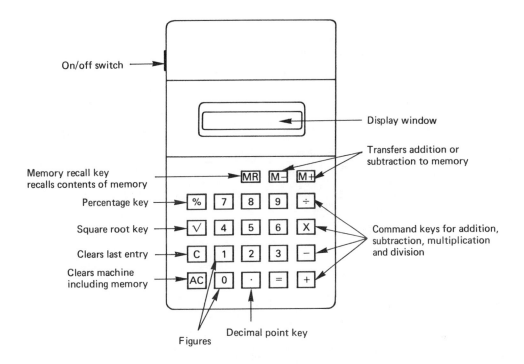

Figure 14.1   A simple, cheap electronic calculator, the Casio HL 805

Check how your calculator face differs from this. Read the instructions which were given with your calculator and make yourself familiar with what it can do.

What happens when you switch on? 0. appears, that is nought followed by a decimal point.

What happens when you press the figure 6? 6. appears in the display window.

When you press 6 and 4? 64. appears.

When you press 6 and then 4 and then 2 and then 5? 6425. appears.

When you press 6, then decimal point key, then 5? 6.5 appears.

When you press 6, then decimal point key, then 0, then 4? 6.04 appears.

14.2 Use of a Calculator

A calculator will do what you tell it to do – it will not think for you, you have to do the thinking; but it will do calculations in a fraction of the time that you normally take.

Switch on. Check that '0.' appears in the display window.
Remember to CLEAR the calculator before beginning a new calculation.

Note: All calculations and operations in this chapter are done on the Casio HL 805, unless stated otherwise.

14.3 Addition

Example 14.1

38 + 19.

Press key 3, then 8, then $\boxed{+}$ then 1, then 9.
Press $\boxed{=}$ key.
Answer   57   Easy!

Get into the habit of looking in the display window after each number or operation so that you see you have recorded the correct figure or instruction. Any mistake is yours; the calculator does not make mistakes.

Example 14.2

302 + 87 + 194.

Press key 3, then 0, then 2, then $\boxed{+}$, then 8, then 7, then $\boxed{+}$, then 1, then 9, then 4. Press $\boxed{=}$ key.
Answer   583

Example 14.3

Add 27.2, 48.6, 3.54, 5.09 and 16.9.

Press keys 27 $\boxed{\cdot}$ 2, then $\boxed{+}$, then 48 $\boxed{\cdot}$ 6, then $\boxed{+}$, then 3 $\boxed{\cdot}$ 54, then $\boxed{+}$, then 5 $\boxed{\cdot}$ 09, then $\boxed{+}$, then 16 $\boxed{\cdot}$ 9. Press $\boxed{=}$ key.
Answer   101.33

Example 14.4

A motorist finds that his car in one year has cost £1309.60 in petrol and oil, £642.38 in repairs, £324.84 in insurance, £110 in tax, and £38.50 for an AA fee. How much does he spend on the car?

Total cost = £1309.60 + £642.38 + £324.84 + £110 + £38.50.
Using a calculator,
1309 $\boxed{\cdot}$ 60 $\boxed{+}$ 642 $\boxed{\cdot}$ 38 $\boxed{+}$ 324 $\boxed{\cdot}$ 84 $\boxed{+}$ 110 $\boxed{\cdot}$ $\boxed{+}$ 38 $\boxed{\cdot}$ 50 $\boxed{=}$ 2425.32.
Answer   £2425.32

Exercise 14.1

Use a calculator to do the following additions:
1 76 + 39   2 247 + 68   3 152 + 64 + 207
4 643 + 38 + 55 + 401   5 6251 + 320 + 809 + 3604

212

6	429	**7**	5739	**8**	47.24 + 38.6
	3806		904		
	87		1056		
	+ 524		+ 295		

9 729.6 + 30.7 + 124.38   **10** 875.42 + 10.05 + 482.21

11   47.08
        304.29
         56.13
         80.06
        +504.26

12 A motorist travels 218.7 miles, 85.4 miles, 150.8 miles, 25.2 miles, and 238.4 miles on successive days. What mileage has he covered in five days?

13 On the Saturday before Christmas a person spent £19.62, £2.46, 65p, £8.09, £2.47 and 92p on presents. What was the total cost of the presents?

14 A batsman scored 85, 26, 39, 7, 16, 124, 63 and 46 in successive innings. How many runs did he score?

14.4 Subtraction

This is carried out as commanded in the question.

Example 14.5

2734 − 1857.

Press keys 2734, then $\boxed{-}$, then 1857. Press $\boxed{=}$ key.

Answer   877

Example 14.6

924 − 85 − 293.

924 $\boxed{-}$ 85 $\boxed{-}$ 293 $\boxed{=}$ 546.

Answer   546

Example 14.7

100 − 28.7 − 30.65.

100 $\boxed{-}$ 28 $\boxed{\cdot}$ 7 $\boxed{-}$ 30 $\boxed{\cdot}$ 65 $\boxed{=}$ 40.65.

Answer   40.65

Example 14.8

− 32 − 56 − 94.

$\boxed{-}$ 32 $\boxed{-}$ 56 $\boxed{-}$ 94 $\boxed{=}$ −182.

Answer   −182

14.5   Addition and Subtraction

This can be done by the calculator in one operation, provided you press the $\boxed{+}$ key or $\boxed{-}$ key as directed.

Example 14.9

$46 - 296 + 385 - 15.$

$46 \boxed{-} 296 \boxed{+} 385 \boxed{-} 15 \boxed{=} 120.$

Answer   120

Example 14.10

$35.6 + 7.08 - 8.29 - 15.74.$

$35 \boxed{\cdot} 6 \boxed{+} 7 \boxed{\cdot} 08 \boxed{-} 8 \boxed{\cdot} 29 \boxed{-} 15 \boxed{\cdot} 74 \boxed{=} 18.65.$

Answer   18.65

Exercise 14.2

1 $324 - 86$	**2** $904 - 386$	**3** $5204 - 783$	**4** $1005 - 749$
5 $24 - 326$	**6** $105 - 464$	**7** $35.26 - 15.3 - 9.68$	
8 $152 - 18.24 - 96.53$		**9** $- 2.7 - 5.6 - 8.4$	
10 $293 - 47 - 68 - 136.4$		**11** $18.74 - 25.8 + 15.07$	
12 $- 36.9 - 18.4 + 75.26$		**13** $200.39 - 18.642 + 7.3 - 108.4$	
14 $3.716 - 36.24 - 25.14 + 100$		**15** $- 63.2 - 4.07 - 82.61 + 300$	

16 $290.65 - 17.24 - 115.08 - 9.263 + 14.309$

17 $0.426 + 2.51 - 0.039 - 0.146$

18 $768.4 - 29.138 - 275.6 + 0.931$

19 $- 0.04 + 0.003 - 16.251 + 35.0$

20 $1524 + 958.2 + 11.06 - 1246 - 38.03$

14.6   Multiplication

Simply press the appropriate command keys.

Example 14.11

$24 \times 47.$

Press keys 24, then $\boxed{\times}$, then 47. Press $\boxed{=}$ key.

Answer   1128

Example 14.12

$134 \times 86.$

$134 \boxed{\times} 86 \boxed{=} 11524.$

Answer   11 524

Example 14.13

57.6×138.2

57 $\boxed{\cdot}$ 6 $\boxed{\times}$ 138 $\boxed{\cdot}$ 2 $\boxed{=}$ 7960.32.
Answer   7960.32

Example 14.14

$42.7 \times 581.6 \times 65.1.$

42 $\boxed{\cdot}$ 7 $\boxed{\times}$ 581 $\boxed{\cdot}$ 6 $\boxed{\times}$ 65 $\boxed{\cdot}$ 1 $\boxed{=}$ 1 616 714.2.
Answer   1 616 714.2

The calculator can only show 8 figures so if the answer contains more than 8 figures, and example 14.14 should contain 10 figures, then the calculator will only show the first 8 significant figures. Any figures after the eighth are 'lost'.

For multiplication of large numbers, where is the decimal point? This is crucial. If the number of *figures before the decimal point* exceeds 8 then most calculators will show an 'E' in the display window.

Example 14.15

$568 \times 568 \times 568.$

568 $\boxed{\times}$ 568 $\boxed{\times}$ 568 $\boxed{=}$ 1.832 504 3 E.
Obviously, the three numbers multiplied together give an answer greater than 1.8.
   What is the answer?
   The answer is found by moving the decimal point 8 places to the right from that shown in the display window.
   True value of 1.8325043 E is 183 250 430.

Example 14.16

$1584 \times 592 \times 403.$

1584 $\boxed{\times}$ 592 $\boxed{\times}$ 403 $\boxed{=}$ 3.779 043 8 E.
'E' occurs in the display window and so to get the true value of the multiplcation sum move the decimal point 8 places to the right.
Answer   377 904 380

Example 14.17

Repeat the question above: $1584 \times 592 \times 403.$
   Now try and multiply or divide by any other number. What happens? Nothing.
   When an 'E' is shown in the display window the calculator will not perform any other function until this 'E' has been cleared.
   Press C (or CE on some calculators) and 'E' disappears. Further calculations can continue *but remember* that the decimal point has to be moved 8 places to the right.

Example 14.18

83 742 × 4691 × 6.43.

83742 ⊠ 4691 ⊠ ... When the second multiplication command is pressed
the 'E' appears.

   Clear 'E' by pressing C (or CE on some calculators) and then multiply by 6.43.
The operation now becomes
83 742 ⊠ 4691 ⊠ **C** ⊠ 6 ⌑ 43 ▣ 25.259 208
Remember the *true position* of the decimal point.
Answer   2 525 920 800

Exercise 14.3

Use your calculator to find
  1 37 × 52   2 8.7 × 5.9   3 25.6 × 18.25
  4 0.867 × 528.1   5 33 × 58.4 × 5.9   6 0.32 × 5.07   7 2974 × 375
  8 26.95 × 808.4   9 624 × 87 × 49.07 10 0.297 × 5.86 × 2.035
 11 374 × 40.06   12 3.92 × 0.004 × 8.426
 13 94.62 × 147.1   14 2.401 × 15.6 × 96.7
 15 56 285 × 6283   16 9428 × 87 × 250
 17 12 683 × 9041   18 2489.7 × 8764.8
 19 38 925 × 4760 × 63   20 98 631 × 7285 × 94
 21 43 797 × 23 850   22 356 × 274 × 132 × 46
 23 82.581 × 7.295   24 176.25 × 9.408
 25 243.041 × 817.57   26 9183 × 75.6 × 29.7
 27 35.082 × 8.58 × 27.28   28 90 507 × 4075 × 36
 29 123 492 × 748.6 × 728.4.
 30 Out of the 29 previous questions, how many are correct answers and how
     many are approximate answers?

14.7   Division

Simply press the appropriate command keys.

Example 14.19

12 312 ÷ 27.

Press keys 12 312, then ÷ , then 27. Press ▣ key.
Answer   456

Example 14.20

53 118 ÷ 78.

53118 ÷ 78 ▣ 681.
Answer   681

Example 14.21

295.1289 ÷ 5.23.

295 $\boxed{\cdot}$ 1289 $\boxed{÷}$ 5 $\boxed{\cdot}$ 23 $\boxed{=}$ 56.43.

Answer   56.43

Example 14.22

387.6 ÷ 27.

387 $\boxed{\cdot}$ 6 $\boxed{÷}$ 27 $\boxed{=}$ 14.355 555.

The question, in this case, would probably ask for the answer to be given to two decimal places or correct to two decimal places.

Answer to 2 decimal places   14.35

Answer correct to 2 decimal places   14.36

Exercise 14.4

1 11 101 ÷ 17	**2** 2254 ÷ 23	**3** 2278 ÷ 34	**4** 17225 ÷ 53
5 10 201 ÷ 101	**6** 27 927 ÷ 87	**7** 106.26 ÷ 4.6	**8** 262.8 ÷ 7.2
9 164.8681 ÷ 2.41	**10** 981.24 ÷ 15.6	**11** 6944.64 ÷ 9.6	
12 3395.52 ÷ 52.4			

Exercise 14.5

Give answers correct to two decimal places.

1 62 ÷ 13	**2** 97 ÷ 8	**3** 156 ÷ 11.4	**4** 297 ÷ 33.3
5 0.87 ÷ 3.6	**6** 18.07 ÷ 11.74	**7** 324.1 ÷ 0.76	**8** 0.903 ÷ 0.46
9 20.02 ÷ 37.8	**10** 3689.4 ÷ 2.91	**11** 0.851 ÷ 4.66	**12** 32.4 ÷ 0.058
13 7348.7 ÷ 93.51	**14** 100 ÷ 15.72	**15** 0.058 ÷ 1.75	
16 0.008 31 ÷ 0.000 51		**17** 36 182 ÷ 73.68	**18** 9 ÷ 46.45
19 38.1 ÷ 127.07		**20** 5207 ÷ 100.8	

14.8   Mixed Operations

The calculator will only do what you tell it to do and so in questions involving more than one different operation you have to know what is meant by the arithmetical part of the question.

Example 14.23

3 + 8 × 4.

If you cannot remember how to work this out look at section 1.7 on priorities. The answer is 35. (3 has to be added to 8 × 4.)

Put this question on the calculator, *as it stands*, and you would have

3 $\boxed{+}$ 8 $\boxed{×}$ 4 $\boxed{=}$ 44.

The calculator adds 3 to 8 and then multiplies the result by 4.

Priorities of an arithmetical calculation are brackets, multiplication and division, addition and subtraction, in that order.

Example 14.23 can be done on the calculator as follows:

8 $\boxed{\times}$ 4 $\boxed{+}$ 3 $\boxed{=}$ 35.

Look carefully to see what must be done first.

Example 14.24

$54 + 16 \div 4 - 32.$

Division is first, and then the rest on the calculator:
$16 \div 4 + 54 - 32.$
(No sign in front of 54 implies it is +.)
16 $\boxed{\div}$ 4 $\boxed{+}$ 54 $\boxed{-}$ 32 $\boxed{=}$ 26

Example 14.25

$(11 + 7) \div 4.$

Brackets are first, with the result divided by 4.
11 $\boxed{+}$ 7 $\boxed{\div}$ 4 $\boxed{=}$ 4.5

Example 14.26

$86 - 32 \div 8 - 24.$

Division first but note − sign in front of 32.
$\boxed{-}$ 32 $\boxed{\div}$ 8 $\boxed{+}$ 86 $\boxed{-}$ 24 $\boxed{=}$ 58

Example 14.27

$$\frac{48.2 \times 39.7}{24.92}.$$

The line means divide:
48 $\boxed{\cdot}$ 2 $\boxed{\times}$ 39 $\boxed{\cdot}$ 7 $\boxed{\div}$ 24 $\boxed{\cdot}$ 92 $\boxed{=}$ 76.78.

Example 14.28

$$\frac{18.96 \times 7.65}{3.06 \times 23.87}.$$

Try this question without further reading. What is your answer? 1131.438? Wrong.

The question asks, what is the result of multiplying 18.96 by 7.65 and then dividing by 3.06 and then by 23.87.

The calculation is
18 $\boxed{\cdot}$ 96 $\boxed{\times}$ 7 $\boxed{\cdot}$ 65 $\boxed{\div}$ 3 $\boxed{\cdot}$ 06 $\boxed{\div}$ 23 $\boxed{\cdot}$ 87 $\boxed{=}$ 1.99

Think what the question is asking before using the calculator.

Give answers correct to two decimal places.

1 $38 \div 8 + 15$ 2 $15 + 8 \div 15$ 3 $(14 + 6) \div 6$

4 $35 + 26 \div 2 - 10$ 5 $54 \div 8 + 9$ 6 $17.5 + 13.4 \div 6 + 12$

7 $(11 - 7.16) \div 14.3$ 8 $27.9 + (15.2 \times 3.7)$

9 $\dfrac{15}{9}$ 10 $\dfrac{18.34}{4.04}$ 11 $\dfrac{25.02 - 13.87}{15.29}$

12 $\dfrac{94.03 \times 0.52}{65.81}$ 13 $\dfrac{48.06 \times 3.27}{0.061}$ 14 $38 - 17.4 \div 6 + 12.06$

15 $\dfrac{29.25 \div 7}{15.25}$ 16 $\dfrac{71.3 \times 0.571}{465 \times 0.025}$ 17 $\dfrac{116.08}{5.217 \times 15.06}$

18 $\dfrac{241.5 + 73.9}{105.4}$ 19 $\dfrac{124 \times 18.71}{0.52 \times 1584}$ 20 $\dfrac{2.07 \times 18.32}{5.65 \times 0.021 \times 17.14}$

14.9   Use of Memory

Electronic calculators have a memory facility, indicated by the keys $\boxed{\text{MR}}$, $\boxed{\text{M+}}$ and $\boxed{\text{M}-}$.

The $\boxed{\text{M+}}$ key transfers the number displayed to the memory and *automatically adds it* into the memory.

The $\boxed{\text{M}-}$ key transfers the number displayed to the memory and *automatically subtracts it* from the memory.

When a number is stored in the memory an 'M' sign appears in the display window to remind you that you are using the memory facility.

The $\boxed{\text{MR}}$ key recalls the result of everything that has gone into the memory.

Read the instructions supplied with your calculator about clearing the calculator *before* a memory calculation. In Fig. 14.1 it is AC for this particular calculator. On others it may be CE or you may have to switch off.

Example 14.29

$3 \times 12 + 7 \times 9$.

$\boxed{\text{AC}}$ 3 $\boxed{\times}$ 12 $\boxed{\text{M+}}$ (36)

       7 $\boxed{\times}$ 9 $\boxed{\text{M+}}$ (63)

$\boxed{\text{MR}}$ 99

Answer   99

$\boxed{\text{AC}}$ makes sure the calculator is completely clear before beginning a memory calculation.

Example 14.30

$(15.6 \times 2.34) + 10 \div 4.2$.

$\boxed{\text{AC}}$ 15 $\boxed{\cdot}$ 6 $\boxed{\times}$ 2 $\boxed{\cdot}$ 34 $\boxed{\text{M+}}$ (36.504)

       10 $\boxed{\div}$ 4 $\boxed{\cdot}$ 2 $\boxed{\text{M+}}$ (2.380 952 3)

$\boxed{\text{MR}}$ 38.884 952.

Answer   38.88 correct to two decimal places

Example 14.31

$$(13.2 \times 0.64) - (2.69 \div 1.25).$$

| AC | 13 | · | 2 | × | 0 | · | 64 | M+ | (8.448)

2 · 69 ÷ 1 · 25 M−   (2.152)

MR 6.296.

Answer   6.296

Example 14.32

Find the total cost of 2 lb of bacon at 132p a lb, 3 loaves at 26p a loaf, 3 pkts of cornflakes at 81p a pkt, and 6 oranges at 8p each.

AC 2 × 132 M+
3 × 26 M+
3 × 81 M+
6 × 8 M+
MR 633.

The display shows 633, all calculations were done in pence, so the answer is 633p, or £6.33.

Answer   £6.33

Example 14.33

$$\frac{7.32 \times 15.6 - 3.25 \times 14.28}{4.68}$$

AC 7 · 32 × 15 · 6 M+
3 · 25 × 14 · 28 M−
MR ÷ 4 · 68 = 14.48.

Answer   14.48

Example 14.34

Sometimes, even using the memory, you have to write a number on a piece of paper before you can complete the calculation. For example:

$$\frac{(15.6 \times 2.42) + (3.25 \times 6.54)}{27.08 - 19.71}$$

The result of the *bottom line* needs to be written on a piece of paper.
27 · 08 − 19 · 71 = 7.37   Remember this figure.
15 · 6 × 2 · 42 M+
3 · 25 × 6 · 54 M+
MR ÷ 7 · 37 = 8.00

Answer   8.00

Or:
15 · 6 × 2 · 42 M+
3 · 25 × 6 · 54 M+
Now do the bottom line:
27 · 08 − 19 · 71 = 7.37
Write 7.37 on a piece of paper.
Bring back the memory MR and ÷ 7.37:
MR ÷ 7 · 37 = 8.00.

Answer   8.00

Exercise 14.7

Use a calculator to find the answer to the following questions (correct to two decimal places):

1 $(15 \times 9) + (27 \times 16)$
2 $(42 \times 65) - (16 \times 32)$
3 $(7.96 \times 3.03) + (0.29 \times 5.06)$
4 $(18.91 \div 2.34) - (75.61 \div 62.4)$
5 $7 \times 9 + 15 \times 7 + 32 \times 5.6$
6 $15.3 \times 27.1 + 9.6 \times 3.4 - 18.7 \times 13.51$
7 $29.2 + 13 \times 5.07 + 2.03 \times 5$
8 $72 - 12 \times 3.51 + 9 \times 2.06$
9 $17 \div 8 + 9 \times 15 + 31 \div 4$
10 $\dfrac{17.25 \times 19.1 + 11.2 \times 9.6}{25.9}$
11 $\dfrac{31.7 \times 0.82 - 3.51 \times 5.06}{9.65}$
12 $\dfrac{19.1 \div 0.27 \times 25.2}{10.4 - 3.27}$

14.10 Using a Constant

There are times when we want to use the same constant number continuously, say π, for a series of multiplications, additions etc.

When a number is set up as a constant a 'K' sign may appear in the display window; again, look at the instructions for the calculator.

The following examples are of the use of a constant on a Casio HL 805.

Example 14.35

Multiply the following numbers by 3.14:
6, 8, 11, 14.6, 15.2.

Key as follows:

3 $\boxed{\cdot}$ 14 $\boxed{\times}$ $\boxed{\times}$ 6 $\boxed{=}$ 18.84
8 $\boxed{=}$ 25.12
11 $\boxed{=}$ 34.54
14 $\boxed{\cdot}$ 6 $\boxed{=}$ 45.844
15 $\boxed{\cdot}$ 2 $\boxed{=}$ 47.728

Note: The double command $\boxed{\times}$ $\boxed{\times}$ keys in the constant 3.14.

Example 14.36

Divide the following numbers by 3.14:
14, 21, 30, 45.

3 $\boxed{\cdot}$ 14 $\boxed{\div}$ $\boxed{\div}$ 14 $\boxed{=}$ 4.46
21 $\boxed{=}$ 6.69
30 $\boxed{=}$ 9.55
45 $\boxed{=}$ 14.33

Figures are correct to two decimal places.

Example 14.37

Add 19.07 to the following numbers:
5.62, 9.42, 13.07, 18.25.

The constant is 19.07.

19 · 07 + + 5 · 62 = 24.69
9 · 42 = 28.49
13 · 07 = 32.14
18 · 25 = 37.32

If you want to keep multiplying (or dividing or adding or subtracting) the same constant by itself, just keep pressing = key.

Example 14.38

Multiply 7 x 7 and so on.

7 × × 7 = 49
= 343   (7 x 7 x 7)
= 2401   (7 x 7 x 7 x 7)
= 16 807   (7 x 7 x 7 x 7 x 7)

Example 14.39

From 200 keep taking 13.625.

The constant is 13.625:

13 · 625 − − 200 = 186.375
= 172.75
= 159.125
= 145.5

Some calculators (for example, the Texet Senator) require the command function to be pressed once only and then the = key continuously without any other command.

Example 14.40

Multiply 3.14 by 5, 6, 7, 8.

3 · 14 × 5 = 15.7
6 = 18.84
7 = 21.98
8 = 25.12

Notice the command position for division.

Example 14.41

Divide the following numbers by 3:
9, 18, 63, 96

$$9 \boxed{\div} \; 3 \boxed{=} \; 3$$
$$18 \boxed{=} \; 6$$
$$63 \boxed{=} \; 21$$
$$96 \boxed{=} \; 32$$

Exercise 14.8

1 Add 15.65 to the following numbers:
   (a) 19.27   (b) 26.94   (c) 3.76   (d) 152.08
   (e) 78.97   (f) 30.03   (g) 68.74   (h) 105.68

2 Subtract 9.057 from the following numbers:
   (a) 20   (b) 52.3   (c) 13.65   (d) 47.287
   (e) 65.32   (f) 92.352   (g) 30.04   (h) 172.191

3 Multiply the following numbers by 3.142:
   (a) 8   (b) 15   (c) 36   (d) 4.5
   (e) 15.62   (f) 46.8   (g) 95.26   (h) 20.04

4 Divide the following numbers by 3.14 (answer correct to two decimal places):
   (a) 20   (b) 52.4   (c) 8.07   (d) 187.5

5 The circumference of a circle is found by multiplying diameter by π. If π = 3.14 find the circumference of circles with a diameter of
   (a) 20 cm   (b) 14.6 in   (c) 186 ft   (d) 95 cm
   (e) 32.7 m   (f) 37.74 cm

6 $D = \dfrac{C}{\pi}$ where D = diameter, C = circumference.

If π = 3.142 find the diameter of a circle correct to two decimal places when the circumference is
   (a) 30 cm   (b) 50 cm   (c) 17.2 in   (d) 130.9 ft
   (e) 7.3 m   (f) 91.7 cm

14.11   Percentage Calculations

The percentage must be at the end of the calculation. Do not put it at the beginning.

Example 14.42

$60 \times 8\%$

60 $\boxed{\times}$ 8 $\boxed{\%}$ → 4.8. There is no need to press the $\boxed{=}$ key.

Answer   4.8

Example 14.43

$32.5 \times 62.5\%$.

32 $\boxed{\cdot}$ 5 $\boxed{\times}$ 62 $\boxed{\cdot}$ 5 $\boxed{\%}$ → 20.3125.

Answer   20.3125

Example 14.44

Find 12% of 150.

Remember 'of' means multiply.
12% × 150:
Put percentage at the end so it becomes 150 × 12%.
150 ☒ 12 ☒% → 18
Answer   18

Example 14.45

What is 15% of £32.40?

This is the same as £32.40 × 15%
32 ☒· 40 ☒ 15 ☒% → 4.86
Answer   £4.86

Example 14.46

What is 250 as a percentage of 400?

In arithmetic this would be changed first to a fraction,
i.e. $\frac{250}{400}$ (or 250 ÷ 400).
   Do this on the calculator and press ☒% .
250 ☒÷ 400 ☒% → 62.5
Answer   62.5%

Example 14.47

What is 32.5 as a percentage of 120?

32 ☒· 5 ☒÷ 120 ☒% → 27.08
Answer   27.08%

Where you increase (or decrease) an amount by a percentage, apply ☒+ or ☒−
after the normal percentage calculation.

Example 14.48

Increase 120 by 30%.

120 ☒ 30 ☒% ☒+ ☒= 156
Answer   156

Example 14.49

Decrease 280 m by 18%.

280 ☒ 18 ☒% ☒− ☒= 229.6
Answer   229.6 m

Example 14.50

How much do you pay for a suit costing £80 if there is a discount of 15%?

Discount is a decrease in price, so the question now becomes decrease £80 by 15%.

80 $\boxed{\times}$ 15 $\boxed{\%}$ $\boxed{-}$ $\boxed{=}$ 68

Answer 68

14.12 Square Root

The square root of a number is what figure multiplied by itself will give you the number.

$9 = 3 \times 3,$ 3 is said to be the square root of 9;

or $\sqrt{9} = 3$.

On a calculator this is very simple; press the $\boxed{\sqrt{}}$ key to find the square root of the number displayed.

Example 14.51

Find the square root of 625.

625 $\boxed{\sqrt{}}$ → 25   No need to press $\boxed{=}$.

Answer 25

Example 14.52

Find the square root of 349.69.

349 $\boxed{\cdot}$ 69 $\boxed{\sqrt{}}$ → 18.7

Answer 18.7

Exercise 14.9

Use a calculator to find

1 (a) 32% of 150; (b) 65% of 60;   (c) 27% of 1500;   (d) 2.5% of £140;
   (e) $12\frac{1}{2}$ of £180; (f) 9% of 1500 m; (g) 22.5% of £60; (h) 18% of £120.

2 Find the price I have to pay if there is a discount of
   (a) 15% on £32; (b) 10% on £75;   (c) 12.5% on £150; (d) 6.25% on £68;
   (e) 40% on £380; (f) 35% on £960;   (g) 7% on £200;
   (h) 25% on £134.60.

3 Find the new cost if there is an increase of
   (a) 5% on £80;   (b) 7.5% on £200; (c) $12\frac{1}{2}$% on £60;   (d) 12% on £820;
   (e) 3.4% on £140; (f) 4.8% on £160.

4 Find the following fractions as a percentage:
   (a) $\frac{3}{8}$;   (b) $\frac{15}{25}$;   (c) $\frac{12}{56}$;   (d) $\frac{3}{7}$;
   (e) $\frac{5}{40}$;   (f) $\frac{7.2}{9.6}$;   (g) $\frac{18}{34}$;   (h) $\frac{9}{22}$.

5 Rates in the coming year are to be increased by 7.2%. Find the new rates where the amount paid last year was:
   (a) £140;   (b) £368;   (c) £596;   (d) £149.40;
   (e) £942;   (f) £468.60;   (g) £752.80;   (h) £615.50.

6 A shop has a sale and gives a discount of 20% of the shop price of any article. Find what you have to pay if the shop price is:

(a) £1.75;   (b) £8.40;   (c) £17.50;   (d) 80p;

(e) £172;   (f) £240.20;   (g) £150;   (h) £418.90.

7 Find the square root of the following numbers:

(a) 3136;   (b) 7396;   (c) 23 104;   (d) 29.16;

(e) 0.0529;   (f) 0.7569;   (g) 282.24;   (h) 12.0409.

8 In a right-angled triangle $a = \sqrt{b^2 + c^2}$.

where a = length of the side opposite the right angle and b and c are the lengths of the other two sides. Find a when:

(a) $b = 3, c = 4$ (b) $b = 5, c = 12$;   (c) $b = 8, c = 15$;   (d) $b = 6, c = 6$;

(e) $b = 9, c = 15$;   (f) $b = 8.4, c = 21.2$;   (g) $b = 32, c = 45$;   (h) $b = 15, c = 24$.

Exercise 14.10

Use your calculator to answer the following questions:

1 An evening meal cost £8.00 plus a service charge of $12\frac{1}{2}\%$. What is the total cost?

2 A college disco ticket costs 75p. 209 students pay for a ticket and the DJ costs £45.

(a) How much profit is made?

(b) 45% of the profit goes to a sports fund; how much goes into the fund?

3 If a country has 22 175 000 people who are eligible for work and there are 3 545 000 unemployed, what percentage of people are unemployed?

4 Ford offer a 14% discount on a Sierra where there is no trade-in. A Sierra 1600L costs £7540. What is the discount price?

5 A woman earning £9600 a year is given a rise of 7.2%. How much extra does she earn per month?

Out of her new yearly salary she has to pay £2100 in income tax, £275 in National Insurance contributions, and £480 in personal pension contribution. What percentage are the total deductions from her total pay?

6 A colour television can be bought for £395. Alternatively, you can pay a deposit of £39.50 and 23 further payments of £18.75. How much extra has it cost by paying in instalments?

7 A motorist travelled 9216 miles a year when petrol cost £1.85 a gallon.

(a) If the car averages 36 mile/gal, how much did the petrol cost?

(b) If car tax was £110, insurance £320, and repairs £564, what was the cost per mile of travelling?

8 A bottle of whisky sells for £7.65. The duty on this bottle is £6.25. What is the duty as a percentage of the price of a bottle of whisky?

9 It is estimated that in a town of 72 000 people, 35% are over the age of 65.

(a) How many people are over 65?

In the over-65s there are 3 women to every 2 men.

(b) How many women in the town are over 65?

10 A house has a floor area of 1300 ft^2. An extension is built which provides an additional 23% extra floor area. The cost is reckoned at £41 per ft^2. What is the new floor area of the house and how much did the extension cost?

15 Assignments

15.1 Introduction

The purpose of this chapter is to present a number of situations showing where mathematics and its applications are always with us at some time or another. The assignments do not demand a higher level of mathematics than that already attempted in this book.

The assignments may be regarded as being in order of difficulty.

Students should go carefully through all the information given in each assignment and try and establish what is being asked for and, therefore, what needs to be worked out.

Since a major stumbling block in attempting to answer a problem is often 'Where do I start?', each assignment has hints relating to the order in which the working out may be attempted, though this does not mean it is the only way or the easiest way.

15.2 The Disco

The youth club has 120 members and the social committee decided to have a Christmas disco on 23 December from 8.00 p.m. to 1.00 a.m. Tickets, including refreshments, were £1 for members and £1.50 for guests.

The DJ charged £10 an hour before midnight and £20 an hour after.

The social committee spent 60p a head on refreshments.

36 dozen bottles of drink were bought at £5.20 a dozen and sold to make a profit of 25%. All were sold.

80% of all club members attended and there were half as many guests as members attending.

Find the profit made on the Christmas disco.

Hints

To find the profit, find the total income (money collected) and subtract total expenditure (money spent or cost).

Income comes from (a) sale of tickets
　　　　　　　　　　(b) sale of drinks.
How many members bought tickets?
How many guests bought tickets?
What was the profit on the drinks sold?

Expenditure was on (a) DJ;
　　　　　　　　　　　(b) refreshments.
How much did the DJ charge?
How much was spent on refreshments?

Now find the profit.

15.3 The Newsagent

From Monday to Friday during one week in April a newsagent stocked the number of daily newspapers shown in Fig. 15.1 (the selling price of each newspaper is also shown on the chart).

Week beginning 20 April	Price	Mon.	Tue.	Wed.	Thur.	Fri.	Sat.
Express	20p	70	70	70	70	70	90
Telegraph	25p	60	60	60	60	60	80
Sun	18p	60	60	60	60	60	80
Mirror	18p	50	50	50	50	50	60
Star	18p	40	40	40	40	40	50
Today	18p	40	40	40	40	40	50
Mail	20p	35	35	35	35	35	45
Guardian	25p	25	25	25	25	25	30
Times	25p	12	12	12	12	12	12
Sporting Life	40p	10	10	10	10	10	20
Financial Times	40p	5	5	5	5	5	8
Morning Advertiser	20p	4	4	4	4	4	4

Figure 15.1   Chart showing numbers of copies of papers stocked

The number of copies remaining unsold at the end of each day was as shown in Fig. 15.2.

The newsagent employed 3 boys and 1 girl to deliver the papers and each one was paid £7.00 per week.

230 customers had their paper delivered and the charge for this service was 20p per week to each customer.

There is a gross profit of 25% on newspapers actually sold.

From the information given, find

(a) how many newspapers were sold on each day of the week for the week beginning 20 April;

(b) what the takings were on each day for the sale of papers;

(c) how much profit or loss there was from the delivery charge to customers over the cost of employing 3 boys and 1 girl;

(d) how much gross profit per week there was from the sale of papers alone, assuming a gross profit of 25% on papers sold.

Hints

(a) Add up the column for the number of papers stocked on each day. Add up the column for the number of copies unsold on each day. The difference will give you the number of copies sold on each day.

Week beginning 20 April	Mon.	Tue.	Wed.	Thur.	Fri.	Sat.
Express	5	7	2	4	3	1
Telegraph	8	6	4	8	5	0
Sun	4	0	2	2	5	3
Mirror	6	2	9	1	3	3
Star	5	3	5	0	2	4
Today	0	11	3	4	4	0
Mail	2	2	1	0	0	2
Guardian	4	2	3	4	2	2
Times	0	0	0	0	0	0
Sporting Life	1	3	1	2	0	0
Financial Times	0	0	0	0	0	1
Morning Advertiser	0	0	0	0	0	0

Figure 15.2   Chart showing numbers of copies of papers unsold

(b) To find the actual takings on each day it may help by drawing a chart similar to the ones shown for stock and unsold copies. Record how many of each paper was sold each day; leave enough room in each column to find the money taken, and then add up the totals.

(c) Find the total money coming in (income) for charging 230 customers at 20p per week. Find how much it costs to deliver the papers, employing 3 boys and 1 girl. The difference is the profit or less.

(d) Find the total takings for the week and find the gross profit by calculating 25% of this figure.

15.4   The Motorbike

John, aged 17, has announced to his father that he is going to buy a new 125-cc motorbike in order to travel more easily to work, which is 10 miles away, and to the local college 5 miles away. His father has told John to estimate the running costs over the course of a year and see how it compares with his bus costs. John has found out the following:

He is at work on 210 days a year and at the local college on 30 days. The bus fare to work is £1.70 a day return and to college is 32p single. A new motorbike is £600 which, paid for on HP over two years, will cost £35 a calendar month. Tax is £18 a year and insurance £120 a year. John is confident the bike will do 75 mile/gal (though the garage quoted 100 mile/gal) and he calculates petrol at £2.00 a gallon for ease of working. He has allowed £40 for oil changes and minor repairs. (Dad has promised to buy the 'gear' and crash helmet.)

What was the difference in cost for travelling to work and college over the year between the bus and using a motorbike?

Hints

There are two things to find:
(a) the cost of going by bus to work and to college over a year;
(b) the cost of going by motorbike.

(a) *Cost by Bus*

How many days does John travel to work?
What is the cost of the bus per day?
What is the cost of the bus to work over the year?
In a similar way find the cost of the bus to college.
Now find the total cost by bus to work and college.

(b) *Cost by Motorbike*

(i) *Fixed costs*

What is cost of buying the bike over a year?
Remember tax and insurance, minor repairs, as well as paying for the bike.

(ii) *Actual running costs*

How many miles in a year does John do travelling to work?
How many miles in a year to college?
Find the total mileage.
How many gallons of petrol will he need?
What is the cost of petrol?

Now find the total cost of running the motorbike.
What is the difference in cost between bus and motorbike?

15.5 Timetables

(a) Using the air timetables given below, what is the earliest time you can reach Plymouth by leaving Papa Westray on a Thursday morning at 0904 hours going via Kirkwall, Edinburgh and London Heathrow?

ORKNEY INTERNAL AIR SERVICE

Reservations: Telephone: Kirkwall 2494

25th MARCH 1985 to 27th OCTOBER 1985

Operating Days		Monday & Wednesday							Tuesday & Thursday					
Flight No.	LC	610	612	614	680	611	613	615	620	622	624	621	623	625
Kirkwall	dep	0830	0935	1025	1200	1430	1535	1620	0830	0930	1030	1430	1530	1630
Westray	arr		0947				1547		0842			1442		
	dep		0957				1557		0852			1452		
Papa Westray	arr								0854			1454		
	dep								0904			1504		
Stronsay	arr			1033	1208			1628		0938			1538	
	dep			1043	1216			1638		0948			1548	
Eday	arr			1048				1643		0953			1553	
	dep			1058				1653		1003			1603	
Sanday	arr	0841		No	1221	1441		No			1041			1641
	dep	0851		Eday	1229	1451		Eday			1051			1651
North Ronaldsay	arr	0856		Call on		1456		Call on						
	dep	0906		Wed		1506		Wed						
Stronsay	arr													
	dep													
Kirkwall	arr	0919	1009	1106	1240	1519	1609	1701	0916	1011	1102	1516	1611	1702

Days		Friday						Saturday				
Flight No.	LC	630	632	634	631	633	635	650	651	652	653	654
Kirkwall	dep	0830	0930	1020	1415	1515	1605	0830	0920	1330	1430	1520
Westray	arr		0941			1527			0932		1442	
	dep		0951			1537			0940		1540	
Papa Westray	arr								0854			1454
	dep								0950	1458		
Stronsay	arr			1423						1338		
	dep			1433						1346		
Eday	arr			1028			1613		0956			
	dep			1038			1623		1004			
Sanday	arr	0841			1438			0841				1531
	dep	0851			1448			0849				1539
North Ronaldsay	arr			1044			1629			1352		
	dep			1054			1639			1400		
Stronsay	arr	0856						0854				
	dep	0906						0902				
Kirkwall	arr	0914	1003	1107	1459	1549	1652	0910	1012	1414	1510	1550

NOTE: LC680 OPERATES ONLY WHEN ALTERNATIVE FLIGHTS ARE FULL.

Part of Loganair summer timetable

FROM LONDON GATWICK

Flight No.	Frequency	Dep.	Arr.	Route	Service
to Birmingham					
BC 203	12345	0835	0920	Direct	CB/BA
BC 205	12345	1130	1215	Direct	BA
BC 207	67	1925	2010	Direct	LR/BA
BC 209	7	1045	1130	Direct	CB/BA
BC 211		1945	2030	Direct	LR/BA
to Exeter					
BC 702	123456	0845	0945	Direct	HD
BC 722	123456	1900	2005	Direct	HD
BC 704	7	0955	1100	Direct	HD
to Isles of Scilly					
BC 702/511•	123456	0845	1130	EXT/PLH	HD
to Plymouth					
BC 702	123456	0845	1015	EXT	HD
BC 722	123456	1900	2030	EXT	HD
BC 704	7	0955	1130	EXT	HD

FROM LONDON HEATHROW

Flight No.	Frequency	Dep.	Arr.	Route	Service
to Isles of Scilly					
BC 803/511•	12345	0915	1130	PLH	HD/BA
BC 805/515•	12345	1245	1530	PLH/NQY	HD/BA
to Newquay					
BC 803	12345	0915	1050	PLH	CB/BA
BC 805	12345	1245	1420	PLH	HD/BA
BC 807	12345	1615	1750	PLH	HD/BA
BC 809	12345	1940	2110	PLH	LR/BA
BC 813	6	1015	1125	Direct	CB/BA
BC 819	7	1940	2050	Direct	LR/BA
to Plymouth					
BC 803	12345	0915	1020	Direct	CB/BA
BC 805	12345	1245	1350	Direct	HD/BA
BC 807	12345	1615	1715	Direct	HD/BA
BC 809	12345	1940	2045	Direct	LR/BA
BC 813	6	1015	1155	NQY	CB/BA
BC 819	7	1940	2125	NQY	LR/BA

ADDITIONAL NOTES:

•Services to Isles of Scilly operate on the following days:
Mondays - 3rd June to 2nd Sept. Tues/Wed/Thurs. - 14th May to 26th Sept.
Fri/Sats. - April to Oct.

HD — Hot Drinks   LR — Light Refreshments   BA — Bar Service   CB — Continental Breakfast

1 — Monday. 2 — Tuesday. 3 — Wednesday. 4 — Thursday.
5 — Friday. 6 — Saturday. 7 — Sunday.

Part of Brymon Airways timetable

EDINBURGH—WICK—KIRKWALL
Reservations: Telephone: 031-344 3341/3247

Operating		25 Mar–26 Oct	26 Mar–24 Oct
Days		Mon, Fri, Sat	Tu, We, Th
Aircraft		SH6	DHT
Flight No.		LC333	LC333
Edinburgh	dep	1040	0835
Wick	arr	1145	0950
Wick	dep	1200	1005
Kirkwall	arr	1215	1020
Flight No.		LC334	LC334
Kirkwall	dep	1235	1040
Wick	arr	1250	1055
Wick	dep	1305	1110
Edinburgh	arr	1410	1225

Part of Loganair summer timetable

From EDINBURGH continued
► London

From	To	Days 1234567	Depart	Arrive	Flight No	Aircraft	Class	Stops	Transfer Arr. Airport	Transfer Dep. Flight	Aircraft Class
		123456-	0710	0820	BA4713	EQV	M	0	Super Shuttle		
		12345--	0810	0920	BA4723	TRD$	M	0	Super Shuttle		
		Daily	0910	1020	BA4733	TRD$	M	0	Super Shuttle		
		Daily	1110	1220	BA4753	EQV	M	0	Super Shuttle		
		Daily	1310	1420	BA4773	757$	M	0	Super Shuttle		
		Daily	1510	1620	BA4793	EQV	M	0	Super Shuttle		
		12345-7	1610	1720	BA4803	B11$	M	0	Super Shuttle		
		12345--	1710	1820	BA4813	757$	M	0	Super Shuttle		
		Daily	1910	2020	BA4833	757$	M	0	Super Shuttle		

Part of British Airways Worldwide Timetable

231

(b) A salesman has to travel from Huntingdon to Aberystwyth in time to attend a 2.00 p.m. meeting in Aberystwyth. Using the rail timetables below he found he could do this with nearly an hour to spare by going via Peterborough and Birmingham (changing at Leicester). At what time did he have to leave Huntingdon by train?

Table 25 **Mondays to Fridays**

London and Hertford North → Royston, Cambridge and Peterborough

Miles	Miles	Miles																						
0	0	—	**London Kings Cross** ⊖ 24, 26 d										0005	0025	0200	0500			0551	0610		0634		
2½	2½	—	Finsbury Park ⊖ 24 d											0030					0557	0615		0641		
12¾	12¾	—	Potters Bar 24 d							0011				0050						0626		0652		
17¾	17¾	—	Hatfield 24 d							0017				0057						0632		0658		
20¼	20¼	—	Welwyn Garden City 24 d							0022				0102						0637		0703		
22	22	—	Welwyn North d							0025										0640		0706		
25	25	—	Knebworth d							0029										0644		0710		
—	—	0	Hertford North d					0014	0016										0631					0707
—	—	4¼	Watton-at-Stone d					0019	0021										0636					0712
27½	27½	9½	Stevenage 26 d					0027	0028	0033			0037	0112		0520			0643	0648		0714		0719
32	32	—	Hitchin d					0033	0034	0039				0118	0240	0528		0638	0649	0654		0720		0725
34¾	—	—	Letchworth d					0038	0039	0043									0654	0658		0724		
36¾	—	—	Baldock d			0001				0046										0701		0727		
41	—	—	Ashwell & Morden d		0005	0006				0051										0706		0732		
45	—	—	Royston a		0014	0017				0104										0715		0741		
—	—	—	d				0022				0109						0630						0744	
48	—	—	Meldreth d				0027				0114						0635						0749	
49¾	—	—	Shepreth d				0031				0118						0639						0753	
51	—	—	Foxton d				0034				0121						0642						0756	
58	—	—	**Cambridge** a				0047				0134						0655						0809	
—	41¼	—	Biggleswade d													0537		0649						
—	44	—	Sandy d													0542		0654						
—	51¾	—	St.Neots d	0002												0549		0705						
—	58¾	—	Huntingdon a	0013									0105		0313	0601		0716						
—	—	—	26 d										0106		0332	0602								
—	76¼	—	**Peterborough §** 26 a										0125		0358	0620								

Table 18 **Mondays to Fridays**

Norwich, Ely, March, Peterborough and Leicester → Birmingham

Miles																	
—	Yarmouth 2 16 d										0558		0650				
0	**Norwich** d										0643		0735			0750	
10¼	Wymondham d										0657					0806	
12¾	Spooner Row d															0810	
16	Attleborough d										0704					0816	
19¾	Eccles Road d															0822	
22¾	Harling Road d															0827	
30½	Thetford d										0719		0811			0844	
37¾	Brandon d										0728		0821			0854	
41½	Lakenheath d										0733					0901	
46¾	Shippea Hill d										0741					0909	
53¾	**Ely** a										0754					0922	
—	London Liverpool Street ⊖ 22 a										0933					1108	
—	Harwich Parkeston Quay 12 d													0717			
—	Ipswich 15 d											0541		0744			0806
—	Cambridge 22 d			0515					0705			0738		0820	0852		0954
—	Kings Lynn 22 d											0640		0750			0850
—	**Ely** d			0533					0724			0759		0851	0910		1012
63½	Manea d								0737			0812			0923		
69½	**March** a			0552					0746			0821	0901		0932		1031
—	d			0552					0746			0821	0901		0932		1031
78	Whittlesea d			0604					0758			0833			0944		1043
84½	**Peterborough** a			0617					0811			0846	0923	0929	0957		1056
—	Doncaster 19, 26 a			0800					0920			1015		1035			1207
—	Leeds 26, 33 a			0954					1049					1115			1310
—	York 26 a			0838					0946					1108	1206		
—	Darlington 26 a			0947					1017					1139	1236		
—	Newcastle 26 a			1029					1054					1212	1310		
—	Edinburgh 26 a			1242					1242				1356	1733	1452		
—	London Kings Cross ⊖ 25, 26 d				0500								0804		0900		
—	Peterborough d				0633				0815				0934		1000		
96¼	Stamford d				0648				0830						1015		
109¾	Oakham d				0710				0851						1037		
121¼	Melton Mowbray d				0724		0820		0904						1051		
136¼	**Leicester** a				0745		0841		0925				1039		1112		
—	d	0633	0732			0757		0846	0926				1044		1121		
143	Narborough d	0644	0742			0809		0857	0938						1133		
150¼	Hinckley d	0655	0754			0820		0908	0949				1104		1144		
155	Nuneaton d	0705	0801			0829		0916	1000				1115		1156		
169¼	Water Orton 56 d	0727	0825			0851		0940	1022						1219		
175¾	**Birmingham New Street** 56 a	0743	0839			0905		0956	1036				1150		1235		

Table 75

Shrewsbury → Aberystwyth
Second Class only unless otherwise shown

Miles																
—	London Euston ...74 d	0555	0730	0935	1140	1340	1540	1740							
—	Birmingham New Street ...74 d	0555	0630	0640	0913	1113	1322	1522	1716	1915				
—	Wolverhampton ...74 d	0630	0725	0944	1144	1352	1552	1746	1945					
—	Cardiff Central ...87 d	0533	0533	0705	0902	1200	1412	1550	1815					
—	Liverpool Lime Street ...87 d	0015	0650	0833	1030	1237	1433	1550	1838					
—	Manchester Piccadilly ...87 d	0042	0628	0719	0900	1033	1233	1433	1533	1855				
—	Crewe ...87 d	0225	0628	0806	1003	1140	1345	1545	1727	1944				
—	Chester ...d	0625	0715	0915	1015	1215	1415	1615	1915					
0	**Shrewsbury** ...d	0410	0753	0850	1055	1240	1442	1650	1840	2042				
19½	Welshpool ...d	0440	0820	0922	1124	1313	1513	1718	1912	2118				
33½	Newtown ...d	0507	0838	0939	1142	1330	1530	1735	1930	2135				
39½	Caersws ...d	0516	0849	0947	1151	1338	1538	1743	1944	2143				
61	Machynlleth ...76 a	0548	0921	1019	1230	1410	1610	1831	2034	2215				
	...76 d	0554	0921	0921	1035	1230	1420	1612	1831	2034	2215			
65	Dovey Junction ...76 d	1048	1622	1843	2041	2225								
86½	**Barmouth** ...76 a	0737	1139	1139	1343	1517	1729	2132						
73½	Borth ...d	0612	0938	0938	1111	1251	1633	1851	2052	2237				
81½	**Aberystwyth** ...a	0631	0953	0953	1126	1306	1648	1909	2107	2252				

(c) A person living near Longridge post office wants to travel by bus to Rotherham and is prepared to travel on the 0723 bus to Blackburn. She sees that by changing in Manchester and going to Sheffield and then on to Rotherham the journey could be done in one day. What is the earliest time she could arrive in Rotherham by leaving Longridge at 0723? How long does the journey take? (*Timetables below and overleaf.*)

Preston · Longridge · Ribchester · Blackburn
(including part Service 10)

Monday to Friday

Stop	Code	Times (⊕ ⊙ 10 ■ shown where applicable)
Preston, Bus Station	dep.	0652 0722 0922 1022 1122 1222 1322 1422 1522 ⊕1535 ⊙1622 1652(10) ■ 1722 1818 1918 2018 2132
Ribbleton, Gamull Lane		0708 0738 0938 1038 1138 1238 1338 1438 1538 1551 1638 1708 1738 1834 1934 2034 2148
Grimsargh, Plough Inn		0713 0743 0943 1043 1143 1243 1343 1443 1543 ‡ 1556 1643 1713 1743 1839 1939 2039 2153
Longridge, Stone Bridge		0721 0751 0951 1051 1151 1251 1351 1451 1551 1553 1604 1651 1723 1751 1846 1946 2046 2200
Longridge, Post Office		0723 0753 0953 1053 1153 1253 1353 1453 1553 1606 1653 1723†→ 1725 1753 1848 1948 2048 2202
Longridge, Corporation Arms		0726 0756 0956 1056 1156 1256 1356 1456 1556 1609 1609 1656 1728 1756 1851 1951 2051 2205
Ribchester, Ribchester Arms		0735 0805 1005 1105 1205 1305 1405 1505 1605 1618 1618 1705 1737 1805 1900 2000 2100 2214
Oaks Bar	0713 0743 0813	1013 1113 1213 1313 1413 1513 1613 1626 1626 1713 1745 1813 1908 2008 2108 2222
Salesbury, Bonny Inn	0715 0745 0815	▲ 1015 1115 1215 1315 1415 1515 1615 1628 1628 1715 1747 1815 1910 2010 2110 2224
Wilpshire, Bulls Head	0718 0748 0818	0918 1018 1118 1218 1318 1418 1518 1618 1631 1631 1718 1750 1818 1913 2013 2113 2227
Lammack, Hare & Hounds Hotel		1921 2021 2121 2235
Four Lane Ends	0726 0756 0826	0926 1026 1126 1226 1326 1426 1526 1626 1639 1639 1726 1758 1826 1922 2022 2122 2236
Blackburn, Boulevard⇌	arr. 0737 0807 0837♥	0937 1037 1137 1237 1337 1437 1537 1637 1650 1650 1737 1809 1837 1932 2032 2132 2246

825

825 **Burnley** – BOLTON – MANCHESTER – BIRMINGHAM – COVENTRY – HEATHROW AIRPORT – **Gatwick Airport** **825**

825 **Rochdale** – OLDHAM – MANCHESTER – BIRMINGHAM – COVENTRY – LEAMINGTON SPA – HEATHROW AIRPORT – **Gatwick Airport** 825

825 **Manchester** – BIRMINGHAM – COVENTRY – LUTON – HEATHROW AIRPORT – **Gatwick Airport** 825

Shows full East Lancashire/Manchester to Birmingham/Coventry service.

For Bank Holiday arrangements see below	806	825	730	924	825	830	825	850	825	825	850	825	923	735	808	820	821
Days of operation	D	D	D	NSuM	D	D	D	D	D	D	D	D	D	D	D	D	D
BURNLEY, Bus Stn., Stand 15 ♿	…	…	…	…	…	0700	…	…	0830	…	…	1230	…	…	…	2130	…
Accrington, Infant St., Stand 'O'	…	…	…	…	…	0715	…	…	0845	…	…	1245	…	…	…	2145	…
BLACKBURN, Boulevard Bus Stn., Stand Y ♿	…	…	…	…	…	0730	…	…	0900	…	…	1300	…	…	…	2200	…
Darwen, Bolton Rd., opp. Belgrave Church	…	…	…	…	…	…	…	…	0910	…	…	1310	…	…	…	2210	…
BOLTON, Moor Lane, Bus Stn.	…	…	…	…	…	…	…	…	0935	…	…	1335	…	…	1735	2235	…
Salford University, Museum & Art Gallery, Bus Stop	0415	…	…	…	…	…	…	…	0955	…	…	1355	…	…	1755	2255	…
ROCHDALE, Yelloway Coach Stn., Weir St.	…	…	…	…	…	…	…	…	…	1105	…	…	…	…	…	…	…
OLDHAM, Yelloway Coach Stn., 3 Mumps	…	…	…	…	…	…	…	…	…	1125	…	…	…	…	…	…	…
Ashton-under-Lyne, Bus Stn., Stand C	…	…	…	…	…	…	…	…	…	1140	…	…	…	…	…	…	…
MANCHESTER, National Coach Stn., Chorlton St. arr.	0425	…	…	…	…	…	…	…	1005	1205	…	1405	…	…	1805	2305	…
MANCHESTER, National Coach Stn., Chorlton St. dep.	0430	…	…	0645	…	0810	…	…	1010	1210	…	1410	1630	…	1810	2310	…
Stockport, Bus Stn., Stand A	…	…	…	…	…	…	…	1030	…	…	1430	…	…	…	…	2330	…
Manchester Airport, Bus Stn., Stand C	0450	…	…	…	…	…	…	…	1045	…	…	1445	…	…	1830	2345	…
Altrincham, Interchange Bus Stn., Stand F	…	…	…	…	…	0835	…	…	…	1235	…	…	…	…	…	…	…
Sandbach Service Area, M6 arr.	…	…	…	…	…	…	…	…	…	…	…	…	…	…	…	0005	…
Sandbach Service Area, M6 dep.	…	…	…	…	…	…	…	…	…	…	…	…	…	…	…	0040	0040
Stoke-on-Trent, Etruria Rd., Bus Stop, nr. Sentinel House (Y)	…	…	…	…	…	…	…	…	…	…	…	…	…	…	1910	…	…
STOKE-ON-TRENT, Hanley, Bus Stn. ♿	0535	…	…	…	…	…	…	…	…	…	…	…	…	…	1920	0100	0100
Wolverhampton, Pipers Row Bus Stn., Coach Stop	…	…	0750	…	…	…	0950	1150	…	1350	1550	…	…	…	…	0135	0135
BIRMINGHAM, National Coach Stn., Digbeth **C** arr.	0635	⊏⊐	0825	0830	⊏⊐	1020	1025R	1225	1220R	1425R	1625	1620R	1815	⊏⊐	2020R	0210E	0210E
BIRMINGHAM, National Coach Stn., Digbeth dep.	⊏⊐	0700	⊏⊐	⊏⊐	0900	1100	⊏⊐	⊏⊐	1300	1500	⊏⊐	1700	1900	2100	⊏⊐	0210E	0210E
COVENTRY, Pool Meadow Bus Stn.	…	0740	…	…	0940	1140	…	…	1340	1540	…	1740	1940	2140	…	0245	0245
LEAMINGTON SPA, Coach Stop, Hamilton Terrace	…	…	…	…	1000	…	…	…	…	1600	…	…	…	…	…	…	…
LUTON, Bute St. Bus Stn. ⊖	…	0905	…	…	…	1305	…	…	…	…	…	…	…	…	…	0445	…
Uxbridge, Bakers Rd., Bus Stn., Stand O.	…	…	…	…	…	…	…	…	1540	…	…	1940	…	…	…	…	0510
HEATHROW AIRPORT, Central Bus Stn. ✈	…	0955	…	…	1155	1355	…	…	1555	1755	…	1955	…	…	…	…	0525
HEATHROW AIRPORT, Terminal 4, Arrivals Forecourt ✈	…	1005	…	…	1205	1405	…	…	1605	1805	…	2005	…	…	…	…	…
GATWICK AIRPORT, Coach Stn., Ground Level ✈	…	1050	…	…	1250	1450	…	…	1650	1850	…	2050	…	…	…	0700	…

For Bank Holiday arrangements see below	352	361	296	352	361	352	361	363	363	363
Periods of operation									1	
Days of operation	D	D	D	D	D	D	D	S	F	D
BLACKPOOL, National Coach Stn., Coliseum	0850	…	0910	1050	…	1250	…	1300	1300	1750
Blackpool, Preston New Rd., Corner	0855	…	…	1055	…	1255	…	…	…	1755
Blackpool, Squires Gate, Fylde Transport Garage, Nat. Exp. stop	…	…	0915	…	…	…	…	1305	1305	…
Blackpool, Pontins Camp, National Express stop	…	…	0917	…	…	…	…	1307	1307	…
St. Annes, Ashton Gardens	…	…	0920	…	…	…	…	1310	1310	…
Ansdell, opp. Fairhaven Hotel	…	…	0925	…	…	…	…	1315	1315	…
Lytham, Baths	…	…	0930	…	…	…	…	1320	1320	…
PRESTON, Bus Station, Stand 68	0930	…	1000A	1130	…	1330	…	…	…	1830
Salford, University Museum & Art Gallery, Bus Stop	1015	…	…	1215	…	1415	…	…	…	1915
MANCHESTER, Nat. Coach Stn., Chorlton St., Stand B arr.	1025	…	…	1225	…	1425	…	…	…	1925R
MANCHESTER, Nat. Coach Stn., Chorlton St., Stand B dep.	⊏⊐	1130	…	⊏⊐	1330	⊏⊐	1530	…	…	2000
Gorton, Hyde Rd., Debdale Park, Bus Stop, opp. Reddish Lane	…	1135	…	…	1335	…	1535	…	…	2005
Hyde, Bus Stn., Stand A	…	1145	…	…	1345	…	1545	…	…	2015
Hollingworth, Memorial, Bus Stop	…	1150	…	…	1350	…	1550	…	…	2020
Flouch Inn	…	1220	…	…	1420	…	1620	…	…	2050
Stocksbridge, Bus Stop, Coach & Horses	…	1230	…	…	1430	…	1630	…	…	2100
Sheffield, opp. Hillsborough Baths	…	1245	…	…	1445	…	1645	…	…	2115
SHEFFIELD, Central Bus Stn., Platform G arr.	…	1255	1400	…	1455	…	1655R	1605	1605	2125
SHEFFIELD, Central Bus Stn., Platform G dep.	…	…	…	…	…	…	1730	1605	1605	2125
ROTHERHAM, Bus Stn., Stand B4	…	…	…	…	…	…	1755	1630	1630	2150

15.6 Going To Work

Anita lives at home, a mile from Watford, and has just got a secretarial job at an agency, which is within walking distance of Euston Station, at a salary of £5500 a year. In her salary slip at the end of the month she notices that national insurance contributions amount to £7.70 per week and a deduction for pension is made which is equivalent to 5% of her gross salary. Income tax was deducted on a scale using an allowance of £2450 and tax rates as given on page 130.

A monthly rail ticket from Watford to Euston is £69.50 whereas a weekly ticket is £18.20. Anita sometimes walks to the station and so bus fares, on average, amount to only £3.40 a week. She is given luncheon vouchers to the value of 85p a day but reckons to spend £1.60 a day.

For travelling to work she thought the cost would include eleven monthly rail tickets and two weekly rail tickets, but bus fares and lunches would be calculable over a 48-week year.

If she gives her mother £30 every week and saves £10 each week in a building society, how much does she have left to spend on other things?

Hints

Calculations of this nature may be done best using annual figures and a 52-week year.

Start with pay and deductions which are made automatically:

—What is her gross salary?
—How much are NI contributions in a year?
—How much are pension contributions?
—What tax is paid? (As a reminder look at page 130 to see how to calculate the amount.)
—How much is her net pay after these deductions?

Now find what she pays out in other ways.

—Find the cost of rail travel and what is spent on bus fares.
—Find what it costs her in lunches, remembering that part is paid by the firm by way of vouchers.
—Find what she gives her mother over a year and also what she saves.

You should now have all the information to work out how much is left to spend on other things.

15.7 Four Teenagers in a House

Four friends after leaving further education college at eighteen decide to stay in the same town and share the rent of a house. They find a furnished terraced house to rent at £160 p.c.m. (per calendar month) plus rates.

The rateable value of the house is £360. Rates are 92.5p in the £ and water rate 30p in the £ plus a standing charge of £14.50.

The landlord shows them the previous tenants' bills for electricity and gas. Electricity each quarter averaged as 760 units at 6.0p per unit plus a quarterly charge of £6.50; gas each quarter averaged as 82 therms at 37.00p per therm plus a quarterly charge of £9.40.

The telephone is a pay-phone in the hall.

The four friends decide to try a kitty of £60 a week to cover food and drink; they hire a colour television at £7.50 p.c.m. and they insure all their personal effects for £800 at a cost of 40p per year for each £100 insured.

Using 52 weeks in a year, how much per week, to the nearest £, is it going to cost each person?

Hints

The only cost given per week is food and drink at £60.
   How much is this per person?
Find the cost of all other things for a year.
   What is the rent p.c.m.?
   How much is the rent per year?
Rates and water rate are an annual payment.
   Find the charge for rates and water rate.
Electricity is a quarterly charge, meaning every 3 months, and there will be 4 in a year.
   Find the cost of electricity for a quarter and then for a year.
   Similarly, find the cost of gas.
The television is charged per month.
   Find the cost per year.
Insurance is an annual charge.
   Find the cost of insuring all personal effects.

Find the total cost of all these items: divide by 52 (to one decimal place) to find the cost per week.
   Now find the cost for each person and don't forget the food and drink.

15.8   The Calorie Diet

(a) The diagrams in Fig. 15.3 are simplified weight tables for men and women.

Using the diagrams, state whether the following people, according to the charts, are underweight, of a suitable weight for their height, fat or very fat:

   (i)   male   5 ft 6 in   weighing 10 stone
   (ii) male   5 ft 10 in weighing 12 stone
   (iii) female   5 ft 2 in   weighing 7 stone
   (iv) female   5 ft 4 in   weighing 10 stone
   (v)   male   5 ft 4 in   weighing 11 stone
   (vi) female   5 ft 6 in   weighing 11 stone

(b) A man of 5 ft 8 in and weighing 13 stone decided to lose weight by going on a diet of about 1500 calories a day. He prepared specimen menus for each day of the week and calculated the calorie content of each menu. His specimen menus for Monday were as follows:

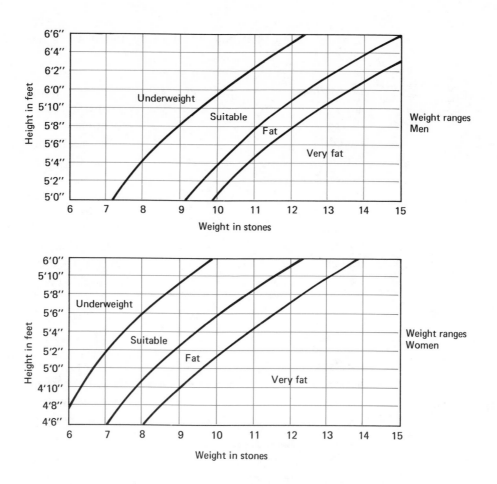

Figure 15.3 Simplified weight tables

Menu A	Menu B	Menu C	Menu D
cup of coffee (milk and sugar)	2 cups of coffee (milk and sugar)	cup of coffee (milk and sugar)	2 cups of coffee (milk and sugar)
2 slices toast and butter	plate of muesli, 2 oz	cornflakes, 1 oz milk, 2 oz	1 slice toast and butter
1 orange, 7 oz		1 slice toast and butter	
chicken leg (roast), 6 oz	Quiche Lorraine (slice)	chips, 6 oz	beef curry, 8 oz
salad, portion	salad, portion	3 grilled sausages	coleslaw, 4 oz
packet of crisps, 1 oz	glass of milk, 6 oz	runner beans, 3 oz	yoghurt, small carton
pint of shandy	ice cream, 2 oz	apple pie, 6 oz	
		cup of coffee (milk and sugar)	
fish, 6 oz, and chips, 6 oz	shepherd's pie, 8 oz	grilled cod, 6 oz	French onion soup, $\frac{1}{2}$ pint
lemon meringue pie, 4 oz	carrots, 4 oz	salad portion	lasagne, 8 oz
peas, 3 oz	jam tart, 4 oz	peas, 3 oz	ratatouille, 8 oz
2 cups of tea (milk and sugar)	1 pint of beer	apple, 5 oz	crème caramel, 6 oz
		cup of tea (milk and sugar)	1 pint of beer

All other liquid intake to be restricted to water. Using the calorie figures given below, find the calorie content of each menu. Which menu was nearest to his aim of 1500 calories per day, and by how much was it less than or greater than 1500 calories?

Item	Calories per oz.	Item	Calories per oz.
gin	65	shepherd's pie	35
sherry	35	apple pie	50
baked beans	20	lemon meringue pie	90
banana	15	carrots	5
runner beans	5	Cheshire cheese	120
roast beef	80	roast chicken leg	25
beefburgers	75	chips	80
cornflakes	105	apple	10
muesli	105	cod, grilled	25
orange	5	cod, fried in batter	55
ice cream	45	double cream	125
lasagne	75	crisps	150
eclairs	105	crème caramel	40
boiled egg	40	tuna	80
fish (haddock, fried)	50	peas	10
fish (sardines)	60	jam tart	120
beef curry	40	milk	20
		coleslaw	15
		ratatouille	20

Item	Item
shandy 80 per $\frac{1}{2}$ pint	brown bread 65 per slice
beer 100 per $\frac{1}{2}$ pint	salad 30 per portion
fried bacon 130 per rasher	toast and butter 110 per slice
fried sausage 150 per sausage	coffee with milk and sugar 60 per cup
grilled sausage 110 per sausage	tea with milk and sugar 60 per cup
chocolate biscuits 120 per biscuit	fish fingers 65 per finger
iced currant bun 360 per bun	Quiche Lorraine, slice 440
French onion soup $\frac{1}{2}$ pint 270	yoghurt, small carton 25

(c) Choose your own food for a day from the list given and total the calories.

15.9   Decorating

Fiona and Adrian want to decorate the living room of a house before they move in. The room was originally two rooms and you can still see the two pillars where the dividing wall was knocked down. After preparing the surfaces they decided to wallpaper the walls, emulsion paint the ceiling, carpet the whole floor together with underfelt, gloss paint the windows, clear varnish the doors, replace the large pane in the front window because it was cracked and have new curtains for front and back windows.

From the diagram (Fig. 15.4) and the information given find the cost involved to complete the job, to the nearest £.

Allow 1 roll of wallpaper for windows and doors.
1 roll of wallpaper is 10.05 m × 52 cm (remember you can only buy whole rolls of paper).
Wallpaper is £4.99 a roll.
Emulsion paint is £2.99 for a litre tin and £5.99 for a $2\frac{1}{2}$ litre tin. 1 litre covers 12 m².

238

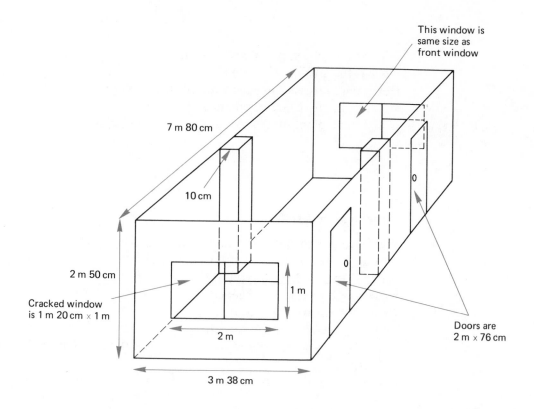

Figure 15.4 Living room to be decorated

1 litre of undercoat (sufficient for windows and skirting board) costs £1.99.
1 litre of gloss paint (sufficient for windows and skirting board) costs £1.99.
1 tin of clear varnish (sufficient for doors) costs £1.99.
Carpet is in 3 m, $3\frac{1}{2}$ m and 4 m widths. Cost is £7.99 per m².
Underfelt is in 4 m widths. Cost is 80p per m².
Glass cut to size is £6 per m².
Curtain material is in 1 m widths and is £4.99 per metre run.

Hints

Find the cost of separate items and then find the grand total. Head each item separately so it is easier to see where a mistake is made.

Wallpaper

Ignore walls and doors. Assume no waste. If necessary draw another diagram of the walls stretched out in one long piece. Find how many strips of wallpaper are needed to go round the room (don't forget the pillars).

Now find the total length of wallpaper required.
What is length of one roll?
How many rolls are needed (remember you cannot buy part of a roll)?
One roll canbe subtracted because of windows and doors.
What is the cost of one roll?
What is the cost of all the wallpaper?

239

Paint

1 litre of emulsion paint covers 12 m².
What is the area of the ceiling?
How many litres are needed to cover the ceiling?
Which is the best buy of emulsion paint?
   The gloss paint, undercoat and varnish are straightforward.

Carpet and underfelt

You have got to buy the width of carpet given — when you cut some off to make it fit across the width you still have to pay for it.
Which carpet width will you use?
What length of carpet is needed?
What area of carpet is required?
Now find the cost of the carpet.
Underfelt — you can allow for bits to be cut off a 4 m width and be used under the carpet.
Find the area of the room and find the cost of the underfelt at 80p per m².

Glass

Find the area of the broken pane.
Find its cost at £6 per m².

Curtains

Allow *twice* the width of the window for a curtain to cover a window and an extra half metre longer than the window to cover the hems at top and bottom.
The material is 1 m wide.
How many widths are required to cover one window using the allowance above?
What length of material is needed to cover one window with the allowances given?
How much is needed for 2 windows?
What is the cost of the curtain material?
What is the cost of the curtains?

Now find the total cost of doing the room.

15.10 The Holiday

Below is part of a ferry timetable for a crossing from Dover to Calais and Calais to Dover giving times and costs.

Dover to Calais		Calais to Dover	
Time	Fare Charge	Time	Fare Charge
0200	D	0015	D
0400	D	0200	D
0600	C	0400	D
0730	C	0600	D
0900	B	0730	C
1030	B	0915	C
1200	B	1045	B
1330	B	1215	B
1500	B	1345	B
1630	B	1515	B
1800	B	1645	B
1930	C	1815	B
2100	C	1945	B
2230	D	2115	C
2359	D	2245	C

All fares are for a single journey only:

Travelling with a Vehicle	Charge D (£)	Charge C (£)	Charge B (£)
Adults (anyone over 14)	11.00	11.00	11.00
Children (4 and under 14; under 4 free)	5.50	5.50	5.50
Vehicles			
Overall length not exceeding 4.00 m	32.00	42.00	50.00
4.50 m	36.00	50.00	60.00
5.50 m	43.00	59.00	70.00

4 students from Sheffield decide to travel by car to Venice for a camping holiday, and for the purpose of estimating how much it is going to cost they make the following assumptions.

They want to catch the cheapest morning ferry from Dover as long as it is not before 0500 hours and they want to return on the 1215 hours ferry from Calais.

The car is 4.40 m long and does 40 miles to the gallon. Petrol in England costs £2 per gallon, in France 6 francs per litre and in Italy 1500 lire per litre.

They work on 1 gallon being 4.5 litres.
Exchange rates are: £1 = 12 francs, £1 = 2500 lire.
Sheffield to Dover is 240 miles.
Calais to the Italian border is 680 miles.
The Italian border to Venice is 220 miles.
Camping fees
per night are: England (1 night): Site (any number of persons) £2.50.
France (4 nights): Site 8 francs plus 4 francs per person.
Venice (10 nights): Site 1250 lire plus 750 lire per person.
Using these figures, how much was the estimate for each student?

Hints

Read the question carefully and try to imagine the journey involved and the costs associated with it. Split the journey into various stages, England, ferry, France,

Italy, and work out the costs in each country, remembering that in France they will be in francs and in Italy in lire. Also, they are not only going from Sheffield to Venice but returning as well.

England

What is the total mileage in England?
Find how many gallons of petrol are wanted and the cost.
Add on the camping fees in England.

Ferry

Which is the cheapest morning ferry after 0500 hours?
Find the cost of taking the car across to Calais with four passengers.
Which ferry is the return journey made on?
Find the cost for the car with four passengers.

France

How much is petrol in France per litre (francs)?
How much is this per gallon (francs)? 4.5 litres = 1 gallon.
What is the cost per gallon in £?
Find the total mileage in France.
Now find the cost of the petrol.
Add on the camping fees in France.

Italy

How much is petrol in Italy per litre (lire)?
How much is this per gallon (lire)?
What is the cost per gallon in £?
Find the total mileage in Italy.
Now find the cost of the petrol.
Add on the camping fees in Italy.

Now find the total estimated cost of the whole journey and how much it will cost each student.

15.11 Office Space Organisation

A firm of solicitors have one main office for all the partners. The office is L-shaped and the measurements of it are as in Fig. 15.5.

The office has to house the following furniture:
3 typing desks, each 4 ft long × 2 ft 6 in wide × 2 ft 6 in high.
3 typing chairs — allow 18 in square for each.
2 document cupboards, each 6 ft 6 in high × 4 ft wide × 18 in deep.
1 open bookcase floor to ceiling, 5 ft wide × 1 ft deep.
1 table 3 ft long × 2 ft 6 in wide × 2 ft 6 in high, with a switchboard
2 ft × 18 in × 1 ft resting on it.
3 ordinary chairs — allow 2 ft square for each.
   Furniture costs are: typing desks £95 each, typing chairs £48 each, document cupboards £84 each, open bookcase £110, table £130, ordinary chairs £42 each (the switchboard is on rental).

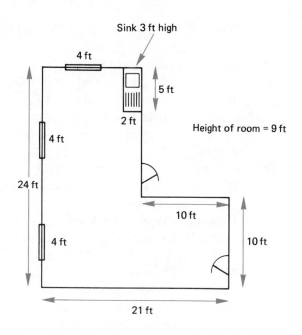

Sink 3 ft high

4 ft

5 ft

2 ft

Height of room = 9 ft

4 ft

24 ft

10 ft

10 ft

4 ft

21 ft

Figure 15.5 Plan of office

Carpeting costs £9 per sq yd fitted and underfelt costs £1.35 per sq yd fitted. The room was decorated at a cost of £256.

The Health and Safety at Work Act states that for each employee in an office there must be at least 40 sq ft of free area and 400 cu ft of free space.

(a) What was the cost of furnishing the office including decorating and carpeting? (Neglect below the sink.)

(b) Draw a scale drawing of the office (scale 2 ft = 1 in) and place the furniture, drawn to scale, in the office so as to leave access to cupboards and filing cabinets.

(c) Calculate how much floor space was left when all the furniture was placed in the office.

(d) What percentage of the total floor area does the furniture take up?

(e) What is the volume of the room?

What volume does the furniture take up? Assume the space below the sink is taken up by cupboards and allow the chairs to be 3 ft high with a base the same as the areas given.

(f) (i) If there are 4 employees in the office would this conform to the Health and Safety at Work Act? (ii) What is the maximum number of employees that would be allowed, by this law, to work in the office?

Hints

(a) Find the cost of the items of furniture.

Check that you have included the correct number of items.

Calculate the area of the room, in sq yd or sq ft.

Now find the cost of carpeting the room at £9 per sq yd and of underfelt at £1.35 per sq yd.

(If you find the area of the room in sq ft then find the cost of carpeting and underfelt per sq ft, remembering that 1 sq yd = 9 sq ft.)

What was the cost of decorating?

243

Now add up cost of furniture, carpeting and underfelt, and decorating to find the total cost.

(b) Make a scale drawing of the office.

You can now draw to scale each item of furniture on the plan of the office.

Or you can draw each item of furniture, cut it out, and start placing it on the office plan to see where might be the best position of each item. It is easier to move the pieces of paper about than to continually rub out pencil drawings.

(c) The floor area was required in (a).

Now calculate how much floor area each item of furniture takes up.

Add them all together.

How much floor space is left?

(d) How much floor area does the furniture take up?

What fraction is this of the total floor area?

Now find the percentage.

(e) Find the volume of the room.

Calculate the volume of each item of furniture, not forgetting the sink or floor to ceiling bookcase, and the chairs.

Add them all together to find the total volume taken up by the furniture.

(f) (i) Work out from question (d) what area of free area there is on the office floor.

Look at the requirements of the Health and Safety at Work Act and see whether 4 employees would be allowed under free area.

From question (f) see whether 4 employees have enough free space under the Act.

If the answer is yes to both questions then 4 employees will be allowed.

(ii) Divide the free area by 40 and the free space by 400. The smallest of these two answers is the maximum number of employees allowed to work in the office.

15.12 The Retail Shop

John got a job as sales assistant at one of a chain of shops whose main products were tobacco, newspapers and periodicals, books and paperbacks, toys, stationery, records and tapes, and gifts.

He had to spend eight weeks in each section in order to make himself familiar with the following tasks: stock control/ordering, buying considerations, receipt of stock, customers' orders, returns from customers etc., display of goods, returns to suppliers, product knowledge, depreciation, equipment.

John asked to go first in the records and tapes section and he was given the task of stock control/ordering for the first week. This consisted of completing a prepared sheet of record sales in tally form and one of the sheets (the one for the top 10) is shown. In that month, December, a single sold at £1.50, an album at £5.50, and the profit on the selling price was 30%.

From the data given on the sales sheet and the figures above calculate:

(a) how many singles were sold in the week;

(b) how many albums were sold in the week;

(c) how much cash was taken on Saturday 14 December;

(d) the cost of total stock held on Monday 9 December at retail prices of (i) singles, (ii) albums;

(e) what was the weekly profit on (i) sale of singles, (ii) sale of albums.

Singles	Stock on 9/12	Mon. 9/12	Tue. 10/12	Wed. 11/12	Thur. 12/12	Fri. 13/12	Sat. 14/12	Stock on 14/12	Sales
I'm Your Man	60	HHT II	IIII	HHT HHT III	III	HHT III	HHT HHT HHT III		
Saving all my Love for You	60	IIII	HHT IIII	HHT II	HHT HHT	HHT HHT	HHT HHT IIII		
See the Day	60	II	HHT HHT HHT	HHT IIII	II	HHT HHT II	HHT HHT I		
A Good Heart	60	HHT III	II	II	HHT II	HHT III	HHT		
Separate Lives	60	III	I	HHT	II	HHT HHT HHT III	HHT III		
Don't Break my Heart	40	II	HHT	HHT III	I	HHT II	II		
The Show	40	II	IIII	HHT HHT	II	III	HHT HHT III		
Road to Nowhere	40	III	HHT	III	HHT	HHT II			
Say You, Say Me	40	HHT HHT II	I	II	HHT	II	HHT HHT IIII		
The Power of Love	40	I	I	III	I	HHT HHT III	HHT HHT III		

Albums	Stock on 9/12	Mon. 9/12	Tue. 10/12	Wed. 11/12	Thur. 12/12	Fri. 13/12	Sat. 14/12	Stock on 14/12	Sales
That's What I Call Music 6	25	II	I	III	I	IIII	HHT II		
Hits 3	25		II	I	III	I	HHT HHT I		
The Single Collections	25	II	II	III	II	IIII	HHT I		
Now – A Christmas Album	25	I		III	III	II	HHT		
Love Songs	25	II	II	II	III	HHT	IIII		
Greatest Hits of 1986	20	I	I	I	II	IIII	HHT IIII		
Brothers in Arms	20		I	I	III	II	HHT I		
The Love Album	20	II	III	II	II	IIII	HHT I		
Promises	20	I	I	II		IIII	HHT II		
Love Hurts	20	III		II	II	HHT	IIII		

Figure 15.6   Record sales sheets

15.13   The Trainee Nurse

Janet is a trainee nurse and one of her tasks, under the guidance of a qualified nurse, has been to look after a patient who had had a prostate operation. She had to take blood pressure, pulse rate and temperature as well as record the intake and output of fluid.

Janet was only on duty for one session and was followed by Christine and Paula.

(a) From the pulse rates and temperatures given draw a graph to show how these changed over the period.

ANY HOSPITAL
FLUID CHART — Record in Millilitres

NAME:

Instructions	Time	Oral	N/gastric	Nature	Total	IVI		Irrigation		Urine	Nature	Total	Drain	Nature	Aspirate	Vomit	Nature
Intravenous infusion — see prescription card	1 a.m.																
	2 a.m.																
	3 a.m.																
	4 a.m.			*NIL ORALLY*													
	5 a.m.																
Oral fluids — water only	6 a.m.																
	7 a.m.																
	8 a.m.			THEATRE						600							
	9 a.m.																
	10 a.m.																
Irrigation 3 litre normal saline	11 a.m.			Returned from theatre													
	12 md.					1000											
	1 p.m.																
	2 p.m.					1st unit blood		3000	normal saline								
	3 p.m.									2000							
Sterivac drain recharge	4 p.m.																
	5 p.m.												50				
	6 p.m.	100		H_2O		2nd unit blood											
	7 p.m.							3000	normal saline	2000							
	8 p.m.																
Observe catheter drainage	9 p.m.									2000						200	
	10 p.m.	100		H_2O		1000	normal saline										
	11 p.m.							3000	normal saline	2000							
	12 mn.					200 absorbed		1000 absorbed		1000			20				
		TOTAL INTAKE:											TOTAL OUTPUT:				

INTAKE — OUTPUT

DATE: WARD:

Figure 15.7 Hospital patient's fluid chart

Time	1300	1400	1500	1600	1700	1800	1900	2000	2100	2200	2300	2400
Pulse rate per min	95	92	90	86	84	81	81	80	80	78	78	80
Time	1300	1400	1500	1600	1700	1800	1900	2000	2100	2200	2300	2400
Temp. (°C)	39.0	38.4	38.0	38.6	37.8	37.5	37.0	37.2	37.3	36.9	37.0	37.0

(b) From the fluid chart given calculate the fluid intake and output up until midnight on the day of the operation.

Hints

Pulse rate graph

Draw time on the horizontal axis (1 cm = 1 hour) and on the vertical axis cover the range 60 to 100 (i.e. begin the vertical scale at 60 and not 0) with a scale 4 cm = pulse rate 10.

Temperature graph

On the horizontal axis use 1 cm = 1 hour and on the vertical axis cover the range 34°C to 42°C with a scale of 2 cm = 1°C.

Fluid chart

Assume a unit of blood is 420 ml of fluid.

Under the heading IVI (intravenous infusion) remember that at 12 midnight only 200 ml have been absorbed out of that put up at 10 p.m.

On the irrigation (fluid) at 12 midnight only 1000 ml have been absorbed from the 3000 ml put up at 11 p.m.

For the total intake, add the IVI to that taken orally.

The total output is found by subtracting the irrigation fluid (drip) put in from the total drainage, the urine (measured by catheter drain), the sterivac drain and the fluid from vomit.

15.14 The Garage

The plans and drawings (Fig. 15.8 and 15.9) are of a garage to be built at the side of a house. (c/c is short for 'between centres'.)

The building consists of concrete foundations ('footings'), single brick walls with double brick piers and corners, a damp-proof course (DPC) of felt, timber joists across the roof on which there is chipboard and mineralised felt, two wooden doors and two windows, and has a concrete floor laid on hardcore. Water is to be allowed to run off. From the information given calculate the approximate cost to a DIY enthusiast (i.e. with no labour charges) of building the garage.

Hardcore is £3 per m^3 and the minimum load is 5 m^3.

Ready-mixed concrete can only be ordered in $\frac{1}{2}$ m^3 loads costing £37 per m^3 and £22 per $\frac{1}{2}$ m^3.

Bricks are £180 per 1000 but £20 per 100 when ordered in hundreds. 60 bricks will give a surface wall area of 1 m^2. Allow 300 bricks for piers and corners.

The damp-proof course felt is a brick wide and costs £4.75 per roll, which is 10 m long.

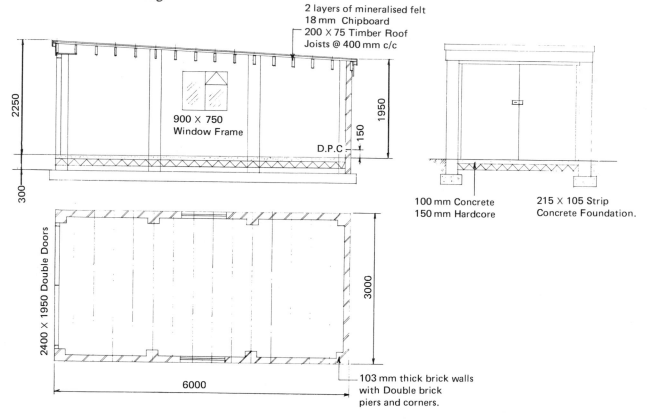

Figure 15.8 Plan and elevations of garage

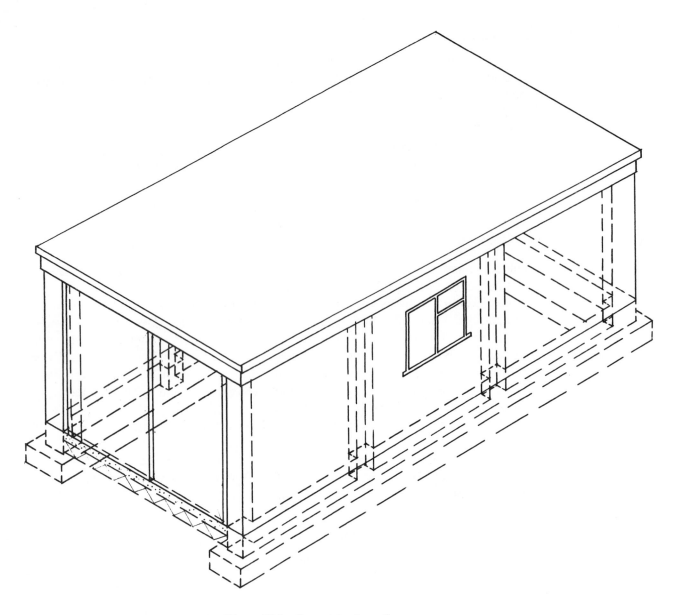

Figure 15.9 Isometric view of garage

Wooden joists 200 mm × 75 mm are 36p per 30 cm, cut to size.

18 mm chipboard is only sold in 250 cm × 125 cm sheets at £7 per sheet.

Mineralised felt is £14.50 a roll, 1 m × 10 m; it is to be laid across the garage roof with a 50 mm overlap all round.

Double doors, including hinges and all fittings, are made for £170.

Window frames 900 mm × 750 mm are £27.50 each.

Glass, cut to size, is £5 per m².

Fascia board, 150 mm × 25 mm, to go all round the garage to cover up the ends of the joists and make a neater job, is £1 per metre run.

Allow £25 for extras, to include paint, making mortar, etc.

Hints

Where do you start?
    Start where you like because one calculation is not dependent on another.

248

Cost of Bricks

What is the surface area of the walls?

Remember there is a window in two of the walls, the piers and corners have a certain surface area, and the walls start at the concrete footings.

60 bricks cover 1 m².

How many bricks are required for the walls? How many for piers and corners?

Work out the cost of bricks at £180 per 1000 and £20 for odd hundreds.

Cost of Hardcore and Concrete

What volume of hardcore is needed?

What will it cost?

What is the volume of concrete for the floor?

What is the volume of concrete for the footings?

Total volume of concrete?

Now find the cost of the concrete.

Cost of Wood

What is the length of one joist?

What will it cost?

How many joists are there?

What is the total cost for the joists?

What length of fascia board is needed for the sides of the garage?

What will it cost?

What lengths are required for front and back?

What will it cost?

Cost of Roof

How many sheets of chipboard are required?

Remember you can only buy whole sheets.

What is the cost?

The mineralised felt has to be laid with an overlap. What length of felt is required to cover the roof allowing for this overlap? (2 layers required.)

How many rolls are required?

What is the cost?

Other Items

How many rolls of damp-proof course felt are needed?

What is the cost?

Calculate the area of glass in each window. Find the cost.

How much are window frames, doors and extras?

Final Cost

Add up all the items to find the total cost.

Answers to Exercises

Exercise 1.1

1 Forty-six	2 Five hundred and eight	3 Seventy-two
4 Forty-eight	5 Eighty-four	6 Two hundred and sixty-seven
7 Five hundred and three		8 Six hundred and seventy
9 Three hundred and nine		10 Eight hundred and twenty-one

11 One thousand four hundred and sixty-three
12 Two thousand five hundred and six
13 Three thousand and eighty-four
14 One thousand and nine
15 Twenty seven thousand two hundred and eighty-three
16 Forty thousand seven hundred and thirteen
17 Twenty thousand and fifty-eight
18 Three hundred and seventy-two thousand five hundred and forty-two
19 Six hundred and twenty thousand four hundred and ninety-one
20 Five million nine hundred and twenty-six thousand four hundred and seventy-three.

Exercise 1.2

1 73	2 109	3 344	4 1308
5 4923	6 2004	7 12 065	8 62 591
9 20 002	10 150 000	11 269	12 280 534
13 506 027	14 832 903	15 1 342 000	16 3 000 000
17 607 607	18 Four hundreds	19 One thousand	20 No ten thousands

Exercise 1.3

1 48	2 24	3 57	4 89
5 82	6 164	7 80	8 100
9 204	10 455	11 770	12 435
13 844	14 1812	15 312	16 979
17 3639	18 4455	19 849	20 4184

Exercise 1.4

1 90	2 414	3 217	4 73
5 2879	6 982	7 4647	8 5731
9 940	10 7398	11 730	12 3520

Exercise 1.5

1 56	**2** 186 798	**3** 149; 107	**4** 19
5 62	**6** 38		

7 (a) 182   (b) 337   (c) 342   (d) 391   (e) 334   (f) 929   **8** 271; 28
9 206   **10** 1 and 6; 5 and 2; 4 and 3

Exercise 1.6

1 17	**2** 178	**3** 32	**4** 36
5 27	**6** 82	**7** 208	**8** 87
9 157	**10** 336	**11** 507	**12** 836
13 1424	**14** 19	**15** 193	**16** 2578
17 178	**18** 257	**19** 939	**20** 286

Exercise 1.7

1 217	**2** 7	**3** 8	**4** 253; 186
5 77	**6** 22; 13	**7** 137	**8** 175
9 398	**10** 14	**11** £46 720	**12** Chester (+37)

Exercise 1.8

1 324	**2** 612	**3** 215	**4** 258
5 301	**6** 256	**7** 504	**8** 1564
9 2613	**10** 3116	**11** 4560	**12** 2652
13 5248	**14** 2910	**15** 2028	**16** 3240
17 11 481	**18** 3920	**19** 4602	**20** 20 824

Exercise 1.9

1 £184	**2** 624	**3** £156	**4** 576 tons
5 110	**6** £1173	**7** £780	**8** 189
9 864	**10** £245	**11** 1253	**12** £783
13 6244	**14** £108		

Exercise 1.10

1 24	**2** 23	**3** 25	**4** 38
5 67	**6** 83	**7** 425	**8** 504
9 607	**10** 394	**11** 54	**12** 68
13 532	**14** 642	**15** 307	**16** 208
17 473	**18** 846	**19** 502	**20** 97

Exercise 1.11

1 £16	**2** 325	**3** 36	**4** 57
5 £94	**6** £29	**7** 11 ft	**8** 72 pkts

9 £244   10 75   11 50 000; more than
12 2 250 000

Exercise 1.12

1 11	2 7	3 24	4 17
5 12	6 10	7 3	8 3
9 9	10 18	11 7	12 3
13 6	14 0	15 13	16 12
17 2	18 18	19 10	20 0

Exercise 1.13

1 3600	2 60	3 150	4 2900
5 16 200	6 92 000	7 1400	8 2400
9 6000	10 7200	11 32 000	12 15 000
13 630 000	14 2200	15 51 000	16 29
17 780	18 15	19 270	20 31
21 1970	22 320	23 5200	24 400
25 20	26 80	27 700	28 610
29 500	30 350		

Exercise 1.14

1 60	2 100	3 90	4 20
5 300	6 600	7 390	8 400
9 0	10 1000	11 5000	12 5000
13 1830	14 1800	15 2000	16 80
17 100	18 2500	19 2000	20 170

Exercise 1.15

1 900	2 42	3 1000	4 1500
5 2800	6 2800	7 16 000	8 7500
9 34 000	10 4800	11 64	12 369
13 97	14 230	15 173	16 160
17 384	18 40	19 62	20 11 000

Exercise 1.16

1 C	2 A	3 D	4 B
5 C	6 A	7 C	8 D
9 C	10 A	11 C	12 B
13 A	14 C	15 B	16 C
17 A	18 B	19 C	20 D

Exercise 2.1

1 $\frac{8}{16}$	2 $\frac{12}{9}$	3 $\frac{2}{4}$	4 $\frac{3}{9}$
5 $\frac{4}{16}$	6 $\frac{9}{6}$	7 $\frac{12}{8}$	8 $\frac{9}{12}$
9 $\frac{12}{18}$	10 $\frac{4}{10}$	11 $\frac{16}{20}$	12 $\frac{14}{16}$
13 $\frac{6}{10}$	14 $\frac{33}{24}$	15 $\frac{24}{20}$	16 $\frac{15}{9}$
17 $\frac{6}{16}$	18 $\frac{20}{32}$	19 $\frac{10}{4}$	20 $\frac{6}{8}$
21 $\frac{12}{16}$	22 $\frac{8}{10}$	23 $\frac{20}{32}$	24 $\frac{4}{6}$
25 $\frac{9}{12}$	26 $\frac{25}{10}$	27 $\frac{16}{12}$	28 $\frac{14}{16}$
29 $\frac{4}{8}$	30 $\frac{20}{16}$		

Exercise 2.2

1 $\frac{3}{4}$	2 $\frac{4}{3}$	3 $\frac{2}{3}$	4 $\frac{3}{4}$
5 $\frac{3}{2}$	6 $\frac{2}{3}$	7 $\frac{3}{4}$	8 $\frac{7}{8}$
9 $\frac{4}{5}$	10 $\frac{7}{16}$	11 $\frac{5}{2}$	12 $\frac{3}{1}$
13 $\frac{8}{5}$	14 $\frac{2}{3}$	15 $\frac{2}{5}$	16 $\frac{3}{8}$
17 $\frac{5}{2}$	18 $\frac{2}{5}$	19 $\frac{3}{4}$	20 $\frac{5}{8}$

Exercise 2.3

1 $\frac{1}{4}, \frac{1}{3}$	2 $\frac{3}{8}, \frac{1}{2}, \frac{7}{10}, \frac{3}{4}$	3 $\frac{2}{3}, \frac{4}{5}$	4 $\frac{1}{3}, \frac{3}{8}, \frac{5}{12}$
5 $\frac{5}{8}, \frac{3}{4}, \frac{5}{6}$	6 $\frac{5}{8}, \frac{2}{3}$	7 $\frac{1}{3}, \frac{1}{2}, \frac{3}{5}$	8 $\frac{5}{8}, \frac{2}{3}, \frac{4}{5}$
9 $\frac{1}{4}, \frac{1}{3}, \frac{5}{12}$	10 $\frac{7}{16}, \frac{1}{2}, \frac{5}{8}$	11 $\frac{1}{2}, \frac{9}{16}, \frac{3}{4}, \frac{7}{8}$	12 $\frac{1}{4}, \frac{9}{24}, \frac{5}{8}$
13 $\frac{1}{4}, \frac{2}{5}, \frac{9}{20}, \frac{7}{12}$	14 $\frac{2}{3}, \frac{3}{4}$	15 $\frac{3}{2}, \frac{7}{4}, \frac{15}{8}$	16 $\frac{2}{3}, \frac{3}{4}, \frac{4}{5}$
17 $\frac{3}{4}, \frac{5}{6}, \frac{11}{12}, 1$	18 $\frac{3}{8}, \frac{7}{16}, \frac{1}{2}, \frac{5}{8}$	19 $\frac{9}{16}, \frac{5}{8}, \frac{23}{32}, \frac{3}{4}$	20 $\frac{17}{20}, 1, \frac{11}{10}, \frac{6}{5}$

Exercise 2.4

1 $1\frac{1}{4}$	2 $2\frac{4}{5}$	3 $2\frac{1}{2}$	4 $1\frac{3}{4}$
5 $3\frac{2}{3}$	6 $1\frac{3}{10}$	7 $1\frac{1}{2}$	8 $1\frac{2}{5}$
9 $2\frac{5}{8}$	10 $2\frac{1}{3}$	11 $3\frac{1}{4}$	12 $4\frac{1}{2}$
13 $2\frac{1}{3}$	14 $4\frac{1}{2}$	15 $3\frac{1}{2}$	16 $1\frac{7}{8}$
17 $2\frac{1}{2}$	18 $5\frac{2}{5}$	19 $6\frac{1}{2}$	20 $3\frac{1}{2}$

Exercise 2.5

1 $\frac{11}{4}$	2 $\frac{23}{6}$	3 $\frac{5}{2}$	4 $\frac{13}{4}$
5 $\frac{11}{6}$	6 $\frac{5}{3}$	7 $\frac{17}{5}$	8 $\frac{19}{8}$
9 $\frac{17}{3}$	10 $\frac{27}{4}$	11 $\frac{29}{8}$	12 $\frac{9}{5}$
13 $\frac{33}{10}$	14 $\frac{23}{8}$	15 $\frac{15}{4}$	16 $\frac{23}{16}$
17 $\frac{11}{5}$	18 $\frac{10}{3}$	19 $\frac{21}{4}$	20 $\frac{31}{8}$

Exercise 2.6

1 $\frac{8}{15}$	2 $3\frac{3}{8}$	3 $\frac{3}{4}$	4 $\frac{7}{8}$
5 $\frac{11}{12}$	6 $1\frac{3}{16}$	7 $1\frac{1}{8}$	8 $1\frac{1}{2}$
9 $1\frac{11}{12}$	10 $3\frac{5}{8}$	11 $5\frac{5}{6}$	12 $5\frac{1}{2}$
13 $4\frac{11}{16}$	14 $4\frac{1}{2}$	15 $4\frac{15}{16}$	16 $3\frac{17}{24}$
17 $4\frac{3}{8}$	18 $2\frac{1}{10}$	19 $2\frac{3}{5}$	20 $5\frac{5}{8}$

Exercise 2.7

1 $\frac{1}{12}$	2 $1\frac{3}{8}$	3 $1\frac{5}{8}$	4 $\frac{9}{16}$
5 $\frac{3}{8}$	6 $\frac{5}{16}$	7 $\frac{5}{12}$	8 $2\frac{5}{16}$
9 $2\frac{7}{24}$	10 $1\frac{7}{16}$	11 $1\frac{5}{12}$	12 $1\frac{5}{12}$
13 $1\frac{15}{16}$	14 $1\frac{19}{24}$	15 $1\frac{3}{8}$	16 $\frac{17}{24}$
17 $\frac{11}{16}$	18 $1\frac{1}{2}$	19 $1\frac{3}{4}$	20 $1\frac{5}{24}$

Exercise 2.8

1 $\frac{1}{2}$	2 $2\frac{5}{6}$	3 90	4 $\frac{3}{8}$
5 $\frac{5}{8}$	6 $\frac{15}{26}$	7 3	8 $3\frac{1}{3}$
9 $4\frac{1}{2}$	10 $1\frac{1}{8}$	11 5	12 $1\frac{17}{32}$
13 $1\frac{3}{4}$	14 $1\frac{3}{16}$	15 $\frac{5}{6}$	16 120
17 72	18 45	19 £45	20 £54

Exercise 2.9

1 $2\frac{1}{5}$	2 $3\frac{3}{8}$	3 $\frac{7}{18}$	4 $2\frac{4}{5}$
5 $2\frac{1}{8}$	6 $4\frac{1}{2}$	7 2	8 $1\frac{1}{4}$
9 $\frac{4}{7}$	10 $\frac{3}{4}$	11 $1\frac{1}{2}$	12 6
13 3	14 $1\frac{1}{8}$	15 $1\frac{11}{16}$	16 $1\frac{5}{9}$
17 $1\frac{3}{4}$	18 $\frac{4}{7}$	19 $2\frac{5}{6}$	20 $\frac{3}{10}$

Exercise 2.10

1 1	2 $\frac{5}{6}$	3 9	4 $1\frac{1}{4}$
5 $2\frac{1}{2}$	6 $2\frac{9}{14}$	7 2	8 $1\frac{1}{4}$
9 3	10 $1\frac{2}{3}$	11 $3\frac{3}{8}$	12 $5\frac{1}{3}$
13 $5\frac{7}{12}$	14 $\frac{5}{8}$	15 $4\frac{4}{9}$	16 34
17 4	18 $1\frac{7}{8}$	19 $2\frac{5}{8}$	20 $4\frac{1}{8}$

Exercise 2.11

1 £40	2 270p	3 £90	4 8 ft
5 £90	6 £60	7 £5	8 £6

9 18 caramels, 6 eclairs   **10** 9 ft

11 (a) £510   (b) £255   (c) £85

12 £600   (b) £93 600   **13** $7\frac{1}{2}$ min   **14** 200

15 16   **16** 18   **17** 90   **18** 60, 30

19 £72m   **20** £14m; £70m

Exercise 2.12

1 C	**2** B	**3** C	**4** A
5 D	**6** B	**7** C	**8** B
9 C	**10** C	**11** C	**12** C
13 A	**14** A	**15** C	**16** C
17 C	**18** C	**19** B	**20** D

Exercise 3.1

1 2.64   **2** three point nought six five   **3** 25.63

4 8.25   **5** 0.59   **6** 107.96   **7** 3.08

8 14.202   **9** 63.078   **10** seven point five two

11 twenty-six point seven nine   **12** eight point four

13 fifteen point nought six   **14** eighteen point nought nought three

15 ten point five six   **16** forty-two point seven nought three

17 one hundred and five point nought two

18 thirty-six point one nought four

19 one tenth   **20** five hundredths

Exercise 3.2

1 0.3	**2** 0.182	**3** 0.4	**4** 0.8
5 0.1	**6** 0.15	**7** 0.27	**8** 0.35
9 0.58	**10** 0.11	**11** 0.72	**12** 0.125
13 0.303	**14** 0.084	**15** 0.006	**16** 0.05
17 0.902	**18** 0.022	**19** 1.5	**20** 3.46

Exercise 3.3

1 $\frac{3}{5}$	**2** $\frac{7}{20}$	**3** $\frac{3}{8}$	**4** $\frac{3}{10}$
5 $\frac{4}{5}$	**6** $\frac{1}{4}$	**7** $\frac{19}{50}$	**8** $\frac{16}{25}$
9 $\frac{3}{4}$	**10** $\frac{22}{25}$	**11** $\frac{33}{250}$	**12** $\frac{5}{8}$
13 $\frac{47}{50}$	**14** $\frac{7}{10}$	**15** $\frac{7}{8}$	**16** $\frac{13}{20}$
17 $\frac{341}{500}$	**18** $\frac{23}{50}$	**19** $\frac{13}{25}$	**20** $\frac{47}{250}$

Exercise 3.4

1 15.52	**2** 145.396	**3** 9.9	**4** 14.4
5 26.59	**6** 47.52	**7** 38.9	**8** 31.89
9 155.4	**10** 33.671	**11** 68.27	**12** 111.38
13 109.46	**14** 7.06	**15** 98.14	**16** 23.762
17 74.122	**18** 30.612	**19** 125.906	**20** 72.163

Exercise 3.5

1 2.8	**2** 7.26	**3** 5.4	**4** 16.23
5 5.2	**6** 22.55	**7** 13.81	**8** 15.92
9 77.36	**10** 61.78	**11** 16.57	**12** 15.62
13 452.71	**14** 29.97	**15** 67.88	**16** 57.75
17 4.66	**18** 45.38	**19** 14.17	**20** 17.92

Exercise 3.6

1 20.64	**2** 301.780	**3** 1.776	**4** 6.9
5 60.2	**6** 202.4	**7** 118.4	**8** 12.04
9 14.4	**10** 23.76	**11** 29.664	**12** 49.64
13 2.24	**14** 7.36	**15** 3.01	**16** 0.1482
17 6.308	**18** 301.2	**19** 0.68	**20** 0.416

Exercise 3.7

1 370	**2** 0.037	**3** 560	**4** 2340
5 1.73	**6** 580	**7** 216 000	**8** 3955.1
9 700	**10** 360	**11** 50	**12** 37.5
13 3.75	**14** 0.375	**15** 0.0028	**16** 0.0056
17 9.24	**18** 0.003 806	**19** 0.000 06	**20** 0.032
21 258 000	**22** 83 090	**23** 0.428	**24** 0.002 31

Exercise 3.8

1 13.6	**2** 3.6	**3** 14.0	**4** 13.8
5 23.4	**6** 16.4	**7** 24.8	**8** 3.5
9 5.1	**10** 6.8	**11** 6.9	**12** 71.0
13 182.0	**14** 64.0	**15** 830.0	**16** 356.0
17 79.0	**18** 0.026	**19** 0.0064	**20** 0.69

Exercise 3.9

1 7.7	**2** 3.0	**3** 3.5	**4** 3.7
5 5.9	**6** 0.3	**7** 1.0	**8** 8.0
9 0.8	**10** 15.1	**11** 29.0	**12** 3.0
13 0.2	**14** 0.1	**15** 2.6	**16** 10.8
17 10.0	**18** 3.3	**19** 1.0	**20** 28.7

Exercise 3.10

1 2.93	**2** 0.72	**3** 8.00	**4** 18.76
5 9.09	**6** 76.18	**7** 0.85	**8** 3.00
9 0.10	**10** 15.33	**11** 1.08	**12** 0.21
13 29.18	**14** 5.40	**15** 12.09	**16** 10.10
17 0.01	**18** 9.20	**19** 75.48	**20** 35.06

Exercise 3.11

1 6500	2 500	3 0.077	4 960
5 2800	6 37 000	7 310	8 18.0
9 19.0	10 3.1	11 7.0	12 0.057
13 0.069	14 4000	15 5.0	16 0.10
17 2100	18 16.0	19 7.9	20 2.5

Exercise 3.12

1 72.8	2 72.9	3 7000	4 0.0239
5 32.5	6 7.64	7 0.298	8 8080
9 8090	10 35.0	11 0.0506	12 50 700
13 4100	14 2.07	15 5.83	16 791.0
17 75.1	18 30.0	19 6000	20 3.08

Exercise 3.13

1 0.6	2 0.375	3 0.66	4 0.5
5 0.4	6 0.25	7 0.75	8 0.625
9 0.33	10 0.7	11 0.875	12 0.8
13 1.66	14 1.75	15 1.4	16 1.375
17 1.5	18 1.25	19 1.33	20 1.8

Exercise 3.14

1 3.725×10^3	2 3.725×10^{-3}	3 7.864×10^3	4 2.975×10^3
5 3.725×10^2	6 3.725×10^4	7 9.87×10^1	8 5.69×10^5
9 8.526×10^2	10 5.7986×10^3	11 2.88×10^1	12 4.72×10^{-3}
13 9.65×10^{-3}	14 2.46×10^{-2}	15 6.5×10^{-4}	16 7.0×10^{-5}
17 1.25×10^{-2}	18 3.0×10^{-3}	19 1.42×10^{-4}	20 3.6×10^{-2}

Exercise 3.15

1 2300	2 0.000 464	3 640	4 82 500
5 3960	6 20	7 412.5	8 58 000
9 79 000 000	10 525 000	11 3400	12 0.017
13 0.000 34	14 0.0094	15 0.43	16 0.0059
17 0.000 068 7	18 0.000 723	19 0.047	20 0.0094

Exercise 3.16

1 C	2 C	3 A	4 C
5 B	6 D	7 A	8 D
9 C	10 B	11 C	12 D
13 B	14 A	15 C	16 D
17 C	18 B	19 C	20 D

Exercise 4.1

1 £68.95	2 £26.53	3 £9.56	4 £15.66
5 £38.18	6 £78.03	7 £157.81	8 £25.81
9 £248.75	10 £765.88	11 £29.35	12 £22.33
13 £23.89	14 £25.66	15 £31.63	16 £90.25
17 £6.51	18 £16.36	19 £27.17	20 £23.38

Exercise 4.2

1 £51.40	2 £400.80	3 £238.26	4 £6.34
5 £9.60	6 £11.94	7 £145.80	8 £368.20
9 £585.08	10 £9.00	11 £7.92	12 £76.16
13 £63.60	14 £334.80	15 £882.00	16 £311.40
17 £203.06	18 £1.80	19 £37.85	20 £2.49
21 £23.54	22 £3.48	23 £23.35	24 £4.75
25 £15.35	26 £18.35	27 £27.25	28 £536.41
29 £3.54	30 £56.45		

Exercise 4.3

1 84p	2 61p	3 64p	4 £1.11
5 £1.04	6 £1.34	7 70p	8 £1.03
9 86p	10 89p	11 £3.18	12 95p
13 £1.09	14 £1.78	15 £1.35	16 £1.22
17 99p	18 £1.31	19 £3.26	20 £1.30

Exercise 4.4

1 £52.73	2 £13.16	3 £1.83	4 £83.91
5 £1.78	6 (a) £3.08	6 (b) £2.53	6 (c) £6.99
6 (d) £9.78	7 £2.17	8 £122.50	9 £4140
10 £46.56	11 (a) £1068 (b) £89.00		12 £956.80
13 £51.24	14 £48.52	15 £3.37	16 £25.70
17 £8.25	18 £140.80	19 £1140	20 (a) £266
20 (b) £192			

Exercise 4.5

1 C	2 A	3 C	4 C
5 D	6 A	7 B	8 D
9 A	10 D	11 C	12 C
13 D	14 C	15 A	16 C
17 B	18 D	19 C	20 A
21 C			

Exercise 5.1

1 (a) 6000 m   (b) 4000 m   (c) 15 000 m   (d) 50 000 m
2 (a) 3600 m   (b) 9500 m   (c) 830 m   (d) 586 m
3 (a) 9 km   (b) 12 km   (c) 25 km   (d) 100 km
4 (a) 4.8 km   (b) 0.6 km   (c) 2.584 km   (d) 0.04 km
5 (a) 4 m 54 cm   (b) 15 m 6 cm   (c) 53 cm   (d) 8 cm
6 (a) 2 kg   (b) 6 kg   (c) 18 kg   (d) 156 kg
7 (a) 1.75 kg   (b) 3.92 kg   (c) 0.84 kg   (d) 0.075 kg
8 (a) 2000 g   (b) 7000 g   (c) 12 000 g   (d) 20 000 g
9 (a) 3250 g   (b) 940 g   (c) 50 g   (d) 6952 g
10 (a) 3 kg 580 g   (b) 16 kg 200 g   (c) 8 kg 405 g   (d) 340 g
11 (a) 5000 ml   (b) 18 000 ml   (c) 2000 ml   (d) 7000 ml
12 (a) 6250 ml   (b) 380 ml   (c) 7051 ml   (d) 11 600 ml
13 (a) 9 ℓ   (b) 18 ℓ   (c) 32 ℓ   (d) 3 ℓ
14 (a) 4.9 ℓ   (b) 2.564 ℓ   (c) 0.38 ℓ   (d) 0.06 ℓ
15 1.9 ℓ   16 240   17 £1.50   18 4.33 kg
19 12 min 42.5 s   20 70

Exercise 5.2

1 (a) 60 in	(b) 240 in	(c) 96 in	(d) 144 in
2 (a) 32 in	(b) 57 in	(c) 76 in	(d) 186 in
3 (a) 7 ft 6 in	(b) 5 ft 10 in	(c) 2 ft 11 in	(d) 9 ft 2 in
4 (a) 18 ft	(b) 45 ft	(c) 8 ft	(d) 37 ft
5 (a) 6 yd	(b) 8 yd 1 ft	(c) 10 yd 2 ft	(d) 4 yd 2 ft
6 (a) 40 cwt	(b) 100 cwt	(c) 35 cwt	(d) 72 cwt
7 (a) 32 oz	(b) 80 oz	(c) 72 oz	(d) 60 oz
8 (a) 16 pt	(b) 27 pt	(c) 41 pt	(d) 37 pt
9 (a) 40 fl oz	(b) 28 fl oz	(c) 64 fl oz	(d) 115 fl oz
10 8 ton 14 cwt	11 18 lb 12 oz	12 232	13 £21.60
14 7 yd 1 ft	15 7	16 3 gal 3 pt	17 £244.80
18 £26.52	19 1 st 8 lb	20 40	

Exercise 5.3

1 22.5 ℓ	2 9 ft	3 1584 m	4 110 lb
5 2.25 m	6 65 kg	7 99p	8 £2.25
9 £1.10	10 114 g		

Exercise 5.4

1 0800 hours	2 1000 hours	3 1600 hours	4 2100 hours
5 0125 hours	6 0736 hours	7 2130 hours	8 1445 hours
9 0630 hours	10 1645 hours	11 2020 hours	12 0852 hours
13 0830 hours	14 2120 hours	15 1918 hours	16 2322 hours
17 1200 hours	18 2215 hours	19 0015 hours	20 1045 hours

Exercise 5.5

1 4 a.m.	2 3 p.m.	3 6.30 p.m.	4 9.50 p.m.
5 2.15 a.m.	6 7.56 a.m.	7 11.25 p.m.	
8 16 min after midnight		9 4.25 a.m.	10 8.10 p.m.
11 7.52 p.m.	12 1.01 a.m.	13 10.38 a.m.	14 9.15 p.m.
15 12.26 p.m.	16 11.05 a.m.	17 8 min to one in the morning	
18 3.46 a.m.	19 2.18 p.m.	20 10.10 p.m.	

Exercise 5.6

1 2 h 30 min	2 5 h	3 7 h 20 min	4 4 h 37 min
5 7 h 51 min	6 5 h 50 min	7 7 h 15 min	8 16 h 10 min
9 7 h	10 6 h 24 min	11 1 h 46 min	12 1 h 54 min
13 4 h 52 min	14 7 h 50 min	15 7 h 40 min	16 21 h 49 min
17 22 h 30 min	18 24 h 20 min	19 5 h 25 min	20 3 h 43 min

Exercise 6.1

1 1 : 2	2 4 : 3	3 3 : 1	4 3 : 4
5 3 : 2	6 3 : 7	7 3 : 2	8 15 : 1
9 3 : 2	10 4 : 1	11 25 : 4	12 11 : 50
13 6 : 5	14 4 : 5	15 1 : 4	16 5 : 3
17 4 : 3	18 7 : 4	19 1 : 5	20 3 : 5
21 9 : 8	22 5 : 3	23 4 : 9	24 16 : 27
25 3 : 4 : 5	26 3 : 5 : 9	27 1 : 2 : 3	28 1 : 4 : 5
29 1 : 4 : 8	30 3 : 5 : 6		

Exercise 6.2

1 (a) 3 : 4 (b) $\frac{3}{7}$ 2 (a) 7 : 4 (b) $\frac{4}{11}$

3 (a) 6 : 1 (b) $\frac{6}{7}$ 4 (a) 3 : 2 (b) $\frac{2}{5}$

5 (a) 5 : 1 (b) $\frac{1}{6}$ 6 (a) 120 g (b) 4 oz

7 9 cwt   8 9 oz   9 (a) 30 g (b) $\frac{1}{2}$ lb

10 (a) 1 lb (b) 100 g   11 3 buckets cement, 48 buckets gravel

12 (a) 9 kg (b) 10 cwt barley, 3 cwt cattle cake

Exercise 6.3

1 £4 : £6   2 £32 : £8   3 £20 : £16   4 £36 : £24

5 £50 : £30 : £20   6 £15 : £30 : £45   7 350 ml : 150 ml   8 60 m : 75 m

9 2.4 kg : 1.6 kg   10 80 cm : 70 cm   11 18 ℓ water, 2 ℓ weedkiller

12 150 g   13 45 rum and butter, 30 vanilla, 60 strawberry

14 150 red, 60 green 15 300 owners   16 120 ml

17 (a) 210 houses, 90 bungalows (b) $\frac{1}{3}$

18 5, 10, 15   19 6 boys   20 1010

Exercise 6.4

1 2.5 km	**2** 2 km	**3** 7.5 km	**4** 6 km
5 5 miles	**6** (a) 25 ft (b) 16 ft 8 in		**7** 50 km
8 40 mm, 38 mm	**9** 48 cm	**10** 22.4 cm	

Exercise 6.5

1 49p	**2** £30	**3** £77	**4** 16 fl oz
5 36 ft	**6** 10 kg	**7** £24	**8** £189
9 $\frac{1}{2}$ pt	**10** £1.20	**11** £48	**12** 21 ft
13 12 oz	**14** 85 cl	**15** 10 oz	**16** £1.98
17 98 kg	**18** 40 ml	**19** 15 kg	**20** £142

Exercise 6.6

1 1 h	**2** 8 h	**3** 8 days	**4** 4 h
5 6 days	**6** 6 days	**7** 12 h	**8** 8 h
9 12 h	**10** 4 days		

Exercise 6.7

1 A	**2** C	**3** D	**4** C
5 A	**6** A	**7** C	**8** D

Exercise 7.1

1 (a) 22	(b) 14	(c) 54	(d) 19
2 (a) £18	(b) £140	(c) £2.55	(d) £77
3 (a) 115 g	(b) 4.72 kg	(c) 4 lb 1 oz	(d) 17 cwt
4 (a) 1 cm 2 mm	(b) 29 km	(c) 5 ft 1 in	(d) 7 yd
5 (a) 15 min	(b) 6 pt	(c) 111 ml	(d) 11 yr 10 mths
6 2 h 11 min	**7** 24.2°C	**8** £2.01	**9** 408
10 £156	**11** 160	**12** 76	**13** 39
14 £125	**15** £1.75	**16** £4.85	**17** £166
18 44	**19** £2.74	**20** £1.08	

Exercise 7.2

1 C	**2** C	**3** B	**4** C
5 D	**6** A		

Exercise 8.1

1 (a) 20 mile/h	(b) 20 km/h	(c) 16 mile/h	(d) 18.5 mile/h
(e) 12.5 mile/h	(f) $20\frac{2}{3}$ mile/h		
2 (a) 20 mile/h	(b) 32 km/h	(c) 16 mile/h	(d) 80 km/h
(e) 50 mile/h	(f) 180 mile/h		

3 (a) 60 miles   (b) 168 km   (c) 94 miles   (d) 285 km
  (e) 3000 miles   (f) 13.5 miles
4 (a) 50 miles   (b) 168 km   (c) 48 miles   (d) 105 miles
  (e) 180 km   (f) 16 miles
5 (a) 3 h   (b) 5 h   (c) 3 h   (d) 8 h
  (e) 4 h   (f) 2 h 30 min
6 (a) 4 h 30 min   (b) 2 h 22 min   (c) 2 h 18 min   (d) 45 min
  (e) 25 min   (f) 45 min
7 $36\frac{2}{3}$ mile/h   8 1800 miles   9 18 mile/h
10 (a) 40 mile/h   (b) $45\frac{1}{3}$ mile/h   11 42 mile/h   12 $66\frac{2}{3}$ mile/h

Exercise 8.2

1 B   2 C   3 C   4 A

Exercise 9.1

1 £141.79   2 £74.64   3 £98   4 £124.60
5 £198.40   6 £391.60   7 £365.56   8 £179.58

Exercise 9.2

1 £260.68   2 £238.37   3 £582   4 £417.90
5 £1497.98   6 £836.25   7 £850.43   8 £176.33

Exercise 9.3

1 24p   2 69p   3 87p   4 22p
5 40p   6 £2.30   7 £2.95   8 £2.10
9 88p   10 £1.44   11 79p   12 51p
13 £1.01   14 £3.52   15 £1.42   16 £1.15
17 45p   18 79p   19 71p   20 £1.64
21 £2.50   22 37p   23 73p   24 £1.83

Exercise 9.4

1 (a) 2675 schillings   (b) 381 marks   (c) 1163 francs
2 (a) 378 dollars   (b) 733 500 lire   (c) 64 200 pesetas
3 (a) 1977.10 francs   (b) 214.20 dollars   (c) 36 380 pesetas
4 (a) 53 500 schillings   (b) 23 260 francs   (c) 4 890 000 lire
5 (a) 95.25 marks   (b) 5350 pesetas   (c) 668.75 schillings
6 (a) 146 700 lire   (b) 75.60 dollars   (c) 697.80 francs
7 (a) 2942.50 schillings   (b) 23 540 pesetas   (c) 419.10 marks
8 (a) 302.40 dollars   (b) 2791.20 francs   (c) 6420 schillings
9 (a) 36 675 lire   (b) 57.15 marks   (c) 3210 pesetas
10 (a) 2093.40 francs   (b) 226.80 dollars   (c) 685.80 marks

Exercise 9.5

1 £10	2 £1000	3 £1000	4 £10
5 £150	6 £25	7 £70	8 £500
9 £180	10 £70	11 £350	12 £27.50
13 £130	14 £1000	15 £45	16 £680
17 10p	18 £22	19 £65	20 £45

Exercise 9.6

1 1163 francs	2 489 000 lire	3 19.05 marks	4 38.10 marks
5 630 dollars	6 42 800 pesetas	7 244 500 lire	8 252 dollars
9 3810 marks	10 63 dollars	11 378 dollars	12 11 630 francs
13 1337.50 schillings		14 11 630 francs	15 91.44 marks
16 37.80 dollars	17 17 120 pesetas	18 1524 marks	19 3489 francs
20 267 500 schillings			

Exercise 9.7

1 1.26	2 26.75	3 3.20	4 4.35
5 211	6 11.20	7 13.80	8 1.26
9 326	10 169	11 12.13	12 3.90
13 220	14 3.30	15 11.59	16 1.85
17 82	18 1.35	19 9.80	20 315

Exercise 9.8

1 £5.05	2 £11.05	3 £10.05	4 £16.05
5 £35.53	6 £38.05	7 £20.05	8 £17.05; £13.50
9 £48.01	10 £36	11 £19	12 £1160
13 £5204			

Exercise 9.9

1 £38	2 £6.40	3 £13.80	4 £560
5 Bank; £218	6 HP; £24		

Exercise 9.10

1 £47.88	2 £96.76	3 £247.86	4 No; £75.30
5 320 therms	6 £309.70	7 £124.96	8 35 998
9 £10.50	10 £123.28		

Exercise 9.11

1 £9	2 £16.10	3 £49.70	4 £57.60
5 £52.80	6 £148.25	7 £64.45	
8 (a) £32.40 (b) £19.70 (c) £48.90		9 £210	
10 (a) £102.60 (b) 5 years			

Exercise 9.12

1 C	2 D	3 B	4 C
5 A	6 A	7 D	8 B
9 C	10 A	11 D	12 A

Exercise 10.1

1 $\frac{1}{2}$	2 $\frac{3}{5}$	3 $\frac{3}{4}$	4 $\frac{7}{20}$
5 $\frac{4}{5}$	6 $\frac{6}{25}$	7 $\frac{18}{25}$	8 $\frac{7}{50}$
9 $\frac{11}{100}$	10 $\frac{1}{8}$	11 $\frac{1}{3}$	12 $\frac{5}{8}$
13 $1\frac{3}{5}$	14 $\frac{9}{40}$	15 $\frac{9}{50}$	16 $2\frac{2}{5}$
17 $\frac{13}{30}$	18 $\frac{21}{40}$	19 $\frac{63}{100}$	20 $2\frac{1}{2}$
21 $\frac{13}{40}$	22 $\frac{7}{15}$	23 $\frac{17}{100}$	24 $\frac{19}{50}$
25 $\frac{9}{400}$	26 $\frac{29}{40}$	27 $\frac{51}{100}$	28 $3\frac{3}{10}$
29 $\frac{33}{50}$	30 $\frac{2}{3}$		

Exercise 10.2

1 0.5	2 0.6	3 0.75	4 0.35
5 0.8	6 0.26	7 0.41	8 1.3
9 0.184	10 0.769	11 0.025	12 0.013
13 2.2	14 0.005	15 0.0082	16 0.035
17 0.825	18 0.6525	19 0.2925	20 0.02
21 3.2	22 0.284	23 0.0027	24 0.0107
25 0.0373	26 0.004	27 1.36	28 0.11
29 0.155	30 0.0525		

Exercise 10.3

1 50%	2 10%	3 20%	4 75%
5 60%	6 70%	7 30%	8 175%
9 150%	10 80%	11 90%	12 12.5%
13 37.5%	14 54%	15 72.5%	16 28%
17 45%	18 225%	19 450%	20 22.5%
21 48%	22 62.5%	23 65%	24 40%
25 125%	26 112.5%	27 46.6%	28 72%
29 125%	30 26.6%		

Exercise 10.4

1 50%	2 25%	3 70%	4 46%
5 3%	6 17%	7 328%	8 112%
9 78%	10 15.9%	11 32.7%	12 52.5%
13 126.4%	14 258%	15 10%	16 5%
17 1.6%	18 7.25%	19 60%	20 92%
21 203%	22 10.4%	23 5.7%	24 102.1%
25 350.2%	26 36%	27 0.4%	28 152.3%
29 50.1%	30 0.75%		

Exercise 10.5

1 50%	2 75%	3 64%	4 37.5%
5 20%	6 31.25%	7 40%	8 62.5%
9 85%	10 45%	11 22.5%	12 33.3%
13 40%	14 48%	15 5%	16 30%
17 26.6%	18 58.3%	19 Girl: 5%	20 24%

Exercise 10.6

1 £3	2 £24	3 £21	4 90p
5 £6.30	6 £1.50	7 £3.30	8 £24
9 £12.90	10 £34.50	11 £16.80	12 £68.80
13 £46	14 £151.20	15 £306	16 £7500
17 £87.80	18 £34 400	19 £153.60	20 £33 000

Exercise 10.7

1 3 km	2 10 cm	3 52.5 kg	4 3.6 ℓ
5 25.92 in	6 6 lb	7 1 h 12 min	8 8 km
9 6.4 g	10 3.75 ml	11 72 pupils	12 1 cm
13 360	14 676	15 12 600	16 357
17 384	18 85.56 million tonnes	19 3990	20 104.5 h

Exercise 10.8

1 £9.20	2 £2070	3 £46	4 £58.65
5 £138	6 £92	7 £46	8 £6.44
9 £496.80	10 £15		

Exercise 10.9

1 £96	2 66p	3 £23	4 70p
5 £11.05	6 £165	7 £98.40	8 £44
9 £43.52	10 £23.66		

Exercise 10.10

1 20% loss	2 25% profit	3 36% loss	4 $33\frac{1}{3}$% profit
5 20% profit	6 15% profit	7 30% profit	8 12% profit
9 18% profit	10 $16\frac{2}{3}$% profit		

Exercise 10.11

1 £20	2 £60	3 £120	4 £80
5 £250	6 £160	7 £50	8 £16
9 £40	10 £60		

Exercise 10.12

1 $33\frac{1}{3}\%$	**2** £287.50	**3** 50%	**4** 35%
5 £80; 40%	**6** 28%	**7** $45\frac{2}{3}\%$	**8** £10.50
9 (a) £34 (b) £25 **10** £24			

Exercise 10.13

1 £16	**2** £19.50	**3** £17.50	**4** £26.25
5 £12	**6** £24	**7** £34	**8** £350
9 £200	**10** £240		

Exercise 10.14

1 £166.40	**2** £61.80	**3** £32.64	**4** £61.50
5 £115.92	**6** £1248.64	**7** £132.40	**8** £126.10
9 £1.60	**10** £3434.70		

Exercise 10.15

1 £20	**2** £42	**3** £60	**4** £9.60
5 £100	**6** £16	**7** £45	**8** £480
9 £980	**10** £271		

Exercise 10.16

1 £2400	**2** £3750	**3** £2176.50	**4** £3540
5 £40	**6** £12 459	**7** £52 574	**8** £2353.50

Exercise 10.17

1 C	**2** A	**3** D	**4** B
5 C	**6** A	**7** C	**8** D
9 A	**10** C	**11** C	**12** C
13 A	**14** D	**15** C	**16** C
17 A	**18** B	**19** C	**20** B
21 A			

Exercise 11.5

1 (a) 35.5 km (b) 12.5 miles   **2** (a) 34 ℓ (b) 6.5 gal
3 (a) 6.6 lb (b) 20 400 g   **4** (a) £222 (b) 504 dollars
5 (a) 4000 pesetas (b) £364   **7** (a) £60 (b) £32
8 (a) £136 (b) £88   **9** (a) 30 (b) 59

Exercise 11.6

1 12	**2** 30	**3** 32	**4** 23
5 33	**6** 7	**7** 8	**8** 13
9 8	**10** 7		

Exercise 11.7

1 (a) 15   (b) 16   (c) 12   (d) 19   (e) 11
2 (a) 9   (b) 32   (c) 34   (d) 31   (e) 24
3 (a) 29   (b) 6   (c) 2   (d) 32   (e) 168
4 (a) 111   (b) 50   (c) 13   (d) 51   (e) 69

Exercise 11.8

1 $S = B + 0.25C$ **2** $P = 2L + M$ **3** $P = 2L + 2B$ **4** $D = T \times S$
5 12   **6** 12   **7** 30   **8** 4
9 72   **10** 36

Exercise 11.9

1 3.5, 6.6, 2.3, 7.9
3 13.1, 6.9, 11.7, 12.8
5 −2.0, 3.6, 13.2
7 6.2, 3.7, 9.7
9 0.5, 1.9, 6.5, 9.9

2 2.1, 15.9, 22.2
4 0.8, 2.9, 5.0, 6.2, 8.0
6 1.7, 4.1, 9.1
8 10.2, 8.3, 6.6, 4.5
10 9.7, 14.5, 19.6

Exercise 11.10

1 (a) 9   (b) 15
3 red

2 6, 14, 10, 18, 14, 22, 18, 26, 22, 30
8 (a) green   (b) yellow   (c) red   (d) red   (e) blue

Exercise 12.1

1 (a) 58°   (b) 116°   (c) 51°   (d) 67°   (e) 58°   (f) 45°   (g) 75°   (h) 60°
3 (a) 40°   (b) 140°   (c) 140°
4 (a) 130°   (b) 50°   (c) 130°   (d) 50°   (e) 130°   (f) 130°   (g) 50°
5 (a) 030° or 30° E. of N.   (b) 130° or 40° S. of E.
   (c) 220° or 50° S. of W.   (d) 255° or 15° S. of W.
   (e) 310° or 50° W. of N.
6 (a) 110°   (b) 80°

Exercise 12.2

1 33 cm 6 mm	**2** 12 cm	**3** 6 cm	**4** 33 cm
5 18 cm			

Exercise 12.3

1 136 cm²	**2** 224 m²	**3** 225 mm²	**4** 117 ft²
5 51 cm²	**6** 94.24 m²	**7** 5880 in²	**8** 368 m²
9 2772 mm²	**10** 72 m²	**11** 114 cm²	**12** 180.375 ft²
13 144 cm²	**14** 162 m²	**15** 171 m²	**16** 1088 ft²
17 264 m²	**18** 216.4 m²		

Exercise 12.4

1 27 m	**2** £47.70	**3** 3.25 m²	**4** 192
5 £71.55	**6** 14 m	**7** £88.50	**8** 7
9 £1.92	**10** £88		

Exercise 12.5

1 22 cm	**2** 27 cm 2 mm	**3** 5 cm 2 mm	**4** 9 cm 2 mm
5 (a) 16 cm²	(b) 30 cm²	(c) 56 mm²	(d) 28 m²
6 (a) 5.2 cm²	(b) 4.8 cm²	(c) 1.5 ft²	(d) 67.2 cm²
7 (a) base = 14 cm	(b) base = 9 mm	(c) base = 5 m	(d) height = 14 ft
(e) height = 36 cm		(f) height = 24.2 cm	
8 (a) 48 cm²	(b) 40 cm²	(c) 84 mm²	(d) 198 mm²
(e) 315 cm²	(f) 640 ft²	(g) 297 cm²	(h) 218 ft²
(j) 2000 cm²	(k) 329 cm²		

Exercise 12.6

1 (a) 110 cm	(b) 198 cm	(c) 132 in	(d) 330 m
2 (a) 132 cm	(b) 44 ft	(c) 176 m	(d) 308 cm
3 (a) $62\frac{6}{7}$ cm	(b) $100\frac{4}{7}$ cm	(c) $18\frac{6}{7}$ m	(d) $6\frac{2}{7}$ ft
4 (a) 31.4 cm	(b) 18.84 cm	(c) 628 cm	(d) 25.12 cm
5 (a) 21 in	(b) 56 cm	(c) 70 cm	(d) 77 mm
6 (a) 14 cm	(b) 5.25 ft	(c) 19.25 cm	(d) 70 mm
7 7 cm	**8** 16.5 cm	**9** 36 cm	**10** 310 m

Exercise 12.7

1 (a) 154 cm²	(b) 1386 m²	(c) 616 in²	(d) 3850 m²
2 (a) $12\frac{4}{7}$ cm²	(b) $78\frac{4}{7}$ in²	(c) 346.5 cm²	(d) 38.5 cm²
3 (a) $28\frac{2}{7}$ cm²	(b) 38.5 m²	(c) $21\frac{21}{32}$ cm²	(d) $86\frac{5}{8}$ cm²
4 (a) 314 m²	(b) 12.56 m²	(c) 28.26 cm²	(d) 3.14 m²
5 346.5 cm²			

Exercise 12.8

1 154 cm²	**2** 173.25 cm²	**3** 3850 cm²	**4** 490 m²
5 610 cm²	**6** 728 m²	**7** 192.5 in²	**8** 539 ft²
9 1197 ft²	**10** 2044 m²		

Exercise 12.9

1 B	2 B	3 D	4 C
5 C	6 C	7 A	8 C
9 C	10 B	11 C	12 D

Exercise 13.1

1 240 cm³	2 48 ft³	3 140 m³	4 876 cm³
5 26 800 cm³	6 2160 cm³	7 7344 ft³	8 2187.5 m³
9 13 860 cm³	10 2772 in³	11 1386 cm³	12 590.625 m³
13 23 400 cm³	14 86 625 mm³		

Exercise 13.2

1 192 cm³	2 3000 cm³	3 9 ft³	4 11 cm
5 90 cm³	6 120 ft³	7 1540 cm³	8 401.92 cm³
9 (a) 1800 cm³	(b) 34.2 kg	10 cube: 73.5 cm³	11 27 cm³
12 $112\frac{1}{2}$ gal	13 600 ft³	14 20 m²	15 517 ft²

Exercise 13.3

1 C	2 A	3 D	4 C
5 D	6 A	7 B	8 B
9 A	10 C	11 C	12 B

Exercise 14.1

1 115	2 315	3 423	4 1137
5 10 984	6 4846	7 7994	8 85.84
9 884.68	10 1367.68	11 991.82	12 718.5 miles
13 £34.21	14 406 runs		

Exercise 14.2

1 238	2 518	3 4421	4 256
5 −302	6 −359	7 10.28	8 37.23
9 −16.7	10 41.6	11 8.01	12 19.96
13 80.648	14 42.336	15 150.12	16 163.376
17 2.751	18 464.593	19 18.712	20 1209.23

Exercise 14.3

1 1924	2 51.33	3 467.2	4 457.8627
5 11 370.48	6 1.6224	7 1 115 250	8 21 786.38
9 2 663 912.1	10 3.541 754 7	11 14 982.44	12 0.132 119 6
13 13 918.602	14 3621.9565	15 353 638 650	16 205 059 000
17 114 667 000	18 21 821 722	19 1 167 728 290 00	
20 67 541 522 000	21 1 044 558 400	22 592 287 160	23 602.428 39
24 1658.16	25 198 703.03	26 20 618 773	27 8211.3771
28 13 277 376 000	29 67 337 747 000	30 14 correct, 15 approx.	

Exercise 14.4

1 653	**2** 98	**3** 67	**4** 325
5 101	**6** 321	**7** 23.1	**8** 36.5
9 68.41	**10** 62.9	**11** 723.4	**12** 64.8

Exercise 14.5

1 4.77	**2** 12.13	**3** 13.68	**4** 8.92
5 0.24	**6** 1.54	**7** 426.45	**8** 1.96
9 0.53	**10** 1267.84	**11** 0.18	**12** 558.62
13 78.59	**14** 6.36	**15** 0.03	**16** 16.29
17 491.07	**18** 0.19	**19** 0.30	**20** 51.66

Exercise 14.6

1 19.75	**2** 15.53	**3** 3.33	**4** 38
5 15.75	**6** 31.73	**7** 0.27	**8** 84.14
9 1.67	**10** 4.54	**11** 0.73	**12** 0.74
13 2576.33	**14** 47.16	**15** 0.27	**16** 3.50
17 1.48	**18** 2.99	**19** 2.82	**20** 18.65

Exercise 14.7

1 567	**2** 2218	**3** 22.59	**4** 6.87
5 347.2	**6** 194.63	**7** 105.26	**8** 48.42
9 144.88	**10** 16.87	**11** 0.85	**12** 250.02

Exercise 14.8

1 (a) 34.92	(b) 42.59	(c) 19.41	(d) 167.73
(e) 94.62	(f) 45.68	(g) 84.39	(h) 121.33
2 (a) 10.943	(b) 43.243	(c) 4.593	(d) 38.23
(e) 56.263	(f) 83.295	(g) 20.983	(h) 163.134
3 (a) 25.136	(b) 47.13	(c) 113.112	(d) 14.139
(e) 49.08	(f) 147.05	(g) 299.31	(h) 62.97
4 (a) 6.37	(b) 16.69	(c) 2.57	(d) 59.71
5 (a) 62.8 cm	(b) 45.844 in	(c) 584.04 ft	(d) 298.3 cm
(e) 102.678 m	(f) 118.5036 cm		
6 (a) 9.55 cm	(b) 15.91 cm	(c) 5.47 in	(d) 41.66 ft
(e) 2.32 m	(f) 29.19 cm		

Exercise 14.9

1 (a) 48	(b) 39	(c) 405	(d) £3.50
(e) £22.50	(f) 135 m	(g) £13.50	(h) £21.60
2 (a) £27.20	(b) £67.50	(c) £131.25	(d) £63.75
(e) £228	(f) £624	(g) £186	(h) £100.95
3 (a) £84	(b) £215	(c) £67.50	(d) £918.40
(e) £144.76	(f) £167.68		
4 (a) 37.5%	(b) 60%	(c) 21.43%	(d) 42.86%
(e) 12.5%	(f) 75%	(g) 52.94%	(h) 40.91%
5 (a) £150.08	(b) £394.50	(c) £638.91	(d) £160.16
(e) £1009.82	(f) £502.34	(g) £807.00	(h) £659.82

6 (a) £1.40   (b) £6.72   (c) £14   (d) 64p
   (e) £137.60   (f) £192.16   (g) £120   (h) £335.12
7 (a) 56   (b) 86   (c) 152   (d) 5.4
   (e) 0.23   (f) 0.87   (g) 16.8   (h) 3.47
8 (a) 5   (b) 13   (c) 17   (d) 8.49
   (e) 17.49   (f) 22.80   (g) 55.22   (h) 28.30

Exercise 14.10

1 £9   2 (a) £111.75 (b) £50.29   3 15.99%
4 £6484.40   5 £57.60; 27.74%   6 £75.75
7 (a) £473.60 (b) 15.92p per mile   8 81.70%
9 (a) 25 200   (b) 15 120   10 1599 ft² ; £12 259

Chapter 15

15.2 The Disco: £68.40
15.3 The Newsagent: (a) Mon. 376   Tue. 375   Wed. 381   Thur. 386   Fri. 387
      Sat. 513   (b) Mon. £78.75   Tue. £78.37   Wed. £80.08
      Thur. £80.39   Fri. £81.38   Sat. £109.40
                      (c) £18 profit   (d) £127.09
15.4 The Motorbike: £341.80
15.5 Timetables: (a) 1715 hours   (b) 0602 hours   (c) 1755 hours; 10 h 32 min
15.6 Going to Work: £685.50 per year
15.7 Four Teenagers in a House: £28
15.8 The Calorie Diet: (a) (i) suitable   (ii) fat   (iii) underweight   (iv) fat
      (v) very fat   (vi) fat
      (b) Menu A   2095 cal   Menu B   1990 cal   Menu C   1820 cal
      Menu D   2105 cal   Menu C nearest, 320 cal greater
15.9 Decorating: £368
15.10 The Holiday £355.70; £88.93
15.11 Office Space Organisation: (a) £1626.10   (c) 280.75 ft²   (d) 20.69%
      (e) 3276 ft³ ; 306 ft³   (f) (i) yes   (ii) 7
15.12 The Retail Shop: (a) 377   (b) 168   (c) £504.50   (d) (i) £750
      (ii) £1237.50   (e) (i) £169.65   (ii) £277.20
15.13 The Trainee Nurse: Total intake 2240 ml, total output 2870 ml
15.14 The Garage: bricks £440, hardcore and concrete £111, wood £75.60,
      roof £121.50, other items £266.25. Total £1014.35.

Index

274